Guide to Records in the New York State Archives

1993

The University of the State of New York
The State Education Department
State Archives and Records Administration
Albany, NY 12230

PREFACE

We are pleased to present this new edition of the *Guide to Records in the New York State Archives*. This publication lists records available for use at the State Archives and Records Administration (SARA) and provides detailed descriptions of the development and current functions of the State agencies creating the records. Since the publication of the first SARA *Guide* in 1981, use of State archival materials has increased fivefold. We hope this new edition brings many more new users to discover these important informational resources.

SARA's records contain unique documentation for anyone wishing to examine past activities of New Yorkers and the significant role taken by State government in supporting this activity. The 3,200 record series listed in the *Guide* document the broad scope of the State's history — from the turbulent colonial and Revolutionary periods, to the rapid settlement of the State during the 19th century, to the innovative government reforms of the early 20th century, to modern day concerns with human rights, the environment, and government accountability. During the past decade, users have undertaken research at SARA relating to topics covering this entire range of New York's history. These researchers have used State archival records to examine social welfare and public health issues, juvenile delinquency and penal reform, women's rights, Native American land claims, treatment of the insane in public institutions, toxic waste and acid rain, educational financing and the relation of religion and schools, and the public lives of New York political and government leaders. These and many other studies have helped to develop remedial legislation, improve existing government programs, and analyze important trends in broad public policy areas.

SARA created this *Guide* to serve as the cornerstone of its efforts to promote the State's archival resources. It also has initiated a number of additional programs to help make these resources available to all. Descriptions of SARA records can be used by researchers through RLIN (the Research Libraries Information Network) a national data base located at many important research institutions throughout the country. The scope of this data base is being expanded to include detailed information on records located in nearly all of New York's archives, libraries, historical societies, historical records repositories, local government archives, and other institutions. Throughout the past decade, SARA also has increased its capability to preserve deteriorating records and make microfilm copies of State archival records widely available elsewhere in New York.

SARA has initiated a comprehensive program to assist State agencies in developing sound records management practices. This is a major part of SARA's involvement in overall information policy and practices in the executive, legislative, and judicial branches of State government to ensure the sound identification and retention of archival records. The efforts to increase use of SARA's material is complemented also by SARA programs that provide funding and advisory services to improve local historical records administration and by its publications and multimedia programs designed to promote an appreciation of historical records throughout the State.

With the publication of this new *Guide* and the development of these other efforts, researchers are able to obtain current information about the State's records of enduring value. Increased use of these records should help us all to a deeper understanding of our past and lead us to new ways to deal with the challenges presented by our increasingly complex society.

Larry J. Hackman
Assistant Commissioner for Archives and Records Administration

ACKNOWLEDGMENTS

The production of this second edition of the *Guide to Records in the New York State Archives* required technical expertise, considerable energy, and a commitment to excellence from many people. Archivists Richard Andress, Elisabeth Golding, and Duncan McCollum, my colleagues in the State Archives, carefully researched and prepared the administrative histories, and organized the series title entries. Elisabeth Golding also undertook the substantial tasks of preparing the index to this *Guide*, and ensuring that recent accessions were incorporated into this publication. The concern of these individuals for promoting awareness and use of the State's valuable archival resources has ensured the quality and accuracy of entries in this *Guide*. Nancy Chacho and Brian LaBombard undertook with skill, perseverance, and good humor the considerable technical tasks involved in producing this *Guide*. Lorne Hunter, Rose Sirtori, Bernice Waldman, and Judy Nowak assisted by handling wordprocessing, filing, and many other unheralded, but essential tasks. Christine Karpiak deftly handled proofreading and copy editing, and coordinated the technical workflow to produce the manuscript of this volume.

Other State Archives and Records Administration staff provided support and assistance. Staff of the Bureau of Records Analysis and Disposition commented on administrative histories. Thomas Mills, Director of the Division of State Government Records, and Christine Ward, Chief of the Bureau of Archival Services, reviewed the full manuscript of the *Guide*. Judy Hohmann, of the Public and Educational Programs Unit, provided congenial assistance throughout the publication process. Bruce Dearstyne, Director of the Division of External Programs, provided assistance with sections relating to local government records programs. Larry J. Hackman, the Assistant Commissioner for Archives and Records Administration, supported the preparation of this second edition of the *Guide*, providing advice throughout its development and production.

Acknowledgment is also due to all of the New York State agencies who work with the State Archives and Records Administration to assure the identification and preservation of the State's archival records. Many State government agency staff members provided welcome assistance by reviewing the administrative histories for their agencies.

The staff of the State Education Department's Division of Electronic Data Processing were instrumental in the technical production of this *Guide*. Allen Lescak, John Meierhoffer, and Tom Preston provided critical automation services needed to develop an automated online catalog. Catherine Sullivan was responsible for the programming necessary to convert the bibliographic information to a wordprocessing format in order to produce the *Guide*. Thanks to these individuals, tools now exist to more easily and accurately produce periodic updates to the published *Guide*.

The considerable efforts of all those noted above have combined to provide increased access to the valuable resources of New York State government. The quality and extent of this *Guide* is a tribute to their commitment.

Kathleen D. Roe
Principal Archivist

CONTENTS

Public Benefit Corporations and Authorities

Temporary War Emergency Agencies

Part II.   LEGISLATIVE BRANCH

Part III.   JUDICIAL BRANCH

APPENDICES

INDEXES

INTRODUCTION

The State Archives is the collective memory of New York State government. Over 52,000 cubic feet of valuable records provide tangible evidence of the organization, functions, policies, decisions, and operations of colonial and State government from the 17th century to the present. The archival records of State government reflect the challenges faced by New York during the evolution of its multicultural, economically diverse, and perpetually dynamic society. This *Guide to Records in the New York State Archives* serves as a point of departure for those interested in learning about New York State government and its archival records. The *Guide* provides an overview of the current functions and organization of each New York State government agency, and summarizes the State Archives' holdings for each agency.

The State Archives and Its Holdings.

The New York State Archives and Records Administration (SARA), part of the Office of Cultural Education in the State Education Department, is the organization responsible for identifying, preserving, and making available the permanently valuable records of State government. In addition to its responsibilities for the archival records of State government, SARA regulates the retention and disposal of State and local government records, provides guidance and services to help governments better manage their records, and supports statewide activities to strengthen historical records programs in both the public and private sectors.

The holdings of the New York State Archives are a unique resource documenting colonial and State government from the Dutch settlement in the 1630s to recent years. State government activities touch on virtually every aspect of society. This is particularly the case in New York, one of the first states to face the complexities of a

1

large, multiracial, multiethnic population, and the pressures of varied socio-economic and political issues that ultimately result from modernization. The concerns of State government over time have covered subjects from the Revolutionary War to the war on drugs, issues from land claims to fair housing, and groups from farmers to feminists. In retrospect, New York's State governmental activity has often been representative of how alternative theories and techniques were applied, and how society has evolved. The State's archival records are an important resource for studying the issues and accomplishments of the past, relating them to current developments, and providing a more reasoned basis for decision making in the present.

Contents of the Guide.

The entries in the *Guide* are organized to reflect the current structure of State government. There are separate parts for the Executive, Legislative, and Judicial branches. The Executive Branch part, by far the largest, contains an entry for each agency, regardless of whether or not the State Archives has archival records from an agency. Each entry consists of two sections: an administrative summary of the agency and a list of agency records, if any, in the State Archives. The administrative summary provides a brief synopsis of the agency's current functions, and its organizational history. Similarly, entries in the Legislative Branch part are organized by the two houses—the Assembly and Senate—with a separate subdivision for joint legislative commissions and committees. For the Judicial Branch, entries are organized by the current major types of courts in the Unified Court System.

The *Guide* contains information on the complete records holdings of the State Archives as of December 1991. Archivists organize records in groups, called record series, which are kept together in logical groups because they represent how the records were used in an agency program unit. A record series may span several months, or several centuries; may be as small as a few items, or as large as thousands of file drawers; may be ink on sheepskin parchment or magnetic impulses on computer tape. There are more than 3,200 records series in the State Archives.

To help readers understand the scope of the Archives' holdings and the use of the information in this *Guide*, the introduction is followed by a brief history of the State Archives and Records Administration and a section on "How to Use this Guide". This *Guide* also contains three appendices. The first provides information about New York's local government records program, and the second contains a list of microfilmed local records housed in the State Archives. The third appendix contains information about how to learn more about other archival collections in over 2,000 historical records repositories such as archives, libraries, museums, and historical societies around the State. Finally, the *Guide* includes an index to significant names and agency functions identified in the administrative summaries.

The information in this *Guide*, and the records described here, can be of benefit to many individuals and groups. Government officials and employees can find information to better understand the historical development of current issues and to inform decision-making and policy analysis. Scholarly researchers will find the information needed to analyze issues, individuals, and activities of the past. Legal researchers will find records that are evidence of the rights and responsibilities of both citizens and the State government. Family and community historians will find important evidence of the socioeconomic development of New York State. The general public will find this *Guide* a useful summary of the history and current functions and organization of State government.

History of the State Archives and Records Administration

The New York State Archives and Records Administration (SARA) has a broad mandate to regulate the disposal and selective preservation of State and local government records, to provide guidance and services to help governments better manage their records, and to support activities that strengthen historical records programs state-wide. This *Guide* results from one of SARA's major responsibilities: to identify, acquire, and make available for research use the archival records of New York State government.

The modern State government archives program that exists today is only about 15 years old, but concern for valuable public records extends back over three centuries. When the Dutch surrendered New Netherland colony to the English in 1664, the articles of surrender stipulated that the colony's records must be retained and protected. After the Revolutionary War, New York colonial records earlier carried off by British authorities were returned to the new State of New York. During the early statehood period New York took several measures to protect its records, including making the theft of records from the offices of courts, city and county clerks, and the Secretary of State, a felony. As early as 1797, the legislature ordered construction of a special building in Albany to protect the public records of the Secretary of State.

The State also took early action to make its colonial records as complete and usable as possible. Beginning in 1818, Governor DeWitt Clinton commissioned the translation of Dutch colonial records, pursuant to a law passed in 1804. The State also sent a special archival agent to Britain, France, and the Netherlands in the 1840s to secure copies of records relating to New York's colonial history, which were later edited and published.

In 1847, the State legislature provided for more continuous responsibility for

5

preservation of historical records. A joint resolution that year directed the Secretary of State to deliver to the Regents of the University of the State of New York "...documents of historic interest relative to and connected with the annals of the state" for preservation in the State Library. Later legislation in 1859, 1881, 1892, and 1907 provided for the transfer to the Library of additional records from the Secretary of State, State Comptroller, and clerks of the Assembly and Senate. These laws led to the establishment in 1881 of a Manuscripts Division (later, Manuscripts and History Section) in the State Library. The Library appointed a historical documents clerk, later given the title of state archivist, to administer both the State records and nongovernmental manuscripts in the Manuscripts Division.

The Library's program received a major setback in 1911 when a fire in the Capitol destroyed or damaged the bulk of its holdings. Two years later, the Library moved to new quarters in the State Education Building, but limited resources made it impossible to completely process and describe all the records that were acquired.

In the meantime, the State developed policies to preserve local government records. In the aftermath of the 1911 fire, the legislature mandated fire protection for these records, and required local public officials to obtain the consent of the Commissioner of Education before destroying records. A Division of Public Records was established in the State Education Department to enforce protection and disposition procedures and provide advice on local government records management. Local governments were also authorized to transfer custody of their noncurrent records to the Division if they were unable to provide adequate storage locally. The Division of Public Records was combined with the Division of History to form the Division of Archives and History in 1915. At the same time, the local government records held by the Division of Public Records were transferred to the State Library's Manuscripts Section.

During the next half century, repeated appeals by State Education Department officials and historical researchers for a comprehensive archival program went unanswered. In 1950, the legislature established a records management program for State agencies and placed it under the direction of the Division of the Budget. This statute regulating the disposition of State government records gave the Commissioner of Education power to review state agency records disposition requests and veto disposition of records with archival value, but this authority was hampered in the absence of a State archival program to systematically accession and care for the records that were saved. In 1960, the records management program was transferred to the Office of General Services. A records center opened in 1966 for temporary storage of non-current agency records, but it was not intended to house archival records.

A State archives law finally was enacted in 1971. The new law established the State Archives in the Education Department to "acquire, appraise, preserve...display, duplicate, and make available for reference and use...those official records that have been determined to have sufficient historical value or other value to warrant their continued preservation by the state." It broadly defined official records, and spelled out the duties of the State Archives.

Several years passed before financial resources were available to implement the new law. In 1976, the Public Records Section of the Office of State History (successor to the Division of Archives and History) was reassigned to the State Archives as part of an administrative reorganization of history services. This gave the fledgling Archives its first permanent professional staff, but also added program responsibilities. The legislature finally provided funding to open an archives facility and launch a comprehensive archives program in 1978.

The State Archives began by accessioning the State government records deposited in the State Library over the previous century, and then continued accepting records directly from agencies. Its holdings currently consist of over 52,000 cubic feet of records in a variety of formats from the three branches of government. The State Archives takes both physical and legal custody of records when they are no longer actively used in State offices. Staff then review records and prepare descriptions of their content, access tools such as finding aids, and administrative histories of their agency creators to facilitate use of the records by researchers. The Archives also ensures the physical survival of archival records through conservation treatments, rehousing of records in archival containers, microfilming, and storage in a controlled environment. Finally, reference staff assist interested users by telephone, mail, or in the Archives' research facility.

In 1987, the legislature transferred the State's records management program to the State Archives, and the State Board of Regents changed the organization's name to the State Archives and Records Administration. These changes made SARA responsible for providing centralized services for the management of current State government Executive Branch records, including authority to approve the final disposition of all agency records. This was an important addition to its functions, because the proper identification of permanently valuable records of State government begins with the effective management and disposition of all records created by the State. A large portion of State government records are of temporary value, and SARA staff assist agencies in scheduling these records for legal disposition at the appropriate time. A smaller percentage of State government records have permanent legal, fiscal, or historical value. SARA staff appraise these records to verify their value, and then arrange for their transfer to the State Archives.

In recent years, SARA has developed a number of new programs and efforts to accomplish its mission. One focus has been to identify valuable records in the judicial and legislative branches of government. From 1984 to 1987, the State Archives participated in a Judicial Records Disposition and Archives Development Project to assist the Office of Court Administration with records surveys and schedule development and to appraise archival court records. Beginning in 1987, the Legislative Archives Program worked with the State legislature to identify its archival records and ongoing records management needs. SARA has also focused on identifying valuable records in nonpaper media. The Center for Electronic Records, established in 1990, will expand on earlier work in identifying and preserving records in a variety of electronic formats.

A local government records law enacted in 1987 expanded SARA's responsibilities for local government records. In addition to continuing authority for issuing records retention and disposition schedules for local records, SARA was authorized to establish regional records offices to provide advisory services and technical assistance to local governments, and to award records management improvement grants to local governments. Establishment by the legislature in 1989 of a special fund allowed SARA to fully implement the local government records law.

SARA also provides grants and advisory services to private nonprofit records repositories through the Documentary Heritage Program, established by law in 1988. To promote the use of historical records in New York, SARA is currently developing plans for access to a statewide computer database that will contain information on records held in State, local government, and private repositories.

New York State has a rich documentary heritage. Ensuring the survival and availability of that resource for all New Yorkers is the aim of the State Archives and Records Administration.

HOW TO USE THIS GUIDE

This *Guide* provides an overview and introduction to New York State government and its archival records. This concise overview of the State's agencies and their archival records serves as a point of departure for further research or information queries.

The *Guide* contains administrative summaries of the current functions and history for the more than 75 current agencies of State government and identifies over 3,200 series of valuable records now preserved in the State Archives. Archival records identified in the *Guide* are listed in the entry for the agency which created and maintained them. The records are organized and described in aggregate units called series. Series are groupings of records created and maintained together because they result from the same activity and often have a common form or subject. Generally, a record series is created by an agency program unit as a direct result of its activities to accomplish a mandated function. This second edition of the *Guide* contains information on every record series held by the State Archives as of December 1991. The State Archives acquires approximately 200 new records series a year. Researchers are urged to contact the Archives directly for the most current information.

ORGANIZATION AND CONTENTS OF THE GUIDE

Major sections. Guide entries are divided into three sections: the Executive Branch, the Legislative Branch, and the Judicial Branch. Within each section, entries are arranged by agency or other major organizational unit. While all three branches of government are represented here, the majority of records in the Archives and entries in this *Guide* are from the Executive Branch. New York's

Executive Branch is limited by the State constitution to 20 specified departments. Within the Executive Department, which is one of the authorized departments, several dozen offices, commissions, divisions, and other units operate independently and are therefore treated comparably in this *Guide* to the 20 Executive departments. The Legislative Branch section is arranged by the Senate, the Assembly, and by joint legislative commissions or committees. Judicial Branch entries are arranged by major types of courts.

Agency entries. Each entry consists of two parts: an administrative summary of the agency, followed by a list of archival records in the holdings of the State Archives. The administrative summary provides an overview of the agency, describing the current functions. It also has an organizational history that identifies predecessor agencies, changes in name, structure, and major functions, and includes citations to the major statutes authorizing creation of the agency and its administrative predecessors. A chart is sometimes included to provide a visual summary of organizational changes over time.

The second part of each agency entry contains a list of agency record series in the State Archives. Often, these lists are subdivided by the names of the predecessor agencies and/or the major program offices or other organizational units which created the records. Current and predecessor agency names (and related agency-level names) appear in all capital letters. Names of agency organizational units appear in upper and lower case letters. A dash before a unit name indicates that it is a subdivision of the preceding unit. A "double dash" is occasionally used to indicate that a unit is a further subdivision of the "single dash" organizational unit that is immediately above. In several agency entries, long record series lists are subdivided by subject categories to make the lists easier for users to review. Subject categories appear in italic type to set them apart from organizational unit names.

Below is an example and an accompanying explanation to illustrate the information provided in a list of agency record series:

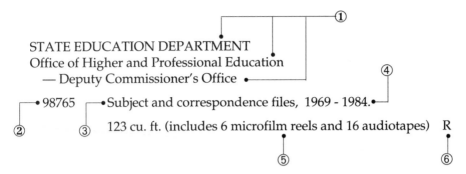

STATE EDUCATION DEPARTMENT
Office of Higher and Professional Education
— Deputy Commissioner's Office

98765 Subject and correspondence files, 1969 - 1984.

123 cu. ft. (includes 6 microfilm reels and 16 audiotapes) R

(1) Agency and subdivision/program unit names. The current and predecessor agency names appear in all capital letters. A subdivision or organizational unit name appears in upper and lower case letters and identifies the organization or unit responsible for creating or maintaining the series. The names used are the official titles of the agencies and units at the time the records were created. In a case where no specific subdivision/program unit existed or was identifiable, the records are listed under the heading "General Agency-level Records." Sometimes subject categories are added in italics in order to make long lists easier for users to review.

(2) Series number. The series number is a control number assigned by the Archives to identify the records, and is used by staff as a unique identifier for management and retrieval purposes.

(3) Series title. The series title is a concise statement of the form, function, and contents of the series.

(4) Dates. Inclusive dates identify the earliest and latest dates of records that are included in a series. If most of the records are from a more limited time period, the entry will also state the "bulk" dates.

(5) Quantity. The quantity of records comprising a series is usually indicated first in terms of cubic feet, a measurement of the amount of space occupied by the records. For a series consisting only of microforms or magnetic tape, the number of reels or tapes is given instead of a cubic foot measure. Information might also appear in parentheses indicating specific forms of material comprising or included in the series (e.g., volumes; sound recordings; audiotapes; microforms that do not duplicate paper records in the series; etc.). In the example, the series is mostly

11

comprised of paper files, and it includes a small quantity of microfilm and audio-tapes. (In the example, the microfilm is not a duplicate copy of any of the paper files.)

(6) Access Restrictions. Access to some or all documents in a records series may be restricted because of the fragile physical condition of the records, or to protect personal privacy, or to conform with legal requirements. If this is the case, the letter "R" appears. Most restricted records may be used under specific terms and conditions. Researchers must contact State Archives staff to ascertain how and under what conditions restricted records may be used.

Appendices. Because the State Archives and Records Administration has responsibility for assisting local governments in caring for their archival records, Appendix A provides a brief overview of the services of the Local Government Records Bureau. Local archival records are in the custody of each local government itself, not in the State Archives. In some cases, the State Archives has microfilm copies of some local records. These microfilmed local records are listed in Appendix B, and can either be used at the State Archives, or borrowed through interlibrary loan.

Appendix C provides a list of New York cultural and educational institutions that have access to the Research Libraries Information Network (RLIN), a national online database of information about library and archival research resources. The State Archives participates in RLIN in order to make information about its holdings more widely available to a nationwide research public. More details on the availability of information about State Archives records through RLIN is contained in the section "Obtaining Further Information," below.

Indexes. The indexes identify important government functions and agency and office names. Index terms refer researchers to the administrative summaries, not to specific record series. Researchers can then review the administrative summary to determine if the agency would have created records on a topic or function, and review individual series titles to make their own decision about which series might be relevant to their research. Researchers with specific questions can call, write, or visit the State Archives directly to discuss research with staff and avail themselves of more detailed access tools.

OBTAINING FURTHER INFORMATION

Researchers interested in more information about a series found in the *Guide* can call, write to, or visit the State Archives. Based on a series number or the combination of the agency name and series title, Archives staff can retrieve additional information about the records, or the records themselves. For over half of the records series identified in this *Guide*, more detailed descriptive information, called a series description, is available. It will have a narrative summary explaining more fully the contents of the series, and might also have a brief listing of container, folder, or volume contents. For a few series, detailed name or subject indexes are available to help researchers locate individual items. All of these "finding aids" are available for use in the State Archives Research Room. Copies of most finding aids can be made and sent to researchers for the cost of duplication.

Written finding aids are complemented by two automated data bases. The first, the Collections Management System (CMS), is a local online public access catalog to the holdings of the State Archives and the New York State Library. The Archives entries are updated regularly, and therefore CMS provides current, comprehensive access to the Archives' records series holdings. CMS provides a descriptive entry for each record series, and has index terms which provide access by name, subject, form of material, function, and geographical location. CMS index terms are more detailed than those provided in this *Guide*. CMS is available for use in the State Archives Research Room, and in the New York State Library, where researchers can use CMS, and staff will provide searching assistance. Access to CMS is also available via Internet.

Information about the Archives' holdings is also contained in the Research Libraries Information Network (RLIN), the national online data base operated by the Research Libraries Group (RLG), a consortium of over 100 major libraries, archives, and other research institutions around the nation. RLIN contains information on the holdings of the State Archives, as well as other repositories in New York State and around the nation. RLIN is a particularly useful tool for research on New York topics because it contains information compiled during the Historical Documents Inventory, a 12-year project initially undertaken by Cornell University and later supported by SARA, to inventory all the historical records in New York State. The inventory was completed in 1990 and nearly all the results have nearly been entered into RLIN, providing a significant research resource. RLIN entries are indexed by name, title, subject, function, form of material, and geographical location. RLIN Archives,

Manuscripts, and Speical Collections members in New York State are listed in Appendix C. Researchers may use RLIN at the State Archives or should contact other RLG member repositories for further information on the availability and use of RLIN. Researchers will need the assistance of professional staff to search RLIN; there may be fees for its use.

The State Archives Research Services Unit can be contacted by mail or telephone for further information about holdings and services. The Archives' holdings are available for use in the Archives Research Room, which is located on the 11th floor of the Cultural Education Center in Albany and is open from 9:00 a.m. to 5:00 p.m., Monday through Friday, except State holidays. Photoduplication services are provided by staff at a nominal cost, and self-service microfilm reader/printers are also available. Copies of microfilmed records can be purchased or borrowed through the New York State Inter-Library Loan network. The State Archives can be contacted at:

Research Services Unit
New York State Archives and Records Administration
The State Education Department
Albany, New York 12230
(518) 474-8955

GREAT INDUCEMENTS FOR

The Union Forever.

VOLUNTEERS

IN U. S. SERVICE !

Cash Down on Examination - - - - -	$238
Ballance U. S. Bounty payable on Discharge, - -	75
State Bonty, Payable Monthly, - - - -	216
U. S. Monthly Pay, $13 per month, making for three years,	468
Besides Clothing and rations	$997
Veterans receive in addition $200, making - -	$1,167

APPLY TO

JAMES W. REED

At office over No. 57 Main Street, Lockport, N. Y.

Special Inducements to Colored Volunteers in way of Bounties,
Full U. S. pay, &c., for service in another State.

☞ APPLY AS ABOVE.

Civil War enlistment broadside from Niagara County. Division of Military and Naval Affairs. Adjutant-General's Office. Correspondence and petitions, 1821-1896.

Civil War veterans at a Gettysburg reunion, 1913. State Education Department. Division of Visual Instruction. Instructional lantern slides, ca. 1856-1939.

Public health education vehicle, ca. 1920. Department of Health. Photographic prints and negatives of department officials, facilities, and activities, ca. 1920-1983.

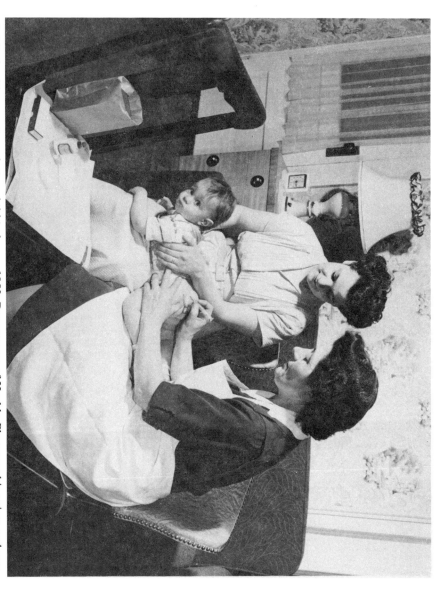

Public health nurse inoculating child in home, 1952. Department of Health. Photographic prints and negatives of department officials, facilities, and activities, ca. 1920-1983.

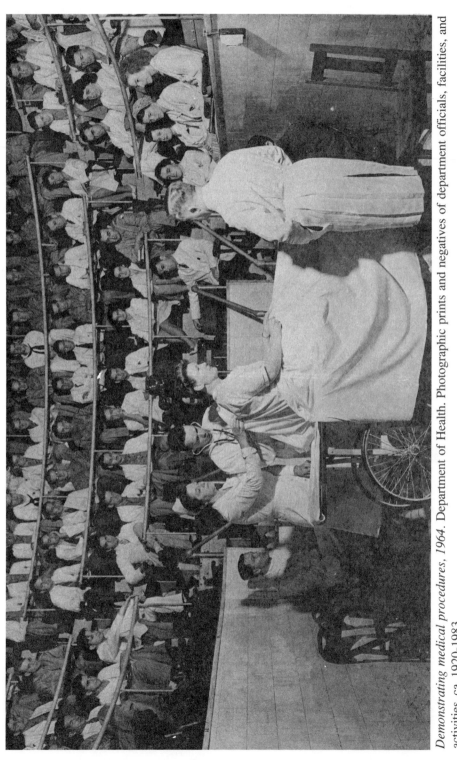

Demonstrating medical procedures, 1964. Department of Health. Photographic prints and negatives of department officials, facilities, and activities, ca. 1920-1983.

Adirondack lumberjacks, ca. 1910. Department of Environmental Conservation. Photographic prints and negatives, 1904–1949.

Conservation Commission Office staff, ca. 1915. Department of Environmental Conservation. Photographic prints and negatives, 1904-1949.

Protecting fish spawning areas, ca. 1920. Department of Environmental Conservation. Photographic prints and negatives, 1904-1949.

Aerial view of section of Far Rockaway, Queens County, 1967. Department of Economic Development. Land Use and Natural Resources Inventory and Land Related Information System aerial photographs, 1967-1974.

Employees of the Remington Typewriter Co., Ilion, 1911. State Education Department. Division of Visual Instruction. Instructional lantern slides, ca. 1856-1939.

Interior of building no. 60, General Electric Works, Schenectady, 1917. State Education Department. Division of Visual Instruction. Instructional lantern slides, ca. 1856-1939.

Students of School #4, Saratoga Springs with bird houses made as class projects, 1910. State Education Department. Office of Elementary Education. Historical sketches and photographs of school systems in cities and villages, ca. 1850-1920.

Part I

EXECUTIVE BRANCH

Office of Governor

Current Functions. The governor, as chief executive officer of the State, is responsible for ensuring that the laws of the State are carried out. The governor exercises executive power and authority over the administrative machinery of State government, including all departments, divisions, offices, bureaus, and commissions established by constitutional provision or by statute.

The governor acts as commander-in-chief of the State's military and naval forces; directs to the legislature an annual message concerning the condition of the State; recommends action to the legislature and approves or vetoes actions proposed by the legislature; convenes extraordinary sessions of the legislature, or of the senate only, when necessary; appoints, and may remove, heads of most State departments; prepares annually for the legislature a comprehensive State budget; and may grant reprieves, commutations, and pardons to persons convicted of crimes (other than treason or impeachment cases).

Organizational History. New York's first constitution in 1777, and subsequent constitutions of 1821, 1846, and 1894, vested supreme executive power and authority in a governor. Colonial precedents for a governor as executive officer were the director general, who administered New Netherland under the Dutch from 1624 to 1664; and the royal governor, who administered the colony under the British until 1776. In April 1777, the Convention of Representatives of the State of New York (renamed the Fourth Provincial Congress) adopted the first State constitution, and two months later George Clinton was elected first governor of New York State.

New York's constitution of 1777 created the office of governor "to take care that the laws are faithfully executed" and "to transact all necessary business with the officers of government." The governor was required to report on the condition of the State at each legislative session, could convene the legislature in special session, prorogue it, and recommend matters for legislative consideration. The governor was designated commander-in-chief of the armed forces and could grant reprieves and pardons to persons convicted of crimes other than treason and murder. The constitution provided for the election of the governor by freeholders for a three-year term, with no limit placed on the number of terms an individual might serve.

Executive power was restricted by means of a systems of checks and balances, including the legislature, a Council of Appointment, and a Council of Revision. The

Council of Appointment, consisting of the governor and four senators elected annually by the assembly, selected nonelective public officials except those otherwise provided for in the constitution. The Council of Revision, made up of the governor, the chancellor of the State's equity courts, and the justices of the supreme court, exercised a veto power over bills passed by the legislature, but a two-thirds vote of both houses of the legislature could override a veto.

Both councils were abolished by the second State constitution of 1821. The legislature assumed the power of electing major government officials (the comptroller, attorney general, secretary of state, state engineer, and treasurer), but the governor retained the power to appoint other state officials with the consent of the senate. Veto power was now vested in the governor alone. The governor could no longer prorogue the legislature, and his term of office was reduced from three to two years. The power to grant pardons and reprieves was amended to exclude only treason and impeachment cases. The other powers and duties of the governor were retained as they were described in the first constitution.

The third (1846) State constitution continued the governor's powers and duties as defined in the second constitution. Constitutional amendments in 1874 increased the term of office to three years, allowed the governor to veto individual items in appropriation bills, and provided that extraordinary sessions of the legislature could consider only matters recommended by the governor.

The fourth State constitution was approved by the voters in 1894 and remains today as the basic legal document of New York government. It continued previous constitutional definitions of the governor's powers and duties, but reduced the term of office to two years.

By the early 20th century, the executive branch of State government had grown to include nearly 200 administrative departments, boards, and commissions. Constitutional amendments in 1925 and 1927 significantly consolidated these administrative offices and expanded the power of the executive office. A 1925 amendment reduced the number of elective officials to four — governor, lieutenant governor, comptroller, and attorney general (the latter two were first made elective posts by the 1846 constitution) — and provided for the consolidation of all administrative agencies into not more than twenty State departments.

One of the authorized departments was the Executive Department. Two laws (1926,

Chapter 546, and 1928, Chapter 676) defined the organization and duties of the Executive Department. It serves as the administrative department of the governor, and through it the governor supervises the activities of all other constitutional departments. The governor was authorized to establish, consolidate, or abolish additional executive department divisions and bureaus, and many such offices have been created or eliminated by executive order or statute since 1928.

In 1927, a constitutional amendment specified that the heads of all departments other than Audit and Control, Law, Education, and Agriculture and Markets be appointed by the governor with the consent of the senate, and that department heads may be removed by the governor as prescribed by law. Another amendment in 1927 required all departments to submit annually to the governor itemized estimates of necessary appropriations and required the governor then to submit to the legislature an executive budget containing a complete plan of proposed expenditures and estimated revenues. In 1937, a constitutional amendment increased the governor's term of office to four years.

The governor and immediate executive office staff, consisting of the secretary to the governor, counsel to the governor, press secretary, appointments officer, and other administrative advisors and assistants, have been generally referred to (both before and after reorganization) as the executive chamber.

OFFICE OF GOVERNOR

General Agency-level Records

13682   Central subject and correspondence files, 1919-1954, 1959-1982.
1,230 cu. ft. and 2,451 microfilm reels

This series includes records of the following gubernatorial administrations:

Alfred E. Smith, 1919-1920, 1923-1928	101 cu. ft. (338 microfilm reels)
Nathan L. Miller, 1921-1922	17 cu. ft.
Franklin D. Roosevelt, 1929-1932	91 cu. ft. (438 microfilm reels)
Herbert H. Lehman, 1933-1942	106 cu. ft. (212 microfilm reels)
Thomas E. Dewey, 1943-1954	560 microfilm reels
Nelson A. Rockefeller, 1959-1973	520 microfilm reels
Malcolm Wilson, 1973-1974	57 microfilm reels
Hugh L. Carey, 1975-1982	915 cu. ft. (326 microfilm reels)

13681   Correspondence name files, 1959-1982.
546 microfilm reels

A0612   Appointment correspondence files, 1883-1936.
220.3 cu. ft.

A3218   Alphabetic card index to governors' correspondence files, 1907-1928.
7.8 cu. ft.

A0114   Messages to the legislature, 1957-1969.
1 cu. ft.

13684   Proclamations, 1976-1982.
7 cu. ft.

A3286   Thanksgiving proclamations by the governor, 1874-1925.
.6 cu. ft.

13685   Executive orders, 1972-1975.
.3 cu. ft.

13687   Addresses, 1975-1982.
2 cu. ft.

A0580   Reports to the governor, 1883-1902.
2 cu. ft.

A0581   Boards of managers reports, ca. 1893-1914.
4 cu. ft.

A0283   Reports and minutes of meetings of boards of officers of State institutions, 1902-1914.
10 cu. ft.

A3251   Proceedings and attendance records of managers of charitable institutions, 1907-1911.
.2 cu. ft. (3 volumes)

A0706   Minutes and public hearings of the Port Authority of New York and New Jersey, 1951-1974.
11 cu. ft.

B0294   Printed reports and studies, 1975-1982.
12 cu. ft.

A0595   Titles of bills received, 1864-1913.
10 cu. ft. (42 volumes)

A0596   Index to titles of bills received, 1872-1912.
6 cu. ft. (40 volumes)

A0602   Titles of bills signed, 1857-1870, 1899.
         3 cu. ft. (4 volumes)

A0630   Administrative files and ledgers, 1862-1923.
         1.3 cu. ft. (18 volumes)

A1887   Treasury warrants, 1702-1776.
         .3 cu. ft. (1 microfilm reel)

A1886   Returns of surveys, 1683-1686.
         .3 cu. ft. (1 microfilm reel)

A1885   Warrants of survey, powers of attorney, Indian deeds, and other
         records, 1721-1776, bulk 1752-1776.
         1 cu. ft. (1 microfilm reel)

A1884   Warrants to prepare letters patent, 1753-1770.
         .3 cu. ft. (1 microfilm reel)

A0597   Executive clemency and pardon case files, ca. 1860-1926.
         133 cu. ft. R

A0626   Clemency ledgers, ca. 1886-1910.
         2 cu. ft. (6 volumes)

A0629   Pardon ledgers, 1857-1937.
         8 cu. ft. (42 volumes)

A0603   Commitments to prisons, 1842-1908.
         12 cu. ft. (32 volumes)

A0601   Reports of prison agents, wardens, and superintendents regarding
         reductions of sentences, 1863-1888.
         1 cu. ft. (3 volumes)

A0604   Discharges of convicts by commutation of sentences, 1883-1916.
         7 cu. ft. (24 volumes)

A0628   Ledgers of restorations to rights of citizenship, 1857-1902.
         1.5 cu. ft. (6 volumes)

A0585   Restoration of citizenship records, 1911-1918.
         11 cu. ft.

A0599   Extradition requisitions and mandates, 1857-1938, bulk 1857-
         1859, 1883-1903, 1913, 1938.
         2 cu. ft. (11 volumes)

A0531   Records of charges, complaints, and investigations, 1877-ca. 1925.
         60 cu. ft.

A0006   Registers of appointments, ca. 1830-1910.
         25 cu. ft. (82 volumes)

A0606   Appointment letterbooks, 1857-1906.
         4 cu. ft. (33 volumes)

A0622   Civil appointments, 1858-1900.
         3 cu. ft. (5 volumes)

A0625   Appointments to office, 1859-1908.
         3 cu. ft. (4 volumes)

A0624   Applications for office, 1864-1905.
         2 cu. ft. (11 volumes)

A0600   Notaries public applications and appointments, 1870-1910.
         9 cu. ft. (51 volumes)

A0540   Records of applications, appointments, and legislative reception,
         1905-1929.
         ca. 52 cu. ft.

13686   Press releases announcing appointments, 1976-1982.
         5.3 cu. ft.

A0574   Press releases, 1923-1949.
         24 cu. ft.

13688   Press releases, 1976-1982.
         11 cu. ft.

13702   Executive Chamber news summary, 1980-1982.
         4 cu. ft.

13703   Public information photographs, 1910-1982, bulk 1945-1982.
         20 cu. ft.

13700   Audio and video tapes, 1951-1982.
         36.8 cu. ft.

A0607   Journals, 1859-1916.
         14 cu. ft. (57 volumes)

A0608   Blotters, 1859-1935.
         48 cu. ft. (77 volumes)

13690   Governor's daily scheduling log, 1978-1983.
         2 cu. ft.

George Clinton, 1777-1795, 1801-1804

A0142   Gubernatorial and personal records, 1725-1854, bulk 1755-1817.
         21.3 cu. ft.

A3189   Letterbook of official correspondence and proclamations, 1787-1795, 1802-1804.
.2 cu. ft. (1 volume)

Daniel D. Tompkins, 1807-1817

A0084   Gubernatorial and personal records, 1792-1823.
15.6 cu. ft.

Edwin D. Morgan, 1859-1862

A0623   Incoming correspondence, 1861-1862.
1 cu. ft. (3 volumes)

A4205   Abstracts of vouchers certified by the governor, 1861-1862.
.2 cu. ft. (1 volume)

David B. Hill, 1885-1891

A3216   Factory inspector appointment files, 1885-1890.
.2 cu. ft.

Benjamin B. Odell, Jr., 1901-1904

A0049   Official tabulation and statement of votes, 1904.
.5 cu. ft.

Charles S. Whitman, 1915-1918

A3217   Executive statements, 1915-1918.
.3 cu. ft.

Nathan L. Miller, 1921-1922

A3215   Board of Estimate and Control report files, 1921-1922.
1 cu. ft.

Herbert H. Lehman, 1933-1942

A0615   Proceedings, recommendations, and background files of the Governor's Conference on Crime, the Criminal and Society, 1935-1936.
3 cu. ft.

A0404   Invitation file, 1933-1942.
8 cu. ft.

Thomas E. Dewey, 1943-1954

A0187   Typescripts of reports from State agencies, ca. 1952-1954.
1.5 cu. ft.

Hugh L. Carey, 1975-1982

13489 Press clippings, 1975-1982.
312 microfilm reels

B1205 Index to Governor Carey's proclamations, press releases, and addresses, 1976-1982.

3 cu. ft.

Counsel to the Governor

12590 Legislative bill and veto jackets, 1884-1897, 1905, 1921-1989.
1,424 cu. ft. (1959-1974: 17,593 microfiche; 1975-1982: 138 microfilm reels; 1983-1989: 7,401 microfiche)

Deputy Secretary to the Governor

14145 Meeting files, 1973-1974.
2 cu. ft.

B1220 Subject files concerning State financial aid for education, 1962-1978.
5 cu. ft.

B1219 National Governors' Conference and related federal issues policy development files, ca. 1972-1974.
7 cu. ft.

Press Office

13704 Governor's speech files, 1975-1982.
23.5 cu. ft.

13705 Transcripts of press conferences, 1975-1982.
4 cu. ft.

13706 Press releases, 1978-1982.
2.3 cu. ft.

Special Assistant to the Governor for Education

B1216 School finance meeting background files, 1975.
1 cu. ft.

B1218 Subject files concerning Governor's Task Force on Equal Employment Opportunity for Women in State Government, 1967-1976.
2 cu. ft.

Public Papers Project

15732   Supporting documents for the published public papers of the governor, 1983-1988.
22 cu. ft.

COMMISSION OF IMMIGRATION

A0491   Typescript of report to the governor, 1909.
.3 cu. ft. (1 volume)

COMMISSIONER TO EXAMINE AND INVESTIGATE THE MANAGEMENT AND AFFAIRS OF THE OFFICE OF THE FISCAL SUPERVISOR OF STATE CHARITIES, THE STATE BOARD OF CHARITIES, THE SITES, BUILDINGS AND GROUNDS COMMISSION, THE BUILDING IMPROVEMENT COMMISSION, AND THE SALARY CLASSIFICATION COMMISSION

A0017   Investigation correspondence, transcripts, and printed materials, 1915-1928.
.7 cu. ft.

MORELAND ACT COMMISSION TO STUDY WORKMEN'S COMPENSATION ADMINISTRATION AND COSTS

10983   Investigation and administration files, 1938-1959.
21 cu. ft. R

COMMISSION FOR INVESTIGATION OF WORKMEN'S COMPENSATION LAW ADMINISTRATION

10997   Research and investigation files, ca. 1928-1944.
34 cu. ft. R

10987   Chief accountant's administrative and investigation files, 1938-1944.
2 cu. ft. R

B1314   Investigation case files and summaries, 1942-1943.
12 cu. ft. R

B1313   Transcripts of public hearings, 1943-1944.
1 cu. ft. R

B1317   Indexed abstracts of witness statements, 1942-1943.
3 cu. ft. R

B1312   Background files on workers' compensation laws in other states, 1937-1943.
1.5 cu. ft.

B1316   Press clippings, 1942-1944.
.6 cu. ft.

B1315   Receipts for records received and returned by the commission, 1943-1944.
1 cu. ft.

COMMISSION TO STUDY, EXAMINE AND INVESTIGATE STATE AGENCIES IN RELATION TO PARI-MUTUEL HARNESS RACING

B1328   Personnel and administration files, 1947-1954.
4 cu. ft. R

B1322   Transcripts of public hearings, 1953-1954.
2 cu. ft. R

B1327   Card indexes to harness racing associations and stockholders, witnesses, and Commission records and staff, ca. 1953-1954.
1.6 cu. ft. R

B1323   Investigation and exhibit files on individuals, 1933-1954.
6 cu. ft. R

10998   Investigation and exhibit files on corporations, ca. 1936-1957.
32 cu. ft. R

B1325   Investigation and bill files of the Joint Legislative Commission to Study the Pari-Mutuel System, 1939-1944.
2 cu. ft. R

B1321   Litigation files, 1953-1954.
3 cu. ft. R

B1326   Questionnaires returned by individuals, 1953.
1 cu. ft. R

B1320   Concessionaire questionnaire and exhibit files, 1932-1954.
8 cu. ft. R

B1319   Stockholder questionnaire files, 1953-1954.
6 cu. ft. R

B1318   Officer, director, and special stockholder questionnaire files, 1953-1954.
4 cu. ft. R

B1324   Press clippings file, 1953-1954.
3 cu. ft.

MORELAND COMMISSION BINGO CONTROL INQUIRY

10986   Public hearing files, 1943-1961.
3 cu. ft. R

MORELAND COMMISSION ON WELFARE

10991   Subject files, 1961-1963.
6 cu. ft. R

MORELAND COMMISSION ON THE ALCOHOLIC BEVERAGE CONTROL LAW

B1310   Subject and correspondence files, 1963-1964.
7 cu. ft. R

B1305   Transcripts of public hearings, 1963.
1 cu. ft.

B1308   Transcripts of public hearings of the Joint Legislative Committee to Study the Alcoholic Beverage Control Law, 1962.
.6 cu. ft.

B1311   Investigation files, 1945-1964.
6.5 cu. ft. R

10990   Questionnaire and interview files, 1963-1964.
11 cu. ft. R

B1309   Background files on alcoholic beverage regulation in other states, 1957-1964.
4.5 cu. ft.

B1306   Press release files, 1963-1964.
.5 cu. ft.

B1307   Press clippings, 1953-1964, bulk 1963-1964.
3 cu. ft.

COMMISSION ON GOVERNMENT INTEGRITY

15823   Investigation project files, 1975-1989.
41 cu. ft. R

15827   Litigation files, 1987-1989.
5 cu. ft. R

15826   Election campaign financial disclosure reports, 1981-1989.
5 cu. ft.

B1339   Informant correspondence files, 1987-1989.
10 cu. ft. R

15830   General information files, 1987-1989.
1 cu. ft.

GOVERNOR'S COMMITTEE ON HOSPITAL COSTS

10993   Correspondence, research, and report files, 1954-1965.
4 cu. ft.

CITIZENS' COMMITTEE ON REAPPORTIONMENT

10988   Correspondence, research, and report files, 1964.
3 cu. ft.

GOVERNOR'S COMMITTEE TO REVIEW NEW YORK STATE LAWS AND PROCEDURES IN THE AREA OF HUMAN RIGHTS

10994   Public hearing, research, and report files, 1966-1968.
4 cu. ft.

GOVERNOR'S COMMISSION APPOINTED TO REVIEW NEW YORK STATE'S ABORTION LAW

10996   Committee reports and public hearing transcript, 1968.
.3 cu. ft.

GOVERNOR'S COMMITTEE ON THE STATE EMPLOYEES' RETIREMENT SYSTEM

10995   Correspondence, research, and report files, 1965-1969.
.6 cu. ft.

POST-VIETNAM COORDINATING COMMITTEE

14222   Correspondence files, 1969-1978, bulk 1969-1972.
1 cu. ft.

TASK FORCE ON FINANCING HIGHER EDUCATION

A0402   Research and report files, 1972-1973.
2.3 cu. ft.

URBAN DEVELOPMENT CORPORATION TASK FORCE

A0506   Report on the Urban Development Corporation, 1974.
.6 cu. ft. (2 volumes)

GOVERNOR'S COMMISSION ON LIBRARIES

B0927   Public hearings files, 1977-1978.
1 cu. ft.

FACT FINDING PANEL ON THE SHOREHAM NUCLEAR POWER FACILITY

B0996   Correspondence and background files, 1983.
.1 cu. ft.

GOVERNOR'S ADVISORY COMMISSION ON LIABILITY INSURANCE

14520   Public hearing and background files, 1986.
4 cu. ft.

EMERGENCY FINANCIAL CONTROL BOARD

12564   Meeting minutes, 1975-1978.
3 cu. ft.

12565   Counsel's correspondence and subject files, 1975-1978.
1 cu. ft.

TEMPORARY EXECUTIVE OFFICES, COMMISSIONS, BOARDS, AND TASK FORCES (CONTINUING)

Law Revision Commission

15162   Report of recommendation on recodification of the Insurance Law (L. 1984, Ch. 367), 1982.
1 cu. ft.

Office of Education Performance Review

A0731   Subject files, ca. 1973-1975.
8 cu. ft.

TEMPORARY EXECUTIVE OFFICES, COMMISSIONS, BOARDS, AND TASK FORCES (DISCONTINUED)

Special Commission on Attica

15855   Investigation and interview files, 1971-1972.
82 cu. ft. R

B1341   Audio tapes and transcripts of Commission hearings, 1972.
6 cu. ft.

B1340   Motion picture film and videotapes of Attica Correctional Facility riot, 1971.
1 cu. ft.

New York and Massachusetts Boundary Commission

A0159   Records, ca. 1790.
.5 cu. ft.

New York and New Jersey Joint Boundary Commission

A0782   Records, 1867-1885.
.3 cu. ft. (3 volumes)

A0040   Minute book, 1888-1889.
.5 cu. ft.

Pennsylvania and New York Joint Boundary Commission

A0121   Records, 1867-1888.
2 cu. ft.

Bridge and Tunnel Commission

A0051   Report, 1921.
.5 cu. ft. (1 volume)

New Capitol Commission

B0700   State Capitol construction plans and drawings, ca. 1869-1900.
10 cu. ft. (ca. 2,000 items)

A1874   Plans of the new State Capitol, ca. 1873.
2.4 cu. ft.

B0701   Capitol construction progress photographs, ca. 1869-1900.
3 cu. ft. (3 volumes)

A1897   Construction photographs of the new State Capitol, ca. 1869-1897.
.5 cu. ft. (1 volume)

A3185   New Capitol Park specifications and map, 1897-1898.
.3 cu. ft.

B0111   Employee time books, 1870-1890.
4 cu. ft.

A3170   Receipt book for work done on the new State Capitol, 1879-1880.
.1 cu. ft. (1 volume)

A3171   Pressbook copy of payroll, 1881-1882.
.5 cu. ft. (2 volumes)

A3172   Roll books, 1891-1896.
.3 cu. ft. (7 volumes)

A3173   Directory of prospective workers, 1883.
.1 cu. ft. (1 volume)

A3174   Account of stonecutters, ca. 1870-1889.
.2 cu. ft. (1 volume)

A3175   Record of granite cut, 1872-1875.
        .3 cu. ft. (2 volumes)

A3176   Labor registers, ca. 1883.
        .3 cu. ft. (2 volumes)

A3177   Record of stone transported by canal boats, 1870.
        .1 cu. ft. (1 volume)

A3178   Record of stone re-cut, 1870.
        .1 cu. ft. (1 volume)

A3179   Register of stone cutters who applied for work, 1883.
        .1 cu. ft. (1 volume)

A3180   Record of hourly wages of workers, ca. 1870-1879.
        .1 cu. ft. (1 volume)

A3181   Record of hours worked, ca. 1870-1879.
        .1 cu. ft. (1 volume)

A3182   Register of running totals of payments to workers, ca. 1870-1879.
        .1 cu. ft. (1 volume)

A3183   Requisition book, 1872-1873.
        .1 cu. ft. (1 volume)

A3184   Payroll index, 1870.
        .1 cu. ft. (1 volume)

A0391   Check book, 1871-1875.
        .5 cu. ft.

New York Civil War Centennial Commission

A1444   Office files, 1961-1964.
        1 cu. ft.

A1445   Tape recordings, 1961-1962.
        .3 cu. ft. (12 tape reels)

B0309   Emancipation Proclamation Centennial motion picture film, 1962.
        1 cu. ft.

A0208   Scrapbooks and clippings, 1961-1962.
        2.5 cu. ft.

Commission on Cultural Resources

> A0736   Administrative and project files, 1970-1973.
> 12 cu. ft.

> B1056   Photoprints of Mental Hygiene and State University of New York buildings, ca. 1970.
> .2 cu. ft.

Commission on the Quality, Cost and Financing of Elementary and Secondary Education

> A0011   Records, 1967-1972.
> 13 cu. ft.

Task Force on State Aid for Elementary and Secondary Schools

> B1064   Day books of correspondence, memoranda, and reports, 1974-1975.
> 1 cu. ft.

Commission on State-Local Fiscal Relations

> B0305   Subject and meeting files, 1962-1965.
> 5 cu. ft. ˙

Commission on Acquisition of Land for Public Defense at Rockaway

> B0237   Administrative files, 1917-1918.
> 1 cu. ft.

> B0240   Card index to the Commission's administrative files, 1917-1918.
> .3 cu. ft.

Commission to Investigate Provision for the Mentally Deficient

> A4222   Correspondence and report files, 1914-1915.
> 1 cu. ft.

> A4229   Letter books, 1914-1915.
> .5 cu. ft. (3 volumes)

> A4231   Administrative reports and meeting minutes, 1914-1915.
> .1 cu. ft.

> A4221   Institutional reference file, 1901-1914, bulk 1911-1913.
> 4 cu. ft.

> A4227   Mental deficiency reference file, 1905-1914, bulk 1912-1914.
> .5 cu. ft.

A4223　　　Public hearing testimony, 1914-1915.
　　　　　　1 cu. ft. (5 volumes)

A4228　　　Photographs of custodial institutions for the mentally deficient,
　　　　　　ca. 1910-1914.
　　　　　　1 cu. ft.

A4224　　　Survey on public school classes for mentally deficient students,
　　　　　　1914.
　　　　　　.2 cu. ft.

A4225　　　Survey of mentally deficient inmates in county jails, 1914.
　　　　　　.2 cu. ft.

A4226　　　Survey of custodial institutions for the mentally deficient, 1914.
　　　　　　.2 cu. ft.

A4230　　　Day book, 1914.
　　　　　　.1 cu. ft.

A4233　　　Blank survey forms, 1914-1915.
　　　　　　.1 cu. ft.

A4232　　　Blank medical forms file, 1910-1914.
　　　　　　.1 cu. ft.

State Study Commission for New York City

A0566　　　Records, 1972.
　　　　　　10 cu. ft.

Commission to Recodify the Public Service Law

A3235　　　Transcripts of proceedings and public hearings, 1929-1930.
　　　　　　2 cu. ft. (6 volumes)

Franklin Delano Roosevelt Centennial Commission, Executive Director's Office

B1002　　　Subject files, 1981-1982.
　　　　　　4 cu. ft.

Board of Trustees of the Schuyler Mansion

A0057　　　Files relating to restoration of the Schuyler Mansion, 1911-1921.
　　　　　　.2 cu. ft.

New York State Committee on Sentencing Guidelines

14508　　　Correspondence and subject files, 1983-1986.
　　　　　　6 cu. ft.

14509   Meeting minutes and background reports, 1983-1985.
2 cu. ft.

14507   Public hearing statements and transcripts, 1985.
2 cu. ft.

Commission to Revise Tax Laws

A3231   Second report ("Depression taxes and economy through reform of local government"), 1933.
.3 cu. ft.

A0136   Confidential material submitted to commission, 1930-1931.
.5 cu. ft. (2 volumes)

Commissioner Appointed to Take Testimony in Matter of Charges Preferred Against Asa Bird Gardiner, District Attorney of New York County

B0986   Transcript of testimony, 1900.
.2 cu. ft.

Committee for the White House Conference on Education

A0618   Correspondence and working files, 1955-1956.
2 cu. ft. (2 boxes)

Commission on Relief for Widowed Mothers

A3107   Correspondence of the Secretary, 1913-1915.
.3 cu. ft.

A3109   Widow's pension legislation research files, 1912-1915.
.3 cu. ft.

A3106   Transcripts of hearings, 1913-1914.
1 cu. ft.

A3110   Register of children of widows committed to institutions by children's court justices in New York City and the Bronx, 1910-1913.
.3 cu. ft.

World's Fair Commission

A0569   Subject and meeting files, 1937-1940.
21 cu. ft.

TEMPORARY STATE COMMISSIONS

Temporary State Commission on Banking, Insurance, and Financial Services

B1105   Dissenting report of commission member Louis J. Lefkowitz, 1984.
.1 cu. ft. (1 item)

Temporary State Commission on the Restoration of the Capitol

L0001   Historic structures report for the Capitol, ca. 1982.
9 cu. ft. (18 volumes)

Temporary State Commission on Revision of the Civil Service Law

14086   Minutes, correspondence, and report files, 1950-1956.
2.4 cu. ft.

Temporary State Commission on the Constitutional Convention

A0001   Minutes, correspondence, and hearing files, 1956-1961.
15 cu. ft.

10992   Hearing, research, and report files, 1966-1967.
6 cu. ft.

Temporary Commission on Revision and Simplification of the Constitution

A0096   Reapportionment files, 1957-1960.
1 cu. ft.

Temporary Commission on the Courts

A0002   Correspondence, memoranda, and report files, 1945-1963.
121 cu. ft.

Temporary Commission on Dioxin Exposure

B0639   Research and report files, 1980-1983.
25 cu. ft.

New York State Temporary Commission on Executive, Legislative, and Judicial Compensation

16006   Background research and correspondence files, 1987-1988.
2 cu. ft.

Temporary State Commission to Recodify the Family Court Act

13980   Minutes, testimony and research files, 1974-1983, bulk 1979-1983.
9 cu. ft.

Temporary State Commission on Fire Laws

    A4217   Liability insurance survey files, 1954.
                 .5 cu. ft.

    A4218   County fire protection district map files, 1953.
                 1 cu. ft.

Temporary State Housing Rent Commission

    A1113   Administrative protest review case files, 1954-1962.
                 16 cu. ft.

Temporary State Commission on the Modernization, Revision, and Simplification of the Law of Estates

    A0564   Minutes, correspondence, draft legislation, and research files, 1961-1967.
                 9 cu. ft.

Temporary State Commission for the Revision and Codification of the Laws Relating to Municipal Finance

    A0003   Correspondence and subject files, 1937-1947.
                 2 cu. ft.

    A0390   Minutes, reports, and correspondence, 1939-1947.
                 37 cu. ft.

Temporary State Commission to Revise the Penal Law and Criminal Code

    13828   Subject, hearing, bill drafting, and report files, ca. 1959-1971, bulk 1962-1970.
                 15 cu. ft.

Temporary State Commission for Postwar Public Works Planning

    B1358   Minutes, 1942-1947.
                 2 cu. ft.

    B1066   Architectural perspectives of proposed State Education Department buildings, 1946.
                 1.5 cu. ft. (10 items)

Temporary State Commission on the Real Property Tax

    15604   Meeting, hearing, and research files, 1978-1987.
                 7 cu. ft.

Temporary State Commission on Rental Housing

13979 Subject, hearing, and report files, 1977-1980.
11 cu. ft.

Temporary Salary Standardization Board

A0032 Report file, 1938.
.3 cu. ft. (1 volume)

Temporary State Commission on the Coordination of State Activities

A0254 Report files, 1946-1951.
1.5 cu. ft.

A0583 Research and report files, 1956-1964.
36 cu. ft.

Temporary State Commission on State and Local Finances

15213 Legal consultant's subject and report files, 1974-1975.
4 cu. ft.

Temporary State Commission on the Need for a State University

A0614 Statewide higher education study files, 1946-1948.
7 cu. ft.

A3036 Research files on inequality of opportunity in higher education, 1946-1948.
6 cu. ft.

Temporary State Commission on Workers' Compensation and Disability Benefits

14484 Minutes, hearing and subject files, 1984-1986.
7 cu. ft.

Office of Lieutenant Governor

Current Functions. The lieutenant governor is designated by the State constitution as president of the senate and votes there in the event of a tie. The lieutenant governor is responsible for assuming the duties of the governor in case of the governor's removal from office by death, disability, impeachment, resignation, or absence from the State.

The lieutenant governor has statutory duties as a member of the court for the trial of impeachments; an ex officio trustee of Cornell University and of the College of

Environmental Science and Forestry; a member of the State Defense Council; and a member of the Committee on Public Access to Records. The lieutenant governor also handles special projects and duties as assigned by the governor.

Organizational History. New York's first constitution in 1777 established the office of lieutenant governor. The constitutional powers and duties of the office have remained unchanged except for the alteration of the term of office from three to two years under the second (1821) constitution, back to three years by an amendment 1876 to the third (1846) constitution, back to two years under the fourth (1894) constitution, and finally to its present four years by an amendment in 1937.

OFFICE OF LIEUTENANT GOVERNOR

B0632   Central subject and correspondence files, 1929-1932, 1983-1985. 35 cu. ft. and 86 microfilm reels

Executive Branch Departments

Executive Department

Current Functions. The Executive Department serves as the administrative department of the governor. In reality, there is no central operating structure for this department. Instead, the department consists of a number of divisions, offices, boards, commissions, councils, and other independent agencies which provide policy advice and assistance to the governor and conduct activities according to statute or executive order.

Organizational History. The Executive Department resulted from the constitutional reorganization of State government in 1925. Prior to reorganization, the executive branch of government had grown to include nearly 200 administrative departments, boards, and commissions. Constitutional amendments in 1925 and 1927 abolished or significantly consolidated these offices and expanded the power of the executive office. In 1925 an amendment provided for the consolidation of all administrative agencies into not more than 20 State departments, including an Executive Department.

Legislation of 1926 (Chapter 546) provided the statutory basis for the Executive Department, directing it to assist and carry out duties assigned by the governor. Five divisions were established within the department and their functions and duties defined: Budget, Military and Naval Affairs, Standards and Purchase, State Police, and Inter-Departmental Relations. The governor was empowered to establish, consolidate, or abolish Executive Department divisions as deemed necessary.

Legislation of 1928 (Chapter 676) abolished the Division of Inter-Departmental Relations, but the informal "governor's cabinet," consisting of the governor as chair, lieutenant governor, secretary to the governor, and heads of State departments who meet at the call of the governor, continued to coordinate interdepartmental activities.

Since 1928, numerous Executive Department divisions, offices, boards, commissions, councils, and other agencies have been established, altered, consolidated, or eliminated. The department currently consists of over thirty such subdivisions, which operate independently and supervise public policy in areas such as housing, human rights, energy, parks and historic sites, consumer protection, veterans' affairs, elections, cable television, and the arts.

Executive Department Subdivisions

Adirondack Park Agency

Current Functions. The Adirondack Park Agency is responsible for state and private land-use development plans within the Adirondacks Park to preserve and protect the natural resources. It establishes public policy for private land use in the Adirondack Park according the Adirondack Park Land Use and Development Plan. A State land master plan, developed by the Agency in conjunction with the Department of Environmental Conservation, guides management of State-owned lands. The agency reviews and issues permits for land-use projects, holds public hearings on proposed projects, assists local governments in developing land-use plans, provides financial assistance to local planning boards, and issues permits for regulated activities on freshwater wetlands or adjacent to designated wild, scenic, or recreational rivers.

Organizational History. This agency was created in 1971 (Chapter 706) to ensure the preservation of the Adirondack wilderness area that had been designated as part of a State forest preserve in 1885, and then as the Adirondack Park in 1892. The agency was directed to cooperate with the Department of Environmental Conservation to prepare master plans for managing State land for approval by the governor and to prepare an Adirondack Park Private Land Use Plan for presentation to the legislature. The legislation gave interim power to the agency to review and approve land development within the park to prevent activities that may have an adverse effect on the park's unique natural resources.

The master plan for management of State-owned land was approved by the governor in 1972; the land use and development plan for private lands was approved by the legislature in 1973. The 1972 New York State Wild, Scenic and Recreational Rivers Act (Chapter 869) placed privately owned land adjacent to designated rivers in a separate regulatory program administered by the agency. In 1975, the Freshwater Wetlands Act (Chapter 614) empowered the agency to review applications for permits to conduct regulated activities (such as draining, construction, or farming) within or affecting freshwater wetlands in the park.

The agency is governed by an 11-member board, including the commissioners of the departments of Environmental Conservation and Economic Development, the secretary of state, and eight others appointed by the governor.

ADIRONDACK PARK AGENCY

General Agency-level Records

14285	Minutes of meetings, 1971-1984. .1 cu. ft. (5 microfilm reels)
14286	Project files, 1973-1984. 14 cu. ft.

Office for the Aging

Current Functions. The New York State Office for the Aging is empowered to advise and assist the governor in developing policies designed to help meet the needs and to encourage the full participation of the aging in society; to coordinate state programs and services; to stimulate community interest in the problems of aging; to promote public awareness of resources available for the aging; to cooperate with and assist political subdivisions in the development of local programs; to foster and support studies, research, and education relating to problems of and services for the aging. The office is the state agency empowered to administer programs under the Federal Older Americans Act. Under Title III—B of this Act, the office designates area agencies on aging that, in turn, are responsible for comprehensive planning and coordination as well as the direct funding of social service programs for the elderly. The office administers the Title III—C program of the Older Americans Act (congregate and home-delivered meals). The office is responsible for administering the governor's discretionary funds under Title V—the Senior Community Service Employment Program. The program provides persons with low incomes who are age 55 and older with part-time employment in human-service activities.

Organizational History. The Office for the Aging is the successor to several legislative and executive bodies. The formulation of policies for the aging began in 1947 with the creation of the Joint Legislative Committee to Study the Problems of the Aging. This committee was reconstituted annually by legislative resolution until 1969. Meanwhile, in 1955, an Interdepartmental Committee on Problems of the Aging was established by executive order to advise the governor on problems and developments affecting the aging and to formulate recommendations for action. The committee consisted of the heads of 12 State agencies and the secretary to the governor, who served as chairperson. In 1960, the governor established by executive order the New York State Committee of One Hundred for the 1961 White House Conference on Aging. The Interdepartmental Committee on Problems of the Aging assisted the Committee of One Hundred in preparing a report on the issue of the aging in New York State. As a result of this report, in 1961 an executive order created an Office for the Aging within the Department of Social Welfare to administer programs of the interdepartmental committee.

In 1965 (Chapter 444), the office was transferred to the Executive Department.

This statute made the Office for the Aging responsible for planning, coordinating, and promoting programs and services for the elderly, and for reviewing and reporting on proposed legislation affecting the elderly. The office served as secretariat to the Interdepartmental Committee until that committee was discontinued in 1974. Since then the office has continued to provide technical assistance and guidance to other State agencies with programs affecting the elderly. In 1965 the governor appointed an advisory committee to assist the director of the office. A 1979 law (Chapter 132) required New York City and each county outside that city to submit to the office an annual plan detailing community services for the elderly. The office reviews and approves these plans and then allocates funds to carry them out.

No records in the State Archives

Division of Alcoholic Beverage Control

Current Functions. The Division of Alcoholic Beverage Control regulates the sale and distribution of alcoholic beverages by issuing licenses and permits to manufacturers, distributors, wholesalers, and retailers; investigating complaints against holders of permits and licenses; conducting disciplinary proceedings; registering brand labels; and controlling wholesale and retail prices.

Organizational History. In the final decades of the 19th century, declining property tax revenues led to a variety of new State taxes, including establishment of a liquor license fee in 1896. The Liquor Tax Law (Chapter 112) of that year abolished all local boards of excise that had previously collected liquor taxes for localities. It created the state commissioner of excise to control liquor traffic under a State fee-licensing system. The commissioner of excise appointed deputies or authorized county treasurers to issue liquor tax certificates and collect fees. Revenues were divided equally between the State and localities until 1915, when the tax was increased by 25 percent and this increase was retained by the State.

The Eighteenth Amendment to the United States Constitution outlawing the manufacture or sale of alcoholic beverages eliminated this source of revenue from 1920 to 1933. Anticipating repeal of Prohibition, the legislature created the Commission on Alcoholic Beverage Control Legislation early in 1933 (Chapter 4). Upon its recommendation, the Division of Alcoholic Beverage Control, headed by an Alcoholic Beverage Control Board, was created within the Executive Department later that year (Chapter 180). The division, which was at first concerned only with beer and wine because it was not expected that the Eighteenth Amendment would be repealed entirely, issued licenses and permits and set standards for the manufacture and sale of those beverages. In 1934 (Chapter 478), the division's jurisdiction was expanded to include all alcoholic beverages, and the board was replaced by the State Liquor Authority that consisted of five members appointed by the governor. It retains this structure to the present.

No records in the State Archives

Council on the Arts

Current Functions. The Council on the Arts promotes and assists the study and presentation of the performing and fine arts by surveying and granting funds to non-profit cultural organizations, local arts councils or consortia, and the New York Foundation for the Arts, which operates a revolving loan program for cultural organizations. The grants, allocated among the counties on a per capita basis, are distributed in program areas such as architecture and environmental arts, arts services, dance, film, literature, museum aid, music, theater, TV/media, visual arts services, special programs, and statewide service programs.

Organizational History. The Council on the Arts is the successor to the New York State Council on the Arts, created as a temporary state commission in 1960 (Chapter 313) to recommend ways of encouraging participation in and appreciation of the arts. In 1961 the council submitted a report to the legislature and subsequently received annual funding for the preservation and encouragement of the arts throughout the State. Four years later (Laws of 1965, Chapter 181) the council, composed of 15 members, was elevated to the status of an agency in the Executive Department.

During its first decade of existence the council sponsored performing group tours and visual arts exhibitions. It conducted special seminars and technical-assistance programs for cultural organizations and community arts councils. Since 1970 the council has also received annual local assistance budget appropriations for distribution as grants-in-aid to cultural organizations and institutions. In 1974 the council's membership was increased to 20 persons "broadly representative of all fields of the performing and fine arts" appointed by the governor. A chairman is designated from among the members by the governor. An executive director and administrative staff carry out the council's programs, including fiscal and program reviews of applicants for local assistance grants.

COUNCIL ON THE ARTS

General Agency-level Records
   14064   Grant application files, 1970-1986.
              1,047 cu. ft. R

Division of the Budget

Current Functions. The Division of the Budget advises the governor on fiscal matters and on the management of State government and formulates and executes the executive budget. To accomplish this the division estimates revenue; analyzes agency appropriation requests; conducts hearings to review agency appropriation requests; investigates, supervises and coordinates State agency expenditures; and conducts management studies of State agencies.

Organizational History. This division was established by legislation in 1926 in anticipation of the adoption of the 1927 constitutional amendment requiring the governor to prepare a State budget and the necessary appropriation bills to put it into effect.

Until the late 19th century the management of State finance rested largely upon the legislature, which appropriated money, and upon the comptroller, who computed the amount of revenue needed to cover the legislative action and notified the counties of the amount they would be required to raise for the State through taxes on real and personal property. During the last two decades of the 19th century, however, this system proved unworkable. The revenue raised from local sources was inadequate to support expanded State regulatory programs and supervision of health and welfare services. Therefore, the legislature added a variety of new taxes, largely collected directly by the State (see Department of Taxation and Finance).

By the end of the 19th century State officials recognized the need for a more unified fiscal management program. The New York Bureau of Municipal Research, a private group organized in 1906 to promote improved public administration, also advocated a systematic State budget system. At the urging of the bureau, the New York State Board of Estimate was established in 1913 (Chapter 281) to formulate a rudimentary budget and prepare appropriation bills. This board, consisting of the governor, lieutenant governor, president pro tempore of the senate, speaker of the assembly, chairpersons of the Senate Finance Committee and Assembly Ways and Means Committee, comptroller, and attorney general, was required to prepare and transmit to the legislature an estimated budget for the administration of State government. Also created in 1913 (Chapter 280) was the Department of Efficiency and Economy, headed by a commissioner who was also ex officio secretary to the Board of Estimate. This department was empowered to study the accounts and methods of operation of administrative agencies and to require and examine annual statements of proposed expenditures from each agency.

Ironically, the board and the department were abolished in 1915 on the eve of a constitutional convention which proposed amendments to increase the governor's responsibility to manage the executive branch and to develop a comprehensive financial plan for the operation of State government. Although the proposed constitution was defeated, the adoption of an executive budget system by the Federal government in 1921 and the progress in other states helped maintain interest in developing a system of budgetary control for New York State.

A Board of Estimate and Control, consisting of the governor, comptroller, and chairpersons of the Senate Finance Committee and Assembly Ways and Means Committee was created in 1921 (Chapter 336). It was responsible for presenting a proposed plan of expenditures to the legislature, although the absence of a constitutional base for budgeting left the legislature more or less free to develop the appropriation bills as it had always done. Constitutional amendments of 1925 and 1927 not only reorganized State government to make the governor the unchallenged head of the executive branch but also established an executive budget system. The enabling legislation that initiated the reorganization provided for the creation of the Division of the Budget within the Executive Department, abolished the Board of Estimate and Control, and transferred its personnel to the new division (Laws of 1926, Chapter 546).

Through an agreement with the legislative leaders, Governor Alfred E. Smith presented the State's first executive budget to the legislature in 1928, thus inaugurating a system that has continued intact until the present day. In the following year, Governor Smith's successor, Franklin D. Roosevelt, presented the first executive budget formally under the new constitutional system. Under this system, executives of all State agencies are required to furnish the division with estimates of the annual financial needs of their respective agencies and to appear at hearings for review of these requests.

DIVISION OF THE BUDGET

General Agency-level Records

16520   General subject files, ca. 1942-1987.
         326 cu. ft.

B1345   Subject heading index to general subject files, ca. 1940-1984.
         2 cu. ft.

14273   Budget request files, 1965-1990.
         226 cu. ft.

16523   Budget and appropriation files, 1983-1987.
         6 cu. ft.

16521   Capital projects files, ca. 1965-1985.
         52 cu. ft.

A0302   Transcripts of budget hearings, 1932-1941.
         6 cu. ft.

A0705   Postwar planning commission maps, ca. 1940.
         4 cu. ft.

A0038   Fiscal reports and studies, 1943-1945.
         .5 cu. ft.

B0919   Governor's town meeting files, 1967-1972.
         2 cu. ft.

16525   Local government files, 1962-1971.
         4 cu. ft.

16526   United States government files, 1981-1983.
         1 cu. ft.

B1055 Correspondence and reports concerning evaluation of the experimental prekindergarten program, 1967-1981.
1 cu. ft.

14150 Levittown v. Nyquist files, 1974-1983.
11 cu. ft.

Executive Offices

16568 Director's subject files, 1953-1983.
8 cu. ft.

16569 Deputy director's office files, 1971-1987.
11 cu. ft.

16524 Alphabetic correspondence files, 1956-1987.
27 cu. ft.

Organization and Management Unit

15000 Management reports, studies, and background files, ca. 1948-1986.
38 cu. ft.

General Government Operations Unit

16567 Management review and labor relations unit files, ca. 1954-1984.
32 cu. ft.

Budget Services Unit

13123 Memoranda on pending legislation, 1970-1982.
44 cu. ft.

Electronic Data Processing Unit

13802 Agency electronic data processing proposal and evaluation files, 1962-1980.
42 cu. ft.

13803 Summaries of the agency electronic data processing progress reports, 1966-1973.
1 cu. ft. (2 volumes)

13804 Day books of correspondence and memoranda, 1972-1978.
4 cu. ft. (15 volumes)

Education Unit

14147 Ford Foundation grant School Finance Law Study files, 1975-1978.
2 cu. ft.

14148   School Finance Law Study working files, 1975-1979.
2 cu. ft.

– Local Assistance Section

14144   Subject files, 1973-1982.
33 cu. ft.

14149   Day books of correspondence and memoranda, 1973-1981.
6.5 cu. ft.

14146   Reports on public education administration and finance, 1973-1974.
1 cu. ft.

Special Assistant for Education

B1217   Meeting files concerning educational finance, 1975-1977.
2 cu. ft.

Public Authorities Control Board

16147   Minutes and resolutions, 1984-1986.
2 cu. ft.

16148   Meeting files and application background materials, ca. 1970-1989.
28 cu. ft.

16146   Applications for board approval, 1983-1988.
25 cu. ft.

Independent Study Task Force

B1051   Working files for report on the Regents External Degree Program and College Proficiency Examination Program, 1983.
1 cu. ft.

Office of Business Permits and Regulatory Assistance

Current Functions. The Office maintains and provides comprehensive State license and permit information to new and expanding businesses. The Office also reviews proposed State agency regulations to ensure compliance with the State Administrative Procedures Act. Further, the Office is charged with helping to ensure that State agencies do not impose requirements that constitute rules without complying with the rule making process under the State Administrative Procedures Act.

Through Executive Orders, the Office is directed to: ensure that the State's administrative hearing system operates in an impartial, efficient and timely manner; review existing State regulations affecting the business community with goal of reducing unnecessary regulatory burdens; and reduce the State's paperwork burden on itself, business, and the public.

Organizational History. The Office of Business Permits was established in 1978 (Chapter 770) to maintain and provide information on business related permits and licenses. The agency was reconstituted in 1984 (Chapter 698) as the Office of Business Permits and Regulatory Assistance and expanded its authority to include the review of State agency rule making procedures. The Laws of 1987, Chapter 610 further expanded the Agency's duties to include helping to ensure that State agencies do not impose requirements that constitute rules without complying with the rule making process under the State Administrative Procedures Act. The Office is assisted by an Advisory Council consisting of the secretary to the governor *ex officio* and 10 members appointed by the governor.

No records in the State Archives

Commission on Cable Television

Current Functions. The Commission on Cable Television oversees and regulates the cable television industry by: encouraging development in accordance with a statewide service plan developed by the Commission; establishing and reviewing franchising practices; providing technical assistance to municipalities in franchise negotiations; and prescribing standards for the construction and operation of cable television systems. The Commission also operates the New York State Community Affairs Network (NY-SCAN), a government access channel that covers hearings, conferences, and other government proceedings.

Organizational History. The Commission was created in 1972 (Chapters 466 and 467). It consists of five members appointed by the governor, one of whom the governor designates as chairperson.

No records in the State Archives

Council on Children and Families

Current Functions. The State Council on Children and Families evaluates, coordinates, and monitors services to children and their families by identifying problems and deficiencies in service programs and recommending changes; reviewing and resolving administrative and regulatory differences among member agencies; and maintaining the Children and Youth Interagency Management Information System, which contains information on children in residential care.

Organizational History. The council was created in 1977 (Chapter 757). The Children and Youth Interagency Management Information System was created by statute in 1982 (Chapter 350). The council consists of the heads of 14 State agencies having programs or services for children or families and is chaired by the governor or his designee. The chairperson appoints an executive director as chief administrator of the council's programs.

No records in the State Archives

Consumer Protection Board

Current Functions. The function of the Consumer Protection Board is to protect the rights of State's consumers. The board coordinates the activities of all State agencies performing consumer-protection functions and intervenes on behalf of consumers in proceedings before the Public Service Commission. The activities of the board include conducting investigations and research in matters affecting consumers; representing the interests of consumers before federal, State, and local administrative and regulatory agencies; initiating and promoting consumer education programs; cooperating with and assisting local governments in developing consumer protection activities; and establishing advisory councils to assist policy formation in specific consumer areas. The board has no adjudicatory or legal enforcement authority.

Organizational History. The Consumer Protection Board was created by the Laws of 1970 (Chapter 294). The board consists of the chairman of the Public Service Commission; the superintendents of the Banking Department and the Insurance Department; the commissioners of the Department of Agriculture and Markets; the

Department of Economic Development; the Department of Environmental Conservation; the Department of Health; and the secretary of state. An executive director, chosen by the governor, serves as chairperson of the board.

CONSUMER PROTECTION BOARD

Executive Director's Office

    14500   Correspondence files, 1973-1985.
                8.5 cu. ft.

Commission of Correction

Current Functions. The Commission of Correction oversees the operation of all State and local correctional facilities. It advises the governor on policies and programs for improving the administration of correctional facilities and promulgates rules and regulations establishing minimum standards for the care, custody, treatment, supervision, and discipline of all persons confined in State and local correctional facilities. It also inspects these facilities to ensure adherence to standards; examines facility operations to ensure adherence to laws governing the inmates rights and prepares recommendations to assist in the development of facility programs for the effective employment of inmates.

Organizational History. The 1894 State constitution and subsequent enabling legislation provided for a State Commission of Prisons consisting of eight gubernatorial appointees. The commission was empowered to visit and inspect all penal institutions and to promote humane and efficient administration of these institutions. In 1901 (Chapter 12), the commission membership was reduced to three appointees and the commissioners were assigned to also serve as a Board of Commissioners for Paroled Prisoners. The board was abolished in 1908 (Chapter 239) and was replaced by a Board of Parole for State Prisons that was independent of the Commission of Prisons. The membership of the Commission of Prisons was increased to seven gubernatorial appointees. As part of the constitutional reorganization of State government in 1925-26, the Department of Correction was created and the name of the Commission of Prisons was changed to the Commission of Correction (Laws of

1926, Chapter 606). The commissioner of the new department became the chairperson of the commission. The Commission of Correction was placed administratively within the Department of Correction but retained independent powers of visitation and inspection. In 1973 (Chapter 398), the commission was established as an independent agency within the Executive Department. The commission functioned with part-time members until 1975 (Chapter 865), when the present commission with three full-time members and support staff was established.

No records in the State Archives

Crime Victims Board

Current Functions. The function of the Crime Victims Board is to mitigate the effects of violent crime by assisting its victims. The board provides relief to eligible claimants who demonstrate financial difficulty as a result of criminal acts, supports local victim and assistance agencies that provide direct support to crime victims, and serves as an advocate for the rights and interests of crime victims. A crime victim may be eligible through this program for reimbursement of medical, counseling, and funeral expenses; attorney fees; and loss of essential personal property, earnings and/or support. The work of the board was augmented by the Federal Victims of Crime Act of 1984, which provides additional funds to victims and to victim-support agencies.

Organizational History. The Crime Victims Compensation Board was created by the Laws of 1966, Chapter 894. Chapter 17 of the Laws of 1982 changed the name to the Crime Victims Board. The board consists of five members selected by the governor, three of whom shall have been admitted to practice law in New York State for at least five years.

No records in the State Archives

Division of Criminal Justice Services

Current Functions. The purpose of the Division of Criminal Justice Services is to conduct research and to provide advisory and technical assistance services to increase the effectiveness of the State's criminal justice system. The division advises and assists the governor in developing policies, plans, programs, and information system projects for improving the administration of the criminal justice system. The division maintains the criminal justice communications network (CRIMNET) as well as a computerized criminal history and statistical data file to identify individuals through comparisons of fingerprints and to provide prior criminal records to Federal, state, and local law enforcement agencies. The division also supports local agencies by providing computer services and technical assistance, conducting training, and management studies, maintaining breathalizer and radar equipment and developing programs in highway safety, crime prevention, and arson awareness. It conducts criminal justice research and acts as a clearinghouse for research and information relating to the administration of criminal justice. The division administers funds for and monitors local initiatives that support innovative probation, parole, community service, and other programs. In addition, the division prepares and evaluates a number of federally assisted juvenile delinquency prevention and justice assistance programs, and it receives and disburses Federal funds.

Organizational History. The Division of Criminal Justice Services was established within the Executive Department in 1972 (Chapter 399). The division resulted from the consolidation of three separate governmental units: the New York State Identification and Intelligence System (NYSIIS), the Office of Local Government's Division for Local Police, and the Office of Planning Service's Division of Criminal Justice. NYSIIS had been established in 1965 (Chapter 353) as a service agency within the Executive Department to gather, computerize, retrieve, and disseminate criminal justice information. The Division for Local Police had been created in 1967 (Chapter 168) to make recommendations for the improvement of local police services and to provide staff services to the Municipal Police Training Council.

DIVISION OF CRIMINAL JUSTICE SERVICES

Office of Justice Systems Analysis

16548   Summaries of uniform crime reports, 1975-1980.
21 cu. ft.

16549   Summaries of felony processing reports, 1974-1979.
             11 cu. ft.

– Bureau of Statistical Services

14319   Criminal court statistical reports, 1948-1979.
             15 cu. ft.

Developmental Disabilities Planning Council

Current Functions. The Developmental Disabilities Planning Council assists and protects the welfare of the developmentally disabled in New York State. The council serves this function by preparing, implementing, monitoring, and evaluating the State plan for the developmentally disabled; analyzing other New York State plans for possible impact on persons with developmental disabilities; collecting, analyzing, and commenting to the Federal government on data concerning the status of public policy issues affecting the developmentally disabled; coordinating State and local service providers to increase the productivity, independence, and integration into the community of persons with developmental disabilities; and supervising a program of grants for facilities and organizations connected with the care and treatment of the developmentally disabled.

In its State plan, the council must provide for elimination of inappropriate placement in institutions of persons with developmental disabilities; early screening, diagnosis, and evaluation of developmentally disabled infants and preschool children; counseling, program coordination, protective services, and other services for developmentally disabled adults; support for noninstitutional, community programs for the care and habilitation of the developmentally disabled; protection of human rights of all developmentally disabled persons receiving treatment, services, or habilitation; utilization of all available community resources including volunteer services; and other requirements specified by Federal law.

Organizational History. The Developmental Disabilities Planning Council was created by a law of 1981 (Chapter 588) to perform the functions and duties required by the Federal Developmental Disabilities Services and Facilities Construction Act of 1970, the Federal Developmentally Disabled Assistance and Bill of Rights Act of 1975, and the Federal Rehabilitation Comprehensive Services and Developmental

Disabilities amendments of 1978.

In 1983, the governor expanded the council's responsibilities to include planning and directing the basic grants program formerly monitored by the Office of Mental Retardation and Developmental Disabilities.

The council consists of at least 20 gubernatorial appointees representing State and local governments, nongovernmental agencies, advocacy organizations, and the developmentally disabled population. The Office of Mental Retardation and Developmental Disabilities is the DDPC's administering agency, assisting it with activities such as personnel and contract management.

No records in the State Archives

Office of Advocate for the Disabled

Current Functions. The Office of Advocate for the Disabled serves as a statewide advocate for disabled persons. The office advises the governor, the legislature, and State agencies about the needs of the disabled; reviews legislation, regulations, and policy changes of State agencies that may affect disabled persons; provides information and referral services to the disabled; and assists local governments and service providers.

Organizational History. The office was first created in 1977 by executive order. In 1982 (Chapter 718) it was made a permanent part of the Executive Department and headed by the advocate for the disabled appointed by the governor. This legislation also created a twenty-one-member Advisory Council to the Advocate, appointed by the governor.

No records in the State Archives

State Board of Elections

Current Functions. The State Board of Elections is responsible for protecting the voting rights of New York State's citizens by administering and enforcing the State Election Law; ensuring complete disclosure of campaign financing and practices; and maintaining the citizens' confidence and full participation in the election process. The board administers the Election Law by supervising the election process, maintaining official records of election results filed by the State Board of Canvassers, issuing rules and regulations for county election boards, and investigating possible violations of the Election Law.

The board ensures compliance with campaign disclosure statutes by auditing statements of election expenditures and receipts. It endeavors to maintain the citizens' confidence and participation by testing and certifying electronic voting equipment, initiating voter registration and voter awareness programs, and providing for servicemen's voting.

Organizational History. The State Board of Elections was created by the Laws of 1974, Chapter 604. This New York State Campaigns, Elections, and Procedures Law, initiating major election reform in the State, was a response to increasing public demand for closer bipartisan government supervision of the electoral process and for more detailed accounting of campaign activities by candidates for public office. The demand had been accelerated by the disclosures of misuse of public office and misappropriation of campaign funds during the Watergate affair.

Prior to the Board's establishment, the secretary of state had been responsible for election administration, and the attorney general had handled election law enforcement. However, the election process was mainly a local government responsibility. During the colonial period elections were conducted by voice vote. The first State constitution called for "a full and fair experiment" of voting by ballot. Laws of 1778 (Chapter 16) provided that the governor and lieutenant governor be elected by ballot while retaining the voice vote for legislators and other officials. In 1787 (Chapter 15), the ballot system was instituted for all elections.

The 1778 (Chapter 16) law also provided for local inspectors of elections who were to give notice of and conduct elections, transcribe voice votes, and examine ballots. Election results were tabulated by the county sheriff, who forwarded them to the secretary of state, except that ballots for the election of the governor and lieutenant governor were delivered by the sheriff to the secretary of state to be examined by a joint committee of six senators and six assemblymen.

The election procedure was modified by the Laws of 1799 (Chapter 51). Inspectors of elections continued to supervise elections and collect results at the town, city, or ward level, but results were then transmitted to the county clerk, who transcribed a county report that was submitted to a State Board of Canvassers consisting of the secretary of state, comptroller, and treasurer. This board was to canvass the county tabulations and publish the results. Later, the attorney general and the surveyor general were added to the board.

Local election procedures changed several times during the ensuing decades. Statutes passed in 1909, 1922, and 1949 created a board of elections in each county and in New York City. These election boards were required to transmit certified copies of local canvassing board statements to the secretary of state and the attorney general.

The Laws of 1926 (Chapter 437), placed the State Board of Canvassers in the Department of State and changed its membership to the attorney general, two senators, and two assemblymen. As before, election records continued to be filed with the secretary of state. The attorney general was responsible for enforcing the Election Law. When this responsibility was assumed by the new State Board of Elections in 1974, the State Board of Canvassers was placed within the Board of Elections. The Board of Canvassers is responsible for canvassing certified copies of statements submitted by county boards of canvassers, preparing election results statements, and filing these records with the State Board of Elections.

STATE BOARD OF ELECTIONS
General Agency-level Records

> 15004   State election campaign financial disclosure statements, 1974-1985.
> 114 cu. ft.

> A0510   Statewide general and special election results, 1800-1964.
> 16 cu. ft.

> 15883   Political advertisements and campaign literature files, 1982-1989.
> 28 cu. ft.

STATE BOARD OF CANVASSERS

> A0155   Returns, ca. 1880-1890.
> .5 cu. ft.

Governor's Office of Employee Relations

Current Functions. The Governor's Office of Employee Relations (GOER) assists State agencies in dealing with labor issues and administers health and safety programs developed through collective bargaining agreements. GOER carries out the State's labor relations responsibilities as an employer in accordance with the Public Employees' Fair Employment Act (the Taylor Law) and other related statutes by negotiating collective bargaining agreements with recognized representatives of State public employees; assisting State agencies to interpret and administer negotiated agreements; helping to define the State's role as a public employer in matters before the Public Employment Relations Board (PERB) and through the continuing contract arbitration process; supporting the appellate function of the Grievance Appeals Board in the review of noncontract-related grievances; and directly overseeing training programs and certain benefit areas for management/confidential (M/C) employees.

Organizational History. The Office of Employee Relations was created by the Laws of 1969 (Chapter 491). The office is headed by a director appointed by the governor. Its basic functions have remained unchanged since 1969, but it has assumed additional responsibilities such as providing partial funding (along with public employee unions) of employee training and development, health benefits, safety and health, and day-care programs.

GOER usually represents management on joint labor-management committees, which since the 1979 collective bargaining agreements with the unions representing State employees, have played an increasing role in the State's labor relations.

GOVERNOR'S OFFICE OF EMPLOYEE RELATIONS

General Agency-level Records

11558   State employees strike hearing and determination files, 1972-1973.
        17 cu. ft.

Executive Division

16243   Subject files, 1972-1987.
        31 cu. ft.

Division of Contract Negotiations and Administration

16227   Director's subject and correspondence files, 1969.
        1 cu. ft.

16223   Contract negotiations history files, 1968-1986.
40 cu. ft.

16226   Correspondence, policy statements, and background materials relating to strikes, 1971-1979.
3 cu. ft.

Legal Division

16231   Grievance arbitration files (litigated), 1971-1980.
32 cu. ft.

State Energy Office

Current Functions. The State Energy Office (SEO) is responsible for assisting the governor and legislature in the development and implementation of State policies relating to energy and energy resources. The State Energy Office carries out its planning and policy analysis functions by conducting studies related to energy supply, demand, and distribution; representing the state in energy and energy resource matters; participating in various energy-related intergovernmental and interagency task forces and working groups; and implementing the office's emergency preparedness, nuclear, and petroleum products programs.

Responsibilities for energy conservation include the development and implementation for the State Energy Conservation Construction Code; the State Lighting Efficiency Standards for Existing Buildings; the Truth-in-Heating requirements related to rentals and sales of residences; average fuel economy standards for passenger automobiles purchased by the State; energy efficiency standards for various appliances; and administration of the State's Federal conservation programs, including the State Energy Conservation Plan.

The conservation program effort is aimed at providing long-term benefits to the State's consumers in restitution for overcharges by many of the nation's major oil companies between 1973 and 1981. A variety of conservation programs, funded with monies recovered by the Federal government, provide energy-saving information, services, training, and technical and financial assistance to all sectors—residential, commercial, industrial, institutional, and the transportation industry.

The office provides public information and educational programs promoting conservation and renewable resources and operates a toll-free statewide hotline for individualized energy assistance. The Energy Office also conducts activities to promote the development of renewable resources and energy resources indigenous to the State.

Organizational History. New York State's official involvement in energy issues dates from 1972, when the legislature determined that the State's continuing economic growth and development, combined with environmental, social, and other economic issues, required a consolidated energy-planning effort. Chapter 386 of the Laws of 1972 established the Joint Legislative Commission on Energy Policy for the State of New York. The commission, consisting of ten members appointed by the majority and minority leaders of the senate and assembly, was mandated to develop and report on a comprehensive State energy policy.

This commission was succeeded in 1975 (Chapter 460) by the Legislative Commission on Energy Systems. This commission, also comprising ten legislative appointees, studied and reported on existing power resources and needs and potential alternate power systems.

Chapter 819 of the Laws of 1976 finally established a permanent State Energy Office to advise State government and the public on energy matters, promote and plan for energy conservation, coordinate State energy programs with federal programs, and develop and implement energy codes and standards. The Emergency Fuel Office (established by Executive Order No. 5, 1974 to regulate supplies and promote conservation of petroleum products during the energy crises of the 1970s) and the Atomic Energy Council created by the Laws of 1968, Chapter 947, to regulate atomic energy and promote its development and peaceful use) were abolished and their related functions transferred to the SEO. The SEO is subject to audit by the Department of Audit and Control every four years. Upon completion of the audit, a commission is appointed to determine if the office should continue unchanged, be changed in some way, or be dissolved.

No records in the State Archives

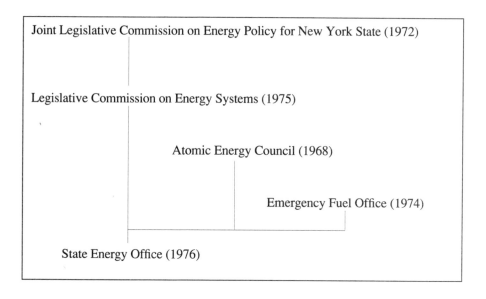

Joint Legislative Commission on Energy Policy for New York State (1972)

Legislative Commission on Energy Systems (1975)

Atomic Energy Council (1968)

Emergency Fuel Office (1974)

State Energy Office (1976)

Division of Equalization and Assessment

Current Functions. The Division of Equalization and Assessment is responsible for carrying out the programs and policies of the State Board of Equalization and Assessment, its directing body. The board's main functions are establishing policies for and regulating tax assessment and assisting local governments in administering the real property tax.

The division implements the board's programs and policies by completing statewide market value surveys, usually every three years, based on which the board establishes equalization rates reflecting the ratio of assessed valuation to full valuation in each assessment jurisdiction. These equalization rates are then used in a number of formulas: to equitably allocate State aid and sales tax revenues, to apportion taxes and costs among special districts covering more than one taxing unit, to calculate constitutional and statutory debt and tax limits, and for other similar purposes.

The division reviews county equalization rates used to adjust assessed valuations of real property in different towns and cities in order to equitably distribute the real property tax for county purposes. The division also carries out its responsibilities by establishing residential assessment ratios; assessing special franchises; approving assessments of taxable State-owned lands; setting railroad ceilings; providing local assessors with technical assistance and training; furnishing advisory appraisals of complex properties and certain special properties; advising on the use of a computerized assessment system; approving local tax maps; and establishing tax map standards.

Organizational History. The State Board of Equalization was established by Laws of 1859 (Chapter 312) to equalize county property value assessments on the basis of which a State property tax was levied. As a result of the 1925-26 State government reorganization, the board was placed in the Department of Taxation and Finance with responsibilities for coordinating and equalizing assessments for use in distributing State aid to municipalities and setting municipal tax limits after the State property tax was discontinued in 1928.

In 1949 (Chapter 346), assessment and equalization functions were transferred to a temporary State commission called the State Board of Equalization and Assessment. The board, consisting of three gubernatorial appointees, one of whom was a state tax commissioner, was directed to establish a program for revision of State equalization rates and to recommend a plan for permanent assignment of the functions, powers, and duties assigned to it.

In 1960 (Chapter 335), the board was reorganized and placed in the Executive Department Office for Local Government. The new board, consisting of the commissioner for local government and four members appointed by the governor, assumed all functions and duties of the previous temporary commission. Policies and procedures established by the board were carried out by an executive director who headed a division within the Office for Local Government. This office was abolished in 1975. Laws of 1975 (Chapter 606) established the Division of Equalization and Assessment as a subdivision of the Executive Department. The division is headed by the Board of Equalization and Assessment, now comprised of five members appointed by the governor, and carries out the board's programs and policies under the direction of an executive director who is appointed by the board.

State Board of Equalization (1859)

State Board of Equalization and Assessment (temporary commission, 1949)

State Board of Equalization and Assessment (Executive Department subdivision, 1960)

State Board of Equalization and Assessment (1975)

Division of Equalization and Assessment (1975)

BOARD OF EQUALIZATION AND ASSESSMENT

15267   Subject files of the chairperson, ca. 1950-1965.
23 cu. ft.

15175   Meeting files and attachments, 1952-1983.
48 cu. ft.

15178   Equalization rate, special franchise, and railroad ceiling complaint files, 1970-1983.
16 cu. ft.

15214   County equalization rate appeal files, ca. 1937-1969.
6 cu. ft.

15215   Special franchise complaint and hearing files, ca. 1907-1983.
20 cu. ft.

15176   Hearing transcripts, 1955-1983.
18 cu. ft.

14473   Hurricane Agnes flood maps, 1972.
2 cu. ft.

B1209   Lists, reports, statistical printouts, and related materials on land affected by Hurricane Agnes floods, 1972.
3 cu. ft. and 7 microfilm reels.

B1208   Emergency Hurricane Agnes flood project manual, 1972.
.3 cu. ft.

DIVISION OF EQUALIZATION AND ASSESSMENT

Executive Director's Office

15217   Subject and correspondence files, 1977-1982.
3 cu. ft.

Executive Assistant to the Director

15212   Subject and correspondence files, 1957-1978.
9 cu. ft.

Bureau of Industrial and Utilities Valuation

15085   Industrial property appraisal files, ca. 1948-1968.
39 cu. ft.

15174   Utility property appraisal files, 1949-1976.
46 cu. ft.

Bureau of Equalization Rights

B1207   Local government applications for State aid under railroad tax
abatement program, 1959-1979.
.4 cu. ft.

Other Records

14395   Statistical tables of real property exempt from taxation, 1967-
1979.
3 cu. ft.

B0925   Applications for State assistance for Hurricane Agnes flood damage, 1973-1977.
1.4 cu. ft.

Office of General Services

Current Functions. The Office of General Services (OGS) is responsible for
developing and administering operations and activities required to support agency
operations. It is also responsible for helping the State's local governments reduce
operating costs.

OGS supports New York State agency operations by carrying out programs in the following areas: building management; centralized purchasing; design and construction of public buildings; space planning and leasing; electronic data processing; telecommunication services; police and security services; operation of visitors' information services and a convention center; food service management in State offices; centralized supply and laundry services; centralized printing and graphics; centralized insurance services; interagency messenger and courier services; assistance to State agencies to increase their business and contracts with businesses owned by minorities and women; surplus property services; parking services; and management of vehicle fleets. It helps local governments reduce costs by distributing federally donated foods and surplus property and by offering local governments the use of its centralized purchasing system.

Organizational History. The Office of General Services was established by the Laws of 1960 (Chapter 459). As part of a plan to reduce the multiplicity of State agencies and duplication of State services, a series of 1960 laws (Chapters 459 through 463) consolidated responsibility for all State administrative support services in OGS, transferring to it the functions of the Department of Public Works relating to the operation and maintenance of public buildings and grounds (including communications systems); the functions of the Division of the Budget relating to retention and disposition of State records and the transfer and disposal of surplus State property; the functions of the Board of Commissioners of the Land Office (in the Department of State) relating to the sale, lease, or other disposition of State-owned lands not devoted to any specific purpose; and the functions of the Division of Standards and Purchase relating to the purchasing and standardization of equipment and supplies. The Board of Commissioners of the Land Office and the Division of Standards and Purchase were abolished.

By 1963, responsibility had been added to OGS for new parking facilities, fleet management, mail and messenger service, tour guide service in the Capitol, central data-processing services, and development of the new South Mall (Empire State Plaza). In 1967, responsibility was transferred to OGS from the Department of Public Works for design, construction, and rehabilitation of State buildings. The federal surplus property and food distribution programs were transferred from the Education Department to OGS in 1973 and 1975. OGS established the Emergency Fuel Office in 1973 to implement the Federal gasoline allocation plan during the gas and fuel oil crisis; this program was subsequently transferred to the newly created New York State Energy Office. OGS served, in 1974, as secretariat to the Committee on Public Access to Records, which was responsible for statewide implementation of the Freedom of Information Law. This function was subsequently transferred to the Department of State. In 1977-78, the State's supply support system was transferred to OGS from the Department of Mental Hygiene. The transfer from the Department of Mental Hygiene to OGS of the first laundry services operation was accomplished in 1982; additional laundries were transferred in 1984-85. By Executive Order No. 21 of 1983, OGS gained responsibility to assist all State agencies in increasing their business and contracts with businesses owned by minorities and women.

OGS's responsibilities relating to the retention and disposition of State records were transferred to the Education Department in 1987 (Chapter 42).

OFFICE OF GENERAL SERVICES

General Agency-level Records

16196   South Mall design drawings, ca. 1965-1975.
         255 cu. ft.

15727   Empire State Plaza (South Mall) construction progress photographs, ca. 1962-1977.
         25.5 cu. ft.

15760   South Mall constructors' semi-annual progress reports on construction of the Cultural Education Center, 1970-1975.
         3 cu. ft.

16187   George A. Fuller Company South Mall project central files, 1965-1982.
         39 cu. ft.

16211   George A. Fuller Company chronological correspondence files, 1966-1979.
         17 cu. ft.

15761   George A. Fuller Company monthly status reports on construction of the Empire State Plaza, 1966-1979.
         13 cu. ft.

15763   Empire State Plaza construction management daily diaries, 1966-1979.
         13 cu. ft.

15759   Executive office capital construction files, ca. 1967-1985.
7 cu. ft.

15764   Walsh-Corbetta project manager's subject files, 1968-1979.
11 cu. ft.

16191   Meuser, Rutledge, Wentworth, and Johnston South Mall project foundation, engineering, and inspection files, 1965-1978.
2 cu. ft.

16188   Harrison and Abramovitz South Mall project design implementation files, 1972-1977.
1 cu. ft.

16195   South Mall project specifications, 1964-1982.
27 cu. ft.

B1005   Contract specifications for Cultural Education Center and Commerce Avenue facilities, 1968-1970, bulk 1968.
.5 cu. ft.

B1350   Index of South Mall project contracts and specifications, 1965-1978.
1 cu. ft.

Office of South Mall Construction

16192   Main project files, 1965-1982.
135 cu. ft.

15762   Central subject files, 1963-1982.
31 cu. ft.

16208   Chronological correspondence files, 1963-1980.
8 cu. ft.

16209   South Mall project site acquisition and clearance files, 1961-1967.
2 cu. ft.

Office of Counsel

16198   South Mall project claims records, 1967-1986.
109 cu. ft.

Division of Land Utilization

B1303   Upland transaction files, 1963.
3 cu. ft.

B1304   Lands under water transaction files, 1943-1965.
52 cu. ft.

13633 Transfer of jurisdiction files, 1972.
3 cu. ft.

Design and Construction

16204 State Coordinating Committee on the South Mall Project monthly progress reports, 1962-1969.
3 cu. ft.

16214 George A. Fuller Company Safety Department records, 1966-1977.
21 cu. ft.

Public Information Office

B0638 Galley proofs of publication on the Executive Mansion in Albany, 1982.
1 cu. ft.

STATE ARCHITECT

B0274 Ledger of office expenses and State facility accounts, 1899-1913.
.3 cu. ft. (1 volume)

B0273 Appropriations and expenses journal for State facilities, 1905-1908.
.3 cu. ft. (1 volume)

DEPARTMENT OF ARCHITECTURE

B0336 State Architect's letter books, 1914-1917, bulk 1914-1917.
.3 cu. ft. (2 volumes)

B0339 State Architect's approvals of Special Fund estimates, 1922-1923.
.3 cu. ft. (1 volume)

BUREAU OF PUBLIC BUILDINGS

A4039 Inventory of the furnishings in State buildings and offices in Albany, 1923.
.3 cu. ft. (1 volume)

OFFICE OF SPECIAL PROJECTS

Executive Director's Office

    B1003   Subject files relating to the Eleanor Roosevelt Centennial
             Commission, ca. 1983-1985.
             8 cu. ft.

Division of Housing and Community Renewal

Current Functions. The Division of Housing and Community Renewal provides
financial and technical assistance for a wide variety of community development
programs and establishes and enforces housing regulations. The division provides
financial assistance by making urban renewal grants to municipalities and nonprofit
organizations and by funding nonprofit neighborhood preservation companies and
rural housing and community preservation organizations. It provides technical
assistance by supervising low- and middle-income housing projects and advising
local municipal-development corporations. The division regulates rents in New
York City, Albany, Buffalo, and a number of other upstate municipalities and provides staff for the State Fire Prevention and Building Code Council, which developed and enforces the Uniform Fire Prevention and Building Code statewide. The
commissioner of housing and community renewal also serves as a member of the
New York State Housing Finance Agency and is chairperson and chief executive
officer of the Roosevelt Island Operating Corporation, both public benefit corporations.

Organizational History. State policies concerning housing date from the creation of
a temporary Tenement House Commission in 1900 (Chapter 279) to study urban housing conditions. The following year the legislature acted on the commission's recommendations by passing the Tenement House Law (Chapter 334), requiring local governments to enforce minimum safety and sanitation standards in apartment buildings.

Housing problems intensified following World War I, and in 1920 the legislature
declared that inadequate housing posed a public emergency. The next year a series of
rent-control and tax-exemption laws were passed to protect renters and to encourage
construction of housing. In 1923 (Chapter 694), a Housing and Regional Planning
Bureau was established in the Department of Architecture to evaluate the effectiveness

of these laws. As a result of the 1925-26 reorganization of State government, this bureau was transferred to the Division of Architecture in the Department of Public Works in 1926 (Chapter 348). That same year the bureau's studies led to the passage of the State Housing Law (Chapter 823), creating a State Board of Housing also within the Division of Architecture. The board consisted of the state architect ex officio plus five members appointed by the governor. It was charged with studying and preparing plans to meet the state's housing needs, cooperating with local housing boards, investigating monopolies in the supply of building materials, approving the formation of limited dividend corporations, and approving and supervising low-rent housing projects undertaken by these corporations. The Bureau of Housing and Regional Planning and the State Board of Housing were both transferred to the Department of State in 1932 (Chapter 507) and designated the Division of Housing under the direction of the Board of Housing.

A major change in state housing policy occurred in 1938 when a constitutional amendment authorized the use of state funds for housing projects. That same year the Division of Housing was transferred to the Executive Department (Chapter 270), and in 1939 (Chapter 809) the State Board of Housing was replaced by a superintendent of housing as head of the division. Enabling legislation establishing procedures for granting State housing loans and subsidies under the constitutional amendment was enacted in 1940 (Chapter 148), and the title of superintendent was replaced with that of commissioner of housing. In 1961 (Chapter 398) the division assumed its present title of Division of Housing and Community Renewal.

Meanwhile, the State began to study the availability and quality of rental housing through the Temporary State Commission to Study Rents and Rental Conditions, created in 1948 (Chapter 675). Two years later (Chapter 250), the Temporary State Housing Rent Commission was created and empowered to establish and enforce maximum rent limits in selected urban areas. All powers and duties of this commission were transferred to the Division of Housing and Community Renewal in 1964 (Chapter 244).

Building code regulation also became an area of state study in the late 1940s. In 1949 (Chapter 700) the State Building Code Commission was created and empowered to formulate and adopt regulations relating to the construction of all buildings in the state. The resulting State Building Construction Code established minimum building construction standards statewide, although responsibility for enforcement of the code remained with local officials. Ten years later (Chapter 198) the commission was abolished and all of its duties transferred to the Division of Housing.

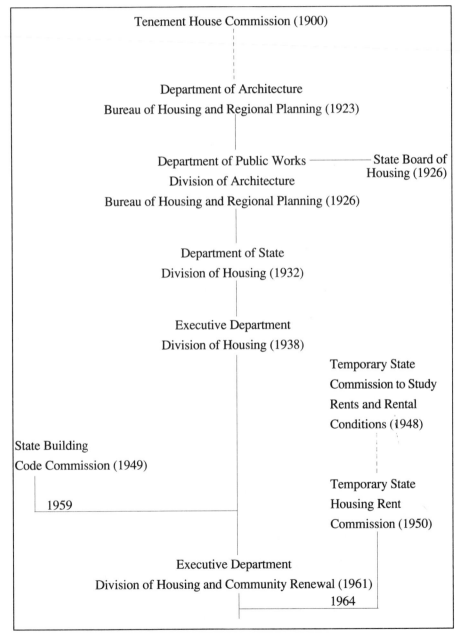

DIVISION OF HOUSING

    13056   Administrative protest review case files of the Temporary State Housing Rent Commission, 1954-1962.
              16 cu. ft.

DIVISION OF HOUSING AND COMMUNITY RENEWAL

Limited Profit Housing Company

    A0419   Assistant to the Commissioner's project files, 1947-1962.
              18 cu. ft.

Division of Human Rights

Current Functions. The Division of Human Rights is generally charged with promoting equal opportunities for all individuals in the economic, cultural, and intellectual life of the state. It does this by enforcing the State Human Rights Law, which prohibits discrimination on the basis of race, creed, color, national origin, sex, age, disability, marital status, arrest record, and some types of conviction records in the areas of employment, housing, public accommodations, nonsectarian tax-exempt educational institutions, credit, and certain commercial practices. The division receives discrimination complaints, holds hearings, and issues orders based on its review of these complaints. The division's decisions are appealable to the courts and the division may seek court orders to ensure enforcement of its decisions.

Organizational History. The origins of the division date to the enactment of the State's Civil Rights Law in 1909 (Chapter 14). This law guaranteed "equal rights in places of public accommodation and amusement" for all people regardless of race, creed, or color, although no specific mechanism was provided for enforcement of its provisions. In 1945 (Chapter 292) New York became the first state to establish the administrative machinery to enforce antidiscrimination laws when it enacted a "Law against Discrimination." This law established the State Commission against Discrimination, consisting of five members appointed by the governor, which was mandated to adopt measures to eliminate and prevent discrimination in employment because of race, color, creed, or national origin. The commission promulgated rules and regulations, investigated complaints, held hearings, and utilized the services of other agencies in enforcing the law.

During the next 15 years various laws placed further restrictions on discriminatory employment practices, and in 1962 (Chapter 165) the commission was renamed the State Commission for Human Rights. The commission was reorganized in its present form as the Division of Human Rights in 1968 (Chapter 958) under a single director (later commissioner). This law also created a Human Rights Review Board in the Executive Department, consisting of six members appointed by the governor, to hear appeals by any party from decisions of the division. Decisions of the board were then reviewable by the courts. The following year the board was renamed the State Human Rights Appeal Board (Chapter 368). In 1984 (Chapter 83) the board was abolished and provisions made for direct judicial review of the division's decisions.

DIVISION OF HUMAN RIGHTS

General Agency-level Records

      10409   Discrimination case files, 1946-1978.
                     378 cu. ft. R

Bureau of Program Planning and Development

      15003   Investigation files, ca. 1965-1975.
                     12 cu. ft.

HUMAN RIGHTS APPEAL BOARD

      15002   Case files, 1969-1984.
                     155 cu. ft. R

Commission on Lobbying

Current Functions. The Temporary State Commission on Lobbying attempts to preserve and maintain the integrity of the governmental decision-making process by monitoring and disclosing the identities, expenditures, and activities of lobbyists seeking to influence actions by the governor, the legislature, or State agencies in rules, regulations, and rate-making proceedings. To fulfill its mandate, the commission registers lobbyists; collects financial and other information on lobbyists, their clients, and public corporations annually spending over $1,000 on lobbying; conducts investigations and public hearings on adherence to regulations; issues advisory opinions to those under its jurisdiction; and reports on its activities to the governor and the legislature.

Organizational History. The Laws of 1906 (Chapter 321) required each lobbyist to submit to the secretary of state an annual statement containing the lobbyist's name, employer, and description of the legislation supported or opposed. The 1906 law remained in force until it was superseded by the Laws of 1977 (Chapter 937) establishing the Temporary State Commission on Regulation of Lobbying as an independent, bipartisan agency of the executive branch. The commission consists of six members, two appointed solely by the governor and four others appointed by the governor on nomination by the temporary president of the senate, minority leader of the senate, speaker of the assembly, and minority leader of the assembly.

No records in the State Archives

Commission on Quality of Care for the Mentally Disabled

Current Functions. This commission protects the health and welfare of the mentally ill, the mentally retarded and developmentally disabled, and alcohol and substance abusers by providing independent oversight and review of the operations of State and State-licensed programs serving these populations. It carries out this responsibility by reviewing the organization and operations of the Department of Mental Hygiene facilities and programs to ensure a uniformly high standard of care for the mentally disabled; reviewing cost effectiveness of the management, supervision, and delivery of mental hygiene programs and procedures; investigating complaints of patients, residents, and employees of mental hygiene facilities, including allegations of patient abuse or mistreatment; training, orienting, and assisting members of boards of visitors of mental hygiene facilities as needed to help them effectively oversee the facilities; reviewing and, where appropriate, investigating deaths of patients in mental hygiene facilities operated or licensed by the State; and administering the State's federally funded Protection and Advocacy Program for the Developmentally Disabled, Client Assistance Program, and Protection and Advocacy Program for Mentally Ill Individuals.

Organizational History. The State Commmission on Quality of Care for the Mentally Disabled was created by a law of 1977 (Chapter 655) to carry out oversight and review of mental hygiene programs and facilities as specified by the law. The governor also assigned the commission to administer the State's Protection and Advocacy Program for the Developmentally Disabled. As a condition of receiving federal funding under the 1975 Federal Developmentally Disabled Assistance and Bill of Rights Act, states were required to have a system to protect and advocate the rights of the developmentally disabled.

In 1984, the governor assigned the commission to administer the State's Client Assistance Program in accordance with a requirement in the Federal Rehabilitation Amendments that states have a system to assist disabled individuals receiving or requesting rehabilitation services. In 1986 the governor assigned the commission to administer the State's federally funded Protection and Advocacy Program for the Mentally Ill. The commission is comprised of three gubernatorial appointees over-seeing the operation of two advisory bodies and seven bureaus.

No records in the State Archives

Division of Military and Naval Affairs

Current Functions. The Division of Military and Naval Affairs administers the State's military forces and facilities and coordinates the State's emergency prepared-ness plans and response to disasters. The military forces consist of the New York Army National Guard, the New York Air National Guard, and the New York Naval Militia, which serve as reserve components to the United States Army, Air Force, and Navy. They can be activated by the Federal government or the governor in times of emergency. The New York Guard is organized in cadre form and provides a State reserve force if the Army National Guard is ordered into Federal service. The divi-sion also administers the State Reserve and Retired Lists of military personnel. The division includes the State Civil Defense Commission, which adopts and promul-gates statewide civil defense and disaster plans.

Organizational History. The first State constitution of 1777 and all subsequent con-stitutions designated the governor as commander-in-chief of the State's armed forces. In

1786 the governor appointed an adjutant general to supervise the militia and all military establishments in the State. The governor was authorized to appoint an adjutant general by the constitutions of 1821 and 1846 in response to the passage of a Federal statute of 1792 requiring each state to appoint such an officer. During the 19th century various staff officers, including inspector general, commissary general, judge advocate, quartermaster general, surgeon general, paymaster general, and engineer-in-chief, were established by statute or by the constitution to assist the adjutant general. In 1862 (Chapter 477) the organized militia was officially designated as the National Guard of New York State. The State Naval Militia was established by law in 1889 (Chapter 492).

The 1894 constitution authorized the governor to appoint a military secretary in addition to the adjutant general. From 1894 until 1926 the military secretary and the adjutant general shared responsibility for supervising the State's defense. A consolidated military law enacted in 1909 (Chapter 41) provided that the adjutant general assume the duties of all existing staff offices.

In 1926 (Chapter 546), a year after ratification of the constitutional reorganization of State government, the Division of Military and Naval Affairs, headed by an adjutant general appointed by the governor, was established within the Executive Department. In addition to assuming responsibility for the State's military and naval staff departments, the Division took over supervision of the State Soldiers' and Sailors' Home at Bath (renamed the State Camp for Veterans), the New York State Monuments Commission for the Battlefields of Gettysburg, Chattanooga, and Antietam, the Bureau for the Relief of Sick and Disabled Veterans, and the New York State Bonus Commission.

The Bath facility was incorporated in 1876 (Chapter 270) as the Grand Army of the Republic Soldiers' Home of the State of New York under the direction of a board of trustees to house honorably discharged veterans of the Civil War. Two years later (Chapter 48), it was taken over by the State and renamed the New York State Soldiers' and Sailors' Home. The Monuments Commission, consisting of three veterans appointed by the Adjutant General, was created in 1913 (Chapter 550) to continue the work of erecting memorials to New York State's participation in the Civil War battles at Gettysburg, Chattanooga, and Antietam. Several earlier commissions were charged with memorializing these battlefields individually. The New York Veterans Relief Commission, consisting of the adjutant general, comptroller, and attorney general, was established in 1922 (Chapter 589) to administer State financial aid to disabled World War I veterans. The following year (Chapter 326) the commission was replaced by the Bureau for the Relief of Sick and Disabled Veterans under the adjutant general. The Bonus Commission, consisting of the adjutant general, comptroller, attorney general, and treasurer, was established in 1924 (Chapter 19) following a 1923 constitutional amendment allowing the State to provide direct bonus payments to honorably discharged veterans of World War I.

When the Division of Veterans Affairs was created in 1945 (Chapter 763) to provide services to returning World War II veterans, the adjutant general was designated chairman of its Veterans Affairs Commission, an advisory body. In 1949 (Chapter 498) the adjutant general was replaced with the newly created position of chief of staff to the governor as head of the Division of Military and Naval Affairs. The State Civil Defense Commission was established in 1951 (Chapter 784) as an independent unit in the Executive Department to prepare for the State's defense in the event of attack. The commission was transferred to the Department of Transportation in 1971 (Chapter 73), and some of its functions were dispersed to other agencies. In 1973 (Chapter 93) the commission was transferred to Division of Military and Naval Affairs, with its former functions reinstated and with the additional responsibility for coordinating statewide disaster planning.

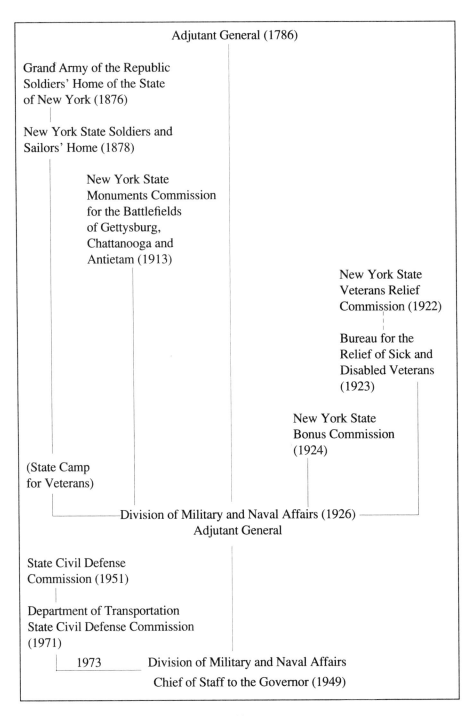

Adjutant General (1786)

Grand Army of the Republic
Soldiers' Home of the State
of New York (1876)

New York State Soldiers and
Sailors' Home (1878)

New York State
Monuments Commission
for the Battlefields
of Gettysburg,
Chattanooga and
Antietam (1913)

New York State
Veterans Relief
Commission (1922)

Bureau for the
Relief of Sick and
Disabled Veterans
(1923)

New York State
Bonus Commission
(1924)

(State Camp
for Veterans)

Division of Military and Naval Affairs (1926)
Adjutant General

State Civil Defense
Commission (1951)

Department of Transportation
State Civil Defense Commission
(1971)

1973   Division of Military and Naval Affairs
Chief of Staff to the Governor (1949)

ADJUTANT-GENERAL'S OFFICE

B0462   Correspondence and petitions, 1821-1896.
         61.5 cu. ft.

A4145   Letter books of outgoing correspondence, 1809-1850, bulk 1832-
         1850.
         .3 cu. ft. (2 volumes)

13722   Register of letters received, 1862-1866.
         3 cu. ft. (14 volumes)

A4130   Duplicate correspondence directed to and received from military
         offices, ca. 1861-1866, bulk 1861.
         .5 cu. ft.

A4153   Registers recording the transmission of documents from the
         Adjutant-General's Office to militia officers, 1858-1863.
         .1 cu. ft. (2 volumes)

A4148   Telegrams received and sent, 1862.
         .6 cu. ft. (2 volumes)

14403   General orders, 1802-1975.
         9.2 cu. ft.

14405   Special orders, 1855-1975.
         93.3 cu. ft. (343 volumes)

14404   Letter orders, 1956-1968.
         4 cu. ft. (19 volumes)

A0172   Certificates of appointment and general and special orders, 1823-
         1864.
         .3 cu. ft.

A0239   Military returns, 1781-1814.
         .5 cu. ft.

13729   Organization rosters of military officers, 1800-1899.
         4 cu. ft. (14 volumes)

13728   Abstract of military commissions issued, 1823-1909.
         4 cu. ft. (15 volumes)

13727   Register of supernumerary officers, 1848-1883.
         .3 cu. ft. (1 volume)

13726   National Guard muster rolls, 1878-1954.
87 cu. ft. (311 volumes)

13723   New York Naval Militia roster of commissioned officers, 1891-1898.
.3 cu. ft. (1 volume)

A0861   Military affairs records, 1806-1840.
.3 cu. ft.

B0810   War of 1812 abstracts of payrolls for New York State Militia, 1812-1814.
50 cu. ft.

B0811   War of 1812 payrolls for New York State Militia units, 1812-1814.
4 cu. ft.

A0020   War of 1812 certificates of claim, ca. 1812-1870.
18 cu. ft.

A4151   Journal of patents for lands in the Military Bounty Land District in Illinois issued to War of 1812 veterans, 1817-1819.
.3 cu. ft. (1 volume)

A3282   Appeals and inspection returns, 1829-1830.
.4 cu. ft.

A4154   Record of militia fines, 1836-1846.
.1 cu. ft. (1 volume)

A4150   Description of New York State Militia by location, ca. 1846-1857.
.6 cu. ft. (2 volumes)

A0162   Putnam Continental Artillery, Company C minute book, 1854-1859.
.3 cu. ft.

A4109   Militia enrollment returns filed by county boards of supervisors, 1858.
.5 cu. ft.

A0563   National Guard records, 1861-1917.
20 cu. ft.

A4152   Roster of officers of New York State volunteer regiments, 1861-1862.
.1 cu. ft. (1 volume)

B0311 Roster of medical staff of New York State volunteer regiments, 1861-1865.
.2 cu. ft. (1 volume)

A4125 Resignation and claim records, 1861-1890, bulk ca. 1870-1880.
.5 cu. ft.

A4166 Twenty-Second New York State Volunteers regimental records, 1861-1865.
.6 cu. ft. (4 volumes)

B0637 Atlas to accompany the official records of the Union and Confederate armies, 1861-1865.
.6 cu. ft. (1 volume)

A0154 Regimental records, 1862-1865.
1.5 cu. ft.

A4155 Registers recording enrollment of persons liable to military duty for Buffalo 1st Ward and Tonawanda, 1862.
.2 cu. ft. (2 volumes)

A4110 Rough abstracts of salaries and ordnance expenditures, 1863-1866.
.5 cu. ft.

A0227 First Artillery New York State Volunteers regimental records, 1863-1865.
.3 cu. ft. (2 volumes)

A4156 Statistical register for enrollment of men liable for National Guard duty, 1864.
.1 cu. ft. (1 volume)

13725 Descriptive Roll of the Howitzer Battery, Eleventh Brigade, National Guard, 1864-1884.
.3 cu. ft. (1 volume)

13774 Town clerks' registers of men who served in the Civil War, ca. 1865-1867.
27.6 cu. ft.

B0633 Descriptive book of the 193rd New York Volunteer Infantry, 1865.
.5 cu. ft. (1 volume)

A4160 Register of United States Colored Troops filing federal claims, 1866-1869.
.2 cu. ft. (1 volume)

A4107   National Guard parade returns for Uniform Fund, 1870-1875.
1.5 cu. ft.

A4122   Telegrams pertaining to the Buffalo Riot, 1892.
.5 cu. ft.

A4123   Monuments and dedication ceremonies records, 1893.
.5 cu. ft.

A4132   Military operations scrapbooks, 1897-1908.
1.5 cu. ft. (3 volumes)

B0809   Abstracts of Spanish-American War service records for New York
National Guard and naval militia units, 1898.
14 cu. ft.

B0801   Abstracts of Spanish-American War muster rolls for National
Guard units mustered into federal service, 1898.
24 cu. ft. (48 volumes)

B0636   Register of payments made to Spanish-American War volunteers,
1907-1934, bulk 1907-1919.
.3 cu. ft. (1 volume)

B0802   Mexican Border Campaign abstracts of muster rolls for National
Guard units mustered into federal service, 1916-1917.
19 cu. ft. (38 volumes)

B0808   World War I abstracts of service records for New York National
Guard and naval militia units, 1917-1919.
238 cu. ft.

B0814   World War I muster rolls of New York National Guard units serving in the United States Army, 1917-1918.
4 cu. ft. (12 volumes)

B1357   World War I veterans bonus cards, 1914-1919.
97 microfilm reels.

INSPECTOR GENERAL'S OFFICE

A4100   Administrative correspondence files, 1859-1875, bulk 1859-1862.
.5 cu. ft.

A4103   Copies of correspondence forwarded from the governor's office,
1861-1862.
.5 cu. ft.

A4133   Letter book, 1863-1868.
.5 cu. ft. (1 volume)

A4101   Annual inspection reports and returns, 1867-1888, bulk 1880-1888.
1 cu. ft.

A4102   Examining Board proceedings, 1874.
.5 cu. ft.

JUDGE ADVOCATE GENERAL'S OFFICE

A4140   Register concerning militia general officers and communications received and sent, 1819-1820.
.3 cu. ft. (1 volume)

QUARTERMASTER GENERAL'S OFFICE

A4106   Administrative correspondence, 1861-1868.
1.5 cu. ft.

PAYMASTER GENERAL'S OFFICE

A4146   Outgoing correspondence, 1865.
.6 cu. ft. (2 volumes)

A4139   Bounty ledgers, 1863-1866.
1 cu. ft. (3 volumes)

A4159   Register of bounty claims, ca. 1864-1865.
.2 cu. ft. (1 volume)

A4161   Bounty payment register, 1865-1867.
.3 cu. ft. (1 volume)

A4165   Register of men claiming bounty money, ca. 1865-1868.
.1 cu. ft. (1 volume)

A4164   Register of bounty applications, 1876-1882.
.1 cu. ft. (1 volume)

A4127   Claims files, 1875-1884, bulk 1880-1883.
.5 cu. ft.

A4128 Bi-monthly accounts of monies received and disbursed, 1883-1886.
.2 cu. ft.

COMMISSARY GENERAL'S OFFICE

A4105 Administrative files, 1861-1886, bulk 1861-1865.
1.5 cu. ft.

A4142 Annual report, 1852.
.3 cu. ft. (1 volume)

OFFICE OF ENGINEER IN CHIEF

A4124 Correspondence on enrollment procedures, 1864.
.5 cu. ft.

SURGEON GENERAL'S OFFICE

A4104 Incoming correspondence from New York State Volunteer units, 1861-1866.
2 cu. ft.

B0312 Register of letters received, 1865-1868.
.2 cu. ft. (1 volume)

A4147 Telegrams received, 1861-1864.
.3 cu. ft. (1 volume)

BUREAU OF MILITARY STATISTICS

A4111 Administrative correspondence files, 1859-1875, bulk 1860-1866.
2 cu. ft.

A4149 Telegrams received and sent by the governor's office, 1861-1862.
1.3 cu. ft. (10 volumes)

A0389 Registers of officers and enlisted men mustered into federal military or naval service during the Civil War, 1861-1865.
6 cu. ft. (6 volumes)

A4134 Historical notes on New York Volunteer regiments, 1861-1865.
2.3 cu. ft. (7 volumes)

A4144   Volunteer relief pay roll of the Joint Volunteer Relief Committee of Albany, 1861-1862.
.5 cu. ft. (2 volumes)

A4114   Accounts submitted by local officials regarding Civil War monies raised and expended, 1861-1866.
3 cu. ft.

A4143   Roster of Staff Officers and Enlisted Men of the 128th Regiment, New York Volunteers, 1862-1865.
.3 cu. ft. (11 volumes)

A4121   Schuyler County Board of Supervisors proceedings, 1862.
.3 cu. ft. R

A4157   Surgeon's report on examinations of Steuben County applicants claiming physical disability exemptions, 1862.
.1 cu. ft. (1 volume)

A4119   Enrollment lists for the 14th District, 1864.
.2 cu. ft.

A4131   Sample ballots and voting records issued to soldiers for the presidential election, 1864.
.5 cu. ft.

A4112   Sample State commissions issued to military officers, 1865.
.2 cu. ft.

BUREAU OF RECORDS OF THE WAR OF THE REBELLION

13775   Civil War muster roll abstracts of New York State Volunteers, United States Sharpshooters, and United States Colored Troops, 1861-1865.
364 cu. ft.

B0800   Civil War muster roll abstracts of National Guard units in federal service, 1861-1865.
39 cu. ft. (92 volumes)

B0803   Civil War muster roll abstracts of the United States Navy, 1861-1865.
48 cu. ft. (96 volumes)

B0804   Civil War muster roll abstracts of the United States Marine Corps, 1861-1865.
1.3 cu. ft. (4 volumes)

B0805   Civil War muster roll abstracts of men unassigned to any State or federal unit, 1861-1865.
2 cu. ft.

B0807   Civil War muster roll abstracts of the 26th Regiment, United States Colored Troops, 1863-1865.
1.5 cu. ft.

B0812   Civil War muster roll abstracts of colored enlisted men unassigned to any unit, 1863-1865.
.5 cu. ft.

B0806   Civil War muster roll abstracts of New York State Veteran Reserve Corps troops, 1863-1865.
.5 cu. ft.

B0813   Civil War muster roll abstracts of substitutes unassigned to any unit, 1863-1865.
1 cu. ft.

AUDITING BOARD

A4116   Claims submitted for expenditures for troops mustered into federal service, ca. 1861-1870.
.5 cu. ft.

A4141   Record of claims, 1862-1868.
.5 cu. ft. (1 volume)

MILITARY BOARD

A3311   Extracts of minutes, 1861.
.2 cu. ft.

A4158   Descriptions and explanations of the second comptroller for war claims against the State, 1861.
.1 cu. ft. (1 volume)

BOARD OF COMMISSIONERS CONSTITUTED IN 1862 TO EXAMINE MILITIA CLAIMS

A4162   Minutes of the Board of Commissioners constituted to examine militia claims for clothing and equipment lost or destroyed while in the service of the United States, 1862-1864.
.1 cu. ft. (1 volume)

A4115   Affidavits of claimants for clothing and equipment lost or destroyed while in the service of the United States, 1862.
.5 cu. ft.

BOARD OF COMMISSIONERS CONSTITUTED IN 1864 TO EXAMINE MILITIA/NATIONAL GUARD CLAIMS

A4163   Minutes of The Board of Commissioners constituted to examine claims for uniforms lost or destroyed by militia or National Guard units while in the service of the United States, 1864-1866.
.1 cu. ft. (1 volume)

MILITIA VOLUNTEERS

A0107   Records of the Independent Corps, Light Infantry, 1862-1864.
.5 cu. ft.

A0189   Quartermaster's abstracts of articles expended, lost, or destroyed in the public service by the 77th Battalion, 1865.
.3 cu. ft.

A0195   Records of the 2nd Regiment, Company B, 1856-1863.
.5 cu. ft.

A0087   Records of the 51st Regiment, 1861-1864.
1.5 cu. ft.

NEW YORK STATE SOLDIERS' DEPOT

A4108   Proceedings and reports of the Board of Managers, 1863-1864.
.5 cu. ft.

NEW YORK MILITARY AGENCY

A4135   Registers of soldiers' claims expedited, 1866-1868.
7 cu. ft. (24 volumes)

A4136   Register of soldiers visiting the Washington office, 1863-1865.
.3 cu. ft. (1 volume)

A4137   Case registers of New York medical agents, 1865-1866.
.3 cu. ft. (2 volumes)

A4138   Superintendent's ledger regarding field offices' accounts,
1865-1867.
.3 cu. ft. (1 volume)

NATIONAL GUARD

13724   Enlistment Roll of the Third Battery, Second Division, 1870-1916.
.3 cu. ft. (1 volume)

13721   World War I service records, 1917-1919.
30 cu. ft. (96 volumes)

A3283   12th Brigade National Guard regimental and brigade files of
Brigadier General James Gibson, 1862-1871.
1 cu. ft.

A3237   12th Infantry Regiment photograph album of Cuba, 1898.
.3 cu. ft. (1 volume)

B0310   Second Division, 3rd Artillery Battery descriptive rolls,
1876-1911.
1 cu. ft. (3 volumes)

MILITARY TRAINING COMMISSION

A0401   Records, 1917-1921.
15 cu. ft.

CIVIL DEFENSE COMMISSION

A3278   Training exercises files, ca. 1950-1960.
5 cu. ft.

Office of Parks, Recreation and Historic Preservation

Current Functions. The Office of Parks, Recreation and Historic Preservation promotes recreation and administers State parks, recreation facilities, and historic sites. It administers 146 State parks in 11 State park regions (a 12th region comprised by the Adirondack and Catskill parks is run by the Department of Environmental Conservation), and 34 State historic sites. Each region is supervised by a regional park, recreation, and historic preservation commission that serves as a liaison with the office. Many historic sites also have local governing boards that are under the supervision of the office. The office also licenses operators of passenger boats and conducts recreation safety training.

Organizational History. Early State park and recreation policies were closely related to conservation efforts. A Temporary State Park Commission, established in 1872 (Chapter 848) to study the feasibility of forming a public park in the "timbered regions" of the Adirondack Mountains, rejected a proposal to create a park for recreational purposes but recommended preservation of the land and timber resources. No action was taken until 1884, when the legislature directed the comptroller to establish a committee to formulate a plan for forest preservation. This committee's recommendations led in 1885 (Chapter 283) to the establishment of the Adirondack and Catskill Forest Preserves administered by a Forest Commission. This commission was abolished in 1895, and its functions transferred to the Fisheries, Game, and Forest Commission. This in turn was superseded in 1900 by the Forest, Fish, and Game Commission, which in 1911 became the Conservation Commission, existing until the constitutional reorganization of 1925. In addition to responsibility for the forest preserve lands, (which were also known as the Adirondack and Catskill parks), the Conservation Commission or its predecessors administered several parks and reservations assigned by law to its jurisdiction, beginning with the State Reservation on the Saint Lawrence in 1896.

Other parks and reservations as well as a number of historic sites and structures were established by law between 1885 and 1925. Each was administered by an independent or regional board of commissioners or trustees. In 1924 (Chapter 189), the State Council of Parks was established as a central advisory agency for all parks, reservations, and places of historic and scenic interest that were not under the authority of the Conservation Commission. The council, consisting of the conservation commissioner, state museum director, and the heads of 10 park and recreation boards, developed plans for a uniform park policy and acted as a clearing house for information on park planning.

In 1926 (Chapter 619), as a result of the constitutional reorganization of State government, jurisdiction of all parks, reservations, and historic sites was centralized in the Conservation Department, Division of Parks. The Council of Parks was continued but placed under the jurisdiction of the conservation commissioner. In addition to its previous advisory and planning functions, the council was empowered to recommend construction or improvement of state and county highways to facilitate public access to recreational areas.

In 1944 (Chapter 603), supervision of 27 historic sites was transferred from the Conservation Department to the State Education Department. Administration of these sites was returned to the Conservation Department in 1966 (Chapter 816) with the creation within that agency of the New York State Historic Trust, a seven-member body composed of four gubernatorial appointees plus the commissioner of education, director of the Council on the Arts, and chairman of the Council of Parks. The director of the Division of State Parks acted as executive secretary of the trust. The Education Department continued to provide advisory services on the operation of the sites.

When the Conservation Department was reorganized as the Department of Environmental Conservation in 1970 (Chapter 140), its Division of State Parks was abolished. All duties and functions relating to parks (except the Adirondack and Catskill preserves), recreation areas, and historic sites were transferred to the newly created Office of Parks and Recreation. A Council of Parks and Recreation and a Historic Trust were reconstituted under administrative jurisdiction of the commissioner of the new office. In 1972 (Chapter 660) a recodified parks and recreation law established centralized management of all parks for the first time, with eleven regional park commissions retaining a local supervisory role. The Council of Parks and Recreation was also continued as an advisory body, and the State Board for Historic Preservation succeeded the Historic Trust in an advisory capacity.

In 1977, an Urban Cultural Parks Advisory Council was created and charged with developing plans for a statewide system of urban cultural parks. This council, whose membership was subsequently increased to 19, consists of a combination of agency heads and gubernatorial appointees chaired by the commissioner of parks, recreation and historic preservation.

The office was renamed Office of Parks, Recreation and Historic Preservation in 1981 (Chapter 679). At the same time the State Council of Parks was renamed the State Council of Parks, Recreation and Historic Preservation.

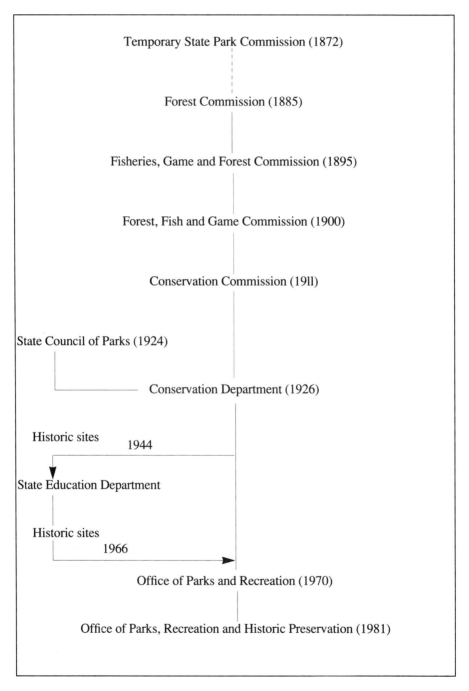

Temporary State Park Commission (1872)

Forest Commission (1885)

Fisheries, Game and Forest Commission (1895)

Forest, Fish and Game Commission (1900)

Conservation Commission (1911)

State Council of Parks (1924)

Conservation Department (1926)

Historic sites   1944

State Education Department

Historic sites   1966

Office of Parks and Recreation (1970)

Office of Parks, Recreation and Historic Preservation (1981)

OFFICE OF PARKS, RECREATION AND HISTORIC PRESERVATION

General Agency-level Records

15376	New York State Maritime Museum administration files, 1969-1980. 16 cu. ft.
15377	Schermerhorn Row Block documentation project files, ca. 1974-1984. 44.5 cu. ft.
15378	Photographs of tall ships celebration in New York Harbor, 1976. 2 cu. ft.

HUDSON RIVER VALLEY COMMISSION

A1115	Correspondence and subject files, 1965-1979. 12 cu. ft.

Division of Parole

Current Functions. Parole is the process of releasing an inmate into the community prior to the expiration of the inmate's maximum sentence of confinement in a State correctional institution. In administering the State's parole system, the Division of Parole performs a number of functions. These include maintaining information on each inmate under the jurisdiction of the Department of Correctional Services; maintaining records on every person on parole; supervising inmates released on parole; conducting investigations in connection with alleged parole violations; and assisting inmates eligible for parole or on parole to secure employment, education, or vocational training. The division also performs similar functions in administering the State's conditional release program.

The Board of Parole is an administrative body within the Division of Parole. The board determines which inmates in a State correctional facility may be released on parole, when the release takes place, and under what conditions the parole is granted. The board also determines the conditions of release of inmates granted a conditional release. The board may revoke the parole or conditional release of any person under the division's supervision and may issue a warrant for the retaking of the person.

Organizational History. The Division of Parole traces its origin to an 1877 law (Chapter 424) empowering the superintendent of state prisons to appoint an agent at each State prison to assist inmates whose terms were about to expire to find suitable homes and employment. An 1889 law (Chapter 382) established a Board of Commissioners for Paroled Prisoners at each prison, composed of the agent, warden, chaplain, physician, principal keeper, and the superintendent of state prisons. Inmates who had served their minimum sentences could apply to these boards for parole. In 1901 (Chapter 260) these separate parole boards were discontinued and the State Commission of Prisons (created in 1894) was designated to serve in a dual capacity as Board of Commissioners for Paroled Prisoners. In 1908 (Chapter 239), the duties of this board were transferred to the newly created Board of Parole for State Prisons, consisting of the superintendent of prisons and two gubernatorial appointees.

Following the reorganization of State government in 1925 and 1926, the Board of Parole for State Prisons was continued and made head of a new Division of Parole within the Department of Correction. The commissioner of correction replaced the superintendent of state prisons on the board. A 1930 law (Chapter 824) transferred the Division of Parole to the Executive Department, where its powers and duties remained the same. The Board of Parole for State Prisons was continued with three gubernatorial appointees as members.

When the Department of Correction was reorganized as the Department of Correctional Services in 1970 (Chapter 475), the Division of Parole became an administrative unit of the new department. The restructured division included a State Board of Parole, which assigned the power to decide cases and conditions of parole and to revoke parole. The Division of Parole was again separated from the Department of Correctional Services in 1977 (Chapter 904) and established as an independent Executive Department agency. The State Board of Parole was continued with the same membership.

No records in the State Archives

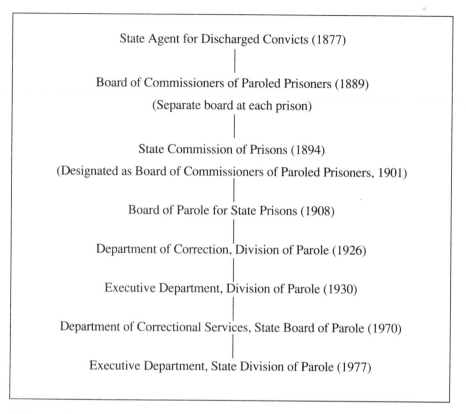

State Agent for Discharged Convicts (1877)

Board of Commissioners of Paroled Prisoners (1889)
(Separate board at each prison)

State Commission of Prisons (1894)
(Designated as Board of Commissioners of Paroled Prisoners, 1901)

Board of Parole for State Prisons (1908)

Department of Correction, Division of Parole (1926)

Executive Department, Division of Parole (1930)

Department of Correctional Services, State Board of Parole (1970)

Executive Department, State Division of Parole (1977)

Division of State Police

Current Functions. The Division of State Police is New York's principal police agency and has statewide jurisdictional authority to enforce the law and preserve the peace. The division provides police services in rural and suburban areas in particular. State Police officers patrol interstate, State, and secondary roads and provide special services in canine, scuba, and hazardous material operations. The division also enforces State vehicle weight and size regulations and is responsible for making the New York State Thruway safe for motorists by decreasing accidents and investigating crimes. Through its Bureau of Criminal Investigation, the division investigates serious and complex crimes relating in particular to organized crime, narcotics, and violent felons. The division also provides support to local and other State law enforcement agencies, including training, communications, data processing, record keeping, aviation support, and criminal laboratory services.

Organizational History. In 1917 (Chapter 161), New York State established a Department of State Police, headed by a superintendent appointed by the governor, to provide law enforcement in the rural areas of the State. The law establishing the department contained a limitation, that remains today, prohibiting the use of State Police within the limits of a city without specific order of the governor. The first contingent of troopers, chosen by the superintendent for two-year enlistments, was organized into four troops stationed at White Plains, Albany, Oneida, and Batavia, respectively. Following the reorganization of State government in 1925-26, the State Police was made a division of the Executive Department by a law of 1926 (Chapter 546). In 1935 (Chapter 697), the division received legislative authorization to operate a scientific laboratory and to organize the Bureau of Criminal Investigation as a separate investigative unit to handle serious or complicated cases. Beginning in 1938, appointments to the force have been permanent, rather than two-year enlistments. The number of state police officers has increased to over 4,000. They are organized into 10 troops located throughout the State.

DIVISION OF STATE POLICE

General Agency-level Records

A0795   Non-criminal investigation case files, ca. 1940-1970.
         109 cu. ft. R

13445   State Police blotters, ca. 1920-1974.
         115.7 cu. ft. R

Division of Probation and Correctional Alternatives

Current Functions. The Division of Probation and Correctional Alternatives oversees the development and execution of New York State's comprehensive system of community-based corrections and alternative punishment. The division is the regulatory and standard-setting agency for all county departments of probation. It promulgates rules and procedures for the delivery of local probation services and correctional alternatives. These services include assisting the intake of cases in family court, investigating cases to facilitate court decisions, and supervising and counseling persons sentenced to probation or alternative correction. The division monitors these services and reimburses localities for approved expenditures. The division also provides training and technical assistance to local probation personnel.

Organizational History. In 1901 (Chapter 372), the legislature passed the State's first probation law, which provided for the appointment of probation officers by justices of various courts. In 1907, a State Probation Commission was established (Chapter 430) to supervise the work of all probation officers. During the reorganization of State government in 1925-26, this commission was continued as the head of the Division of Probation within the Department of Correction. In 1970 (Chapter 479), the Division of Probation was removed from the Department of Correction and made a division within the Executive Department. A division director, appointed by the governor, became head of the agency and served on the State Probation Commission along with four other gubernatorial appointees. In 1971, the membership of the commission was changed to consist of nine members: three community members appointed by the governor; two local probation administrators or officers appointed by the governor; and the directors of court administration of each of the four State judicial departments. A year later, the division director was added as chairperson, and the State's administrative judge of the unified court system replaced the four judicial department directors. In 1985 (Chapter 134), the Division of Probation was renamed the Division of Probation and Correctional Alternatives. This law merged the functions of the Division of Probation with the Comprehensive Alternatives Program that previously had been part of the Division of Criminal Justice Services.

No records in the State Archives

Permanent Commission on Public Employee Pension and Retirement Systems

Current Functions. The Permanent Commission on Public Employee Pension and Retirement Systems assists public employees and retirees by advising the governor and legislature on provisions for retirement and related benefits for public employees in New York State. It carries out this function by providing continuing evaluation of public employee pension and retirement systems. It conducts studies on types and costs of pension/retirement benefit systems, the strengths and weaknesses of such systems, and ways to improve them; as well as on the impact of retirement programs on government efficiency; and the subject of retirement in general. The commission publicizes its findings and reports on them to the governor and legislature. It also makes recommendations on proposed legislation to the governor and legislature.

Organizational History. The Permanent Commission on Public Employee Pension and Retirement Systems was preceded by several commissions charged with studying and making recommendations on public employee pensions. The first, established by a law of 1918 (Chapter 414), was directed to study retirement pensions, allowances, and annuities for State and municipal officers and employees and to recommend proposed legislation to the governor and legislature. As a result of this commission's work, the New York State Employees' Retirement System was established in 1920 (Chapter 741).

The State Commission on Pensions, established by a law of 1922 (Chapter 269), was the first permanent State advisory commission on pensions, assuming the analysis and reporting functions of the earlier commission. Legislation of 1954 (Chapter 98) repealed the 1922 law and continued the State Commission on Pensions in the Executive Department. The legislation enumerated several types of ongoing studies to be conducted and granted the commission jurisdiction in granting extensions in service beyond the mandatory retirement age of 70.

A law of 1960 (Chapter 330) transferred the commission and its functions to the Department of Civil Service and renamed it the Advisory Council on Pensions. This council continued operating until it was discontinued in 1968.

Legislation of 1971 (Chapter 733) established the Permanent Commission on Public Employee Pension and Retirement Systems to resume the analytical, advisory, and reporting duties of the previous commissions. Operating under this law as amended in 1976 (Chapter 890), the current commission consists of five gubernatorial appointees, including one recommended by the temporary president of the senate and one recommended by the speaker of the assembly. The governor also appoints three nonvoting observers to the commission, one representing public employers, one representing employee organizations, and one representing the interests of the general public.

No records in the State Archives

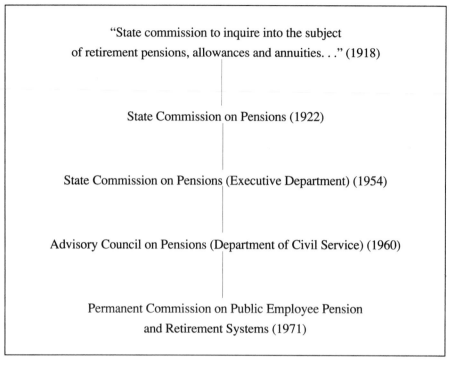

"State commission to inquire into the subject
of retirement pensions, allowances and annuities. . ." (1918)

State Commission on Pensions (1922)

State Commission on Pensions (Executive Department) (1954)

Advisory Council on Pensions (Department of Civil Service) (1960)

Permanent Commission on Public Employee Pension
and Retirement Systems (1971)

State Racing and Wagering Board

Current Functions. The State Racing and Wagering Board regulates and supervises all the State's horse-racing activities and all pari-mutuel betting activities, including the State's six regional off-track betting corporations. The board collects fines and penalties for racing infractions and conducts drug tests at all tracks in the State to determine the presence of drugs in race horses. The board also monitors the conduct of bingo and other games of chance by authorized nonprofit organizations to ensure compliance with existing laws and regulations.

Organizational History. This board was created in 1973 (Chapter 346) to consolidate responsibility for the licensing and regulation of racing and wagering activities that had formerly been exercised by five separate commissions. A State Racing Commission, consisting of three gubernatorial appointees, was created in 1926 (Chapter 440) to issue or deny annual licenses to corporations conducting horse races and steeplechases. In 1940 (Chapter 254), this commission was transferred to the

Department of State and granted additional powers to appoint stewards for race meetings and to issue licenses for and regulate pari-mutual betting. By the same year, a State Harness Racing Commission, consisting of three gubernatorial appointees, was placed in charge of a new division in the Department of State and given regulatory responsibilities for harness racing similar to those of the State Racing Commission for other racing.

Two laws enacted in 1970 further expanded the Department of State's responsibility for regulating racing and wagering. A State Quarter Horse Racing Commission was granted jurisdiction over pari-mutuel quarter horse racing activities (Chapter 1023), and a State Off-Track Pari-Mutuel Betting Commission governed the operation of an off-track betting system (Chapter 143).

In 1973, these four commissions, along with the State Lottery Commission from the Department of Taxation and Finance, were consolidated under the newly created State Racing and Wagering Board, with the original commissions remaining as advisory bodies to the board in their respective areas of jurisdiction. In 1976 (Chapter 960), the State Bingo Control Commission, formerly in the Department of State, was transferred to the board and the board's authority over wagering was expanded to include all bingo games or other games of chance held by approved nonprofit corporations. In that same year, however, responsibility for the State Lottery was removed from the board and reassigned to the Division of the Lottery in the Department of Taxation and Finance (Chapter 92). The Racing and Wagering Board consists of three members appointed by the governor, and one of the members is designated board chairperson and chief executive office.

No records in the State Archives

State Racing Commission (1926)   State Harness Racing Commission (1940)

   (Department of State - 1940)   (Department of State)

     State Off-Track Pari-Mutuel   State Quarter Horse

     Betting Commission (1970)   Racing Commission (1970)

     (Department of State)   (Department of State)

State Racing and Wagering Board (1973)

State Lottery Commission (1967)

(Department of Taxation and Finance)

State Bingo Control Commission (1962) 1976 State Lottery Commission

(Department of State)   1976   (Department of Taxation and Finance)

Office of Rural Affairs

Current Functions. The State Office of Rural Affairs is responsible for developing recommendations for the governor and legislature on appropriate policies, programs, and long-range plans to promote cooperative and integrated efforts among agencies and programs to meet the needs of the State's rural communities. It holds statewide conferences to assess the needs of rural communities, operates a statewide information network, and conducts studies of rural affairs issues.

Organizational History. The office was created within the Executive Department in 1986 (Chapter 890). It is headed by a director appointed by the governor.

No records in the State Archives

Science and Technology Foundation

Current Functions. The New York State Science and Technology Foundation is a public corporation that promotes economic development by encouraging scientific and technological education, research, and development. The foundation administers a range of financial- and technical-assistance programs designed to stimulate the creation of jobs through the transfer of technology from the laboratory to commercial application. The foundation includes three major programs. The first, the Centers for Advanced Technology Program, encourages new and high technology product and service development through programs in research and development, technology transfer between the academic sphere and industry, and education and training. The Corporation for Innovation Development finances existing technology-based ventures and firms involving technological innovations. The Small Business Innovation Research Program assists start-up companies seeking Federal grants.

Organizational History. The foundation was established by the Law of 1963 (Chapter 432) and was continued and reconstituted by Public Authorities Law, Article 10-A. The foundation is governed by a 13-member board of directors, comprised of the commissioners of the departments of Economic Development,

Education, and Health and the chairman of the Urban Development Corporation. In addition, nine private-sector members are appointed by the governor.

No records in the State Archives

Board of Social Welfare

Current Functions. The Board of Social Welfare is responsible for overseeing the quality of State policies and programs relating to child and adult care to protect the welfare of needy and dependent persons. It does this by visiting and inspecting public and private agencies caring for the aged, the disabled, neglected or delinquent children, and other dependents; reviewing and making recommendations to the governor and legislature regarding quality of supervision exercised by State and local supervisory agencies; studying State policies and programs affecting child and adult care and advocating their improvement; and conducting special human services studies as requested by the governor.

Organizational History. The Board of Commissioners of Public Charities, established in 1867 (Chapter 951) to visit and inspect public almshouses and all charitable and correctional institutions (except prisons) receiving State aid, was the first State supervisory body to coordinate public welfare programs. Before this, public assistance programs were independently operated by county and town authorities and private agencies. The board consisted of eight gubernatorial appointees, one from each judicial district.

The board was renamed the State Board of Charities in 1873 (Chapter 571). The board was enlarged to 11 members, with 1 additional member from Kings County and 2 additional members from New York County. Its powers were extended to all (public or private) institutions for the insane and to charitable, correctional (except prisons), and reformatory institutions whether or not they received public funds. The board licensed all insane asylums and visited each institution before issuing a license. This licensing function was transferred to the state commissioner in lunacy in 1874 (Chapter 446). In 1889 (Chapter 283), the board's remaining supervisory duties relating to insane asylums were transferred to the newly established State Commission in Lunacy.

Article VIII of the Constitution of 1894 made the Board of Charities a constitutional body responsible for the supervision, visitation, and inspection of all charitable, correctional, and reformatory institutions except those supervised by the Commission in Lunacy or the Prison Commission. The State Charities Law of 1896 (Chapter 546) limited the board's supervision to institutions receiving State aid but extended its authority to dispensaries. Another member from New York County was added, enlarging the board to 12 members.

The Poor Law of 1896 repealed most previous poor laws and clarified the role of local poor relief officers and the board's duties regarding the poor. The board was to administer laws concerning the poor; investigate conditions of the poor and plan for their relief; advise and regulate almshouse managers on their management, the treatment of inmates, and related issues; visit and inspect almshouses; and approve plans and designs for almshouse construction. The superintendent of State alien and poor and the county superintendents of the poor were to report to the board annually.

The constitutional reorganization of State government in 1925-26 transferred the board's responsibilities for supervision of mental health and correctional facilities to the new departments of Mental Hygiene and Correction. A 1926 law (Chapter 651) established the Department of Charities with the Board of Charities as its executive body. The department assumed the board's functions except for that of visitation and inspection, which the board retained.

In 1929 (Chapter 654), the board was renamed the Board of Social Welfare, and the department was renamed the Department of Social Welfare. The board was reorganized in 1936 (Chapter 873). The 12-member, eight-year term board was abolished, and the governor appointed a new 15-member, five-year term board. The board had power to appoint and remove a commissioner of public welfare, and its role toward public welfare institutions and officials became more regulatory and less administrative. The board was to make rules regarding administration of social welfare programs; determine the principals upon which the State and local governments would provide public relief; advise local welfare institutions and officials; establish general rules for the functioning of institutions; and inspect institutions. The board's inspection function was further clarified by a constitutional amendment in 1938.

The 1940 law (Chapter 619) combining the Public Welfare Law and the State Charities Law continued the board as the executive body of the Department of Social

Welfare with authority to establish public-assistance policies and advise local welfare officials and agencies.

In 1971 (Chapter 110) the board was removed from the Department of Social Services (which had been renamed in 1967) and established as a separate agency in the Executive Department. The department's Bureau of Proprietary Organizations, which had the power of approval of certificates of incorporation for public welfare agencies and institutions, was removed from the Department of Social Services and placed under the board. The power to name a commissioner of social services was transferred from the board to the governor. The board's authority to regulate the administration of local public assistance was transferred to the Department of Social Services, and its direct supervision of child- and adult-care institutions was transferred to other State agencies. The board continued to exercise its traditional, constitutional activities relating to the visitation, inspection, and setting of standards for institutions and agencies caring for dependent, neglected, or delinquent children; the aged; indigent; disabled; and disadvantaged.

A 1977 law (Chapter 669) further clarified and expanded the board's responsibility to act as an independent overseer of institutions under its purview; to review, report, and make recommendations concerning implementation of State policies and programs for child and adult care; and to monitor the quality of administration of these programs by responsible State and local agencies. The board's responsibility for regulation of charitable fund raising (begun under a 1956 law) was transferred to the Department of State.

BOARD OF SOCIAL WELFARE

General Agency-level Records

14251	Minutes of the Board and the Committee of the Whole, 1867-1987. 24.5 cu. ft.
A3257	Charities regulation reference file, 1927-1932. .1 cu. ft.
B1302	Litigation files, 1962-1978. 3 cu. ft.

STATE BOARD OF CHARITIES

General Administrative Records

A1977   Correspondence, 1867-1902.
         26.7 cu. ft. (30 microfilm reels)

A3103   List of incorporated charities' officers' addresses, 1870.
         .1 cu. ft. (1 microfilm reel)

A3104   Lists of physicians, 1871.
         .1 cu. ft. (1 microfilm reel)

A0010   Printed reports, 1884-1915.
         .4 cu. ft.

Reports of Charitable Institutions and Organizations

A1986   Annual reports of dispensaries, 1869-1896.
         1.7 cu. ft. (25 volumes) (3 microfilm reels)

A1984   Annual reports of incorporated charities, 1870-1871.
         .3 cu. ft. (2 volumes) (1 microfilm reel)

A1985   Annual reports of orphan asylums and homes for the friendless,
         1873-1896.
         4 cu. ft. (24 volumes) (12 microfilm reels)

A1982   Questionnaires on hospital accommodations of county poorhouses,
         1881.
         .2 cu. ft. (1 volume) (1 microfilm reel)

A1981   Annual reports of hospitals, 1873-1896.
         2 cu. ft. (20 volumes) (4 microfilm reels)

A1988   Annual reports on poorhouses and almshouses, 1869-1896.
         1.3 cu. ft. (28 volumes) (3 microfilm reels)

Reports of Dependents

A1978   Census of inmates in almshouses and poorhouses, 1875-1921.
         96.6 cu. ft. (225 microfilm records) R

A1987   Examinations of dependents in county and city institutions, 1874-
         1875.
         6 cu. ft. (82 volumes) (11 microfilm reels)

A1979   Census of non-institutionalized insane and idiots, 1871.
         1 cu. ft. (16 volumes) (3 microfilm reels)

A1990   Registers of tramps applying for relief, 1875-1876.
1.3 cu. ft. (6 volumes) (2 microfilm reels)

A1989   Register of insane in county poorhouses, 1871.
1 cu. ft. (1 volume) (1 microfilm reel)

A1980   Register of children removed from poorhouses, 1873-1874.
.2 cu. ft. (1 volume) (1 microfilm reel)

A1991   Reports on institutionalized epileptics, 1895.
.1 cu. ft. (1 volume) (1 microfilm reel)

A1992   Reports on non-institutionalized epileptics receiving public relief,
1895.
.2 cu. ft. (6 volumes) (1 microfilm reel)

A3154   Albany County Alms House daily reports of admissions and discharges, 1903-1904.
.2 cu. ft.

Visits and Investigations

A3105   Reports of visits to institutions, 1878-1879.
.1 cu. ft. (1 volume) (1 microfilm reel)

A3155   Investigation background files concerning the International
Sunshine Society, 1909-1916.
.3 cu. ft.

A1983   Records of an investigation into the administration of the
Rensselaer County Almshouse, 1905-1906.
.2 cu. ft. (2 volumes) (1 microfilm reel)

A3156   Hearing transcripts of the Strong Investigation of charges against
the State Board of Charities, 1916.
.2 cu. ft.

Photographs

A1993   Photographs and floor plans of charitable institutions, ca. 1867-
1903.
5 cu. ft. (5 volumes) (1 microfilm reel)

A1994   Photographs of custodial facilities in New York and other states,
ca. 1890-1915.
1 cu. ft. (1 microfilm reel)

A1995   Photographs of State Training School for Boys, ca. 1908-1909.
1.3 cu. ft. (1 microfilm reel)

St. Lawrence-Eastern Ontario Commission

Current Functions. This commission was established to protect, preserve, and develop the scenic, historic, recreational, and natural resources of the St. Lawrence River and eastern Lake Ontario region. The commission carries out this mission by assisting in the development of land-use plans, conducting project reviews, and preparing informational materials on the region.

Organizational History. The commission was established in 1969 (Chapter 394). In 1971 (Chapter 74), the commission was continued in the Office of Planning Services. It was reestablished as an independent commission in 1974 (Chapter 701) with a mandate to complete a comprehensive development plan for the St. Lawrence and eastern Lake Ontario region by 1977. In 1977 (Chapter 648), the commission was relieved of the responsibility of completing a comprehensive plan and was authorized to prepare a coastal-management program for the region for submission to the governor and legislature.

The commission is comprised of the commissioner of environmental conservation; the secretary of state; the commissioner of economic development; and 14 members appointed by the governor, 12 of whom must be residents of the counties under the commission's jurisdiction and 2 who reside outside the commission's jurisdiction.

ST. LAWRENCE-EASTERN ONTARIO COMMISSION

General Agency-level Records

    13405   Project review files, ca. 1971-1978.
                 3 cu. ft.

Governor's Traffic Safety Committee

Current Functions. The Governor's Traffic Safety Committee protects and educates citizens by conducting New York State's highway safety program to reduce traffic accidents and the resultant deaths, injuries, and property damage. It carries out this responsibility by providing for comprehensive driver-training programs, including school driver education programs; training and certification of qualified school instructors; appropriate regulation of other driver training schools, including licensing of the schools and certification of their instructors; adult driver training and retraining programs; adequate research, development, and procurement of practice-driving facilities, simulators, and other teaching aids for school and other driver-training use; and coordination and approval of highway safety programs of State, local, and other public and private agencies and of individuals and organizations. The committee acts as the State's official liaison with the National Highway Traffic Safety Administration and the Federal Highway Administration in carrying out provisions of the Federal Highway Safety Act of 1966.

Organizational History. The State Traffic Commission, established by the legislature in 1936 (Chapter 910), was New York State's first agency with traffic safety responsibilities, but its main responsibilities related to traffic engineering and traffic control. The first State agency responsible solely for traffic safety was the Traffic Safety Policy Coordination Committee, established by an executive order of May 4, 1957, to advise the governor and coordinate State traffic safety efforts.

In response to the increasing number of traffic-related deaths, in 1959 Governor Rockefeller ordered the creation of an Interdepartmental Traffic Safety Committee to recommend ways to improve highway safety and reduce the number of accidents. Twelve State agencies with traffic safety interests were members of the committee, among them the Department of Motor Vehicles, Division of State Police, Department of Public Works (later the Department of Transportation), State Traffic Commission, and State Thruway Authority. The committee conducted several major studies, including one on traffic accident records and reporting (1961) that proved to be a model for the nation.

To expedite its work, the committee set up a steering committee in 1963 comprised of representatives of the Department of Motor Vehicles, Department of Health, Education Department, Division of State Police, and Department of Public Works. The steering committee met regularly, supported traffic legislation, and annually recommended a Governor's Traffic Safety Program.

The Federal Highway Safety Act of 1966 required states to establish ongoing highway safety programs with ultimate responsibility for program administration to rest with the governor of each state. New York State passed enabling legislation in 1967 (Chapter 620), establishing a statewide highway safety program to integrate and coordinate safety efforts and giving the governor responsibility for the program. An executive order promulgated on the same day (Executive Order 22, April 27, 1967) reestablished the Interdepartmental Traffic Safety Committee, designating it as the agency to administer the State's highway safety program.

Called the Governor's Traffic Safety Committee since 1980, the committee currently consists of the commissioner of motor vehicles as chair and the heads of other State agencies with traffic concerns: the State Education Department, the Department of Health, the Division of Alcoholism and Alcohol Abuse, the Division of Criminal Justice Services, the Division of State Police, the Insurance Department, the Thruway Authority, the Department of Transportation, the Department of State, the Division of Substance Abuse Services, the Division of Probation and Correctional Alternatives, and the State Liquor Authority.

No records in the State Archives

State Traffic Commission (1936)

Traffic Safety Policy Coordination Committee (1957)

Interdepartmental Traffic Safety Committee (1959)

Interdepartmental Traffic Safety Committee (1967)

Governor's Traffic Safety Committee (1980)

Division of Veterans' Affairs

Current Functions. The Division of Veterans' Affairs is part of a multitiered system that includes the Federal Veterans' Administration, city and county veterans' service agencies, and voluntary organizations. The division coordinates programs and activities to aid members of the armed forces, veterans, and their families. The principal function of the division is to counsel veterans and their dependents and survivors in identifying entitlements and preparing claims for Federal veterans' benefits and in obtaining New York State veterans' benefits relating to unemployment insurance, tax exemptions, tuition assistance, civil service, and burial. Division counselors advise active duty personnel on military law and the military medical system.

In addition, the division coordinates veterans' programs and services offered by other State agencies and analyzes veterans' needs and advocates at the State and Federal level for those needs. The division administers the veterans' blind annuity-assistance program that provides financial aid to blind veterans and eligible widows.

Organizational History. The Division of Veterans' Affairs was created by the Laws of 1945, Chapter 763. The head of the division, appointed by the governor, must be a veteran and is designated as the New York State director of veterans' affairs. A Veterans' Affairs Commission assists the director in the formulation of policies affecting veterans and in the coordination of all operations of State agencies relating to veterans' affairs. This commission includes the adjutant general, the director of the budget, the president of the Civil Service Commission, and the commissioners of the departments of Agriculture and Markets, Economic Development, Education, Health, Mental Health, and Social Services. In addition, the commission includes five veterans appointed by the governor.

No records in the State Archives

Division for Women

Current Functions. The Division for Women has a number of responsibilities, including providing advice to the governor on a range of issues relating to women, working with agencies to ensure women's interests are considered in the formulation of public policy, and acting as an advocate on issues affecting women. The division recommends, reviews, and monitors proposed legislation, State policies and procedures, and programs. It also collects and disseminates data on the condition of and opportunities for women.

Organizational History. In 1967, Governor Nelson A. Rockefeller established a Women's Unit within the Office of the Secretary to the Governor to serve as an information clearing house for State departments dealing with issues of specific interest to women. The unit resulted in part from recommendations of a 1966 Governor's Conference on Women. The status of the unit and the resources available for its work were upgraded by Governor Hugh Carey in Executive Order 8 of 1975, which established the Women's Division in the Executive Chamber. The order defined specific powers and duties of the new division. Governor Mario Cuomo continued the division and further charged it to organize an Interagency Task Force composed of representatives from all departments and agencies. The director of the division serves as a member of the governor's cabinet.

WOMEN'S DIVISION

13697	Correspondence and subject files, 1975-1982. 22 cu. ft.
13698	Press clippings, 1975-1982. 9 cu. ft.
13699	Newsletter files, 1975-1982. 2 cu. ft.

Division for Youth

Current Functions. The Division for Youth is responsible for preventing delinquency among the State's youth and for the care and rehabilitation of adjudicated juvenile offenders, juvenile delinquents, and persons in need of supervision. To fulfill these responsibilities the division operates over forty residential facilities for the rehabilitation of youth placed or sentenced by the courts and provides guidance and financial aid to localities to develop and operate delinquency prevention programs and to maintain locally operated youth detention or rehabilitation facilities.

Organizational History. In 1944, Governor Thomas E. Dewey appointed an interdepartmental committee to study the problem of juvenile delinquency. Upon the recommendation of this committee, the New York State Youth Commission, a temporary state commission comprised of a chairperson appointed by the governor and the commissioners of the departments of Correction, Education, Health, Mental Hygiene, and Social Welfare, the industrial commissioner, and the chairperson of the Board of Parole, was established in 1945 (Chapter 556). The commission, which was extended until 1956, studied and made recommendations on the problems of youth guidance, prevention of juvenile delinquency, and treatment of youthful offenders and provided local municipalities with financial and technical aid for delinquency prevention projects.

In 1955 (Chapter 603), a year before the temporary state commission was scheduled to terminate, the Temporary State Commission on Youth and Delinquency—a bipartisan group of legislators, public officials, and laymen—was established to review public policy in this area. As a result of this commission's analysis, the State Youth Commission was reestablished as a permanent Executive Department agency in 1956 (Chapter 636). Commission membership was nine persons appointed by the governor for five-year terms.

Three years later, Governor Rockefeller appointed a Task Force on Youth and Juvenile Delinquency to again study State youth policy. Based on legislation drafted by this task force, the Division for Youth was created in 1960 (Chapter 881) to supersede the Youth Commission. This division, under a director appointed by the governor, assumed all the functions of the Youth Commission and was also authorized to establish and operate centers for the rehabilitation of delinquent adolescents. The Youth Commission was renamed the Council on Youth and continued to exist as an advisory body to the director of the division. Youth-care facilities operated by the Department of Social Services were transferred to the division in 1971 (Chapter 947).

NEW YORK STATE AGRICULTURAL AND INDUSTRIAL SCHOOL (WESTERN HOUSE OF REFUGE)

Administrative Records

    A1972   Administrative correspondence, 1870-1913.
                6 cu. ft. (11 microfilm reels)

A1976   Parole agent's correspondence regarding paroled, transferred or escaped inmates, 1898-1911.
.3 cu. ft.

A3069   Directives to the Superintendent, 1903-1940.
.6 cu. ft. (2 volumes)

A1904   Superintendent's orders to staff, 1891-1943.
2.5 cu. ft. (5 volumes) (1 microfilm reel)

A1996   Register of outgoing mail, 1896-1897.
.1 cu. ft. (1 volume)

A3117   Memoranda concerning orders, requests, or actions of institution officials, 1894-1904.
.3 cu. ft. (1 volume)

A3129   Financial records of the institution, 1884-1893, bulk 1890-1893.
.3 cu. ft.

A3130   Superintendent's record of officer's attendance, 1895-1912.
.3 cu. ft. (1 volume)

A3061   Register of employee leave time used and accumulated, 1917-1941.
.5 cu. ft. (1 volume)

A1967   Daily population summaries, 1876-1944.
2 cu. ft. (8 volumes) (2 microfilm reels)

A1963   Inmate questionnaires concerning institution facilities, 1894.
.3 cu. ft. (1 volume)

A3126   Registers of points and prizes awarded at Annual Exhibitions, 1911-1937.
.1 cu. ft.

A1900   Minutes of the Board of Managers and Board of Visitors, 1849-1940.
3 cu. ft. (12 volumes) (2 microfilm reels)

A1901   Minutes of the Acting Committee (Executive Committee) of the Board of Managers, 1849-1898.
1.5 cu. ft. (3 volumes) (1 microfilm reel)

A1964   Minutes of the Board of Classification, 1893-1909.
1 cu. ft. (3 volumes)

A3128   Superintendent's monthly reports to the Board of Visitors, 1926-1936.
.3 cu. ft.

A3060   Monthly reports of the Board of Visitors, 1902-1936.
.5 cu. ft.

A3056   Inspector's reports on conditions at the State Industrial School, 1902-1906.
.3 cu. ft. (1 volume)

A3057   Minutes of meetings of a special committee of the Board of Visitors, 1938.
.1 cu. ft.

A3058   Transcript of testimony taken by a special committee of the Board of Social Welfare investigating conditions at the school, 1938.
.1 cu. ft. (1 volume)

A3064   Minutes of the Benefit Association of the Civil Service Employees of Industry, N.Y., 1910-1914.
.1 cu. ft. (1 volume)

A1903   Superintendent's daily journal, 1849-1889.
1 cu. ft. (7 volumes) (2 microfilm reels)

A1905   Matron's daily journals for the female department, 1887-1896.
.5 cu. ft. (6 volumes) (1 microfilm reel)

Admission, Parole, and Discharge Records

A1970   Admission registers, 1876-1960.
3 cu. ft. (6 volumes) (2 microfilm reels)

A1965   Boys receiving books, 1896-1911.
.5 cu. ft. (2 volumes) (1 microfilm reel)

A1962   Lists of inmates returned to the institution, 1898-1904.
.3 cu. ft. (1 volume) (1 microfilm reel)

A3053   Registers of commitments, 1896-1942.
.5 cu. ft. (2 volumes)

A3127   Orders assigning inmates to religious divisions, 1899-1912.
.5 cu. ft. (1 volume, 2 folders)

A1966   Inmate rosters, 1896-1907.
1 cu. ft. (3 volumes) (1 microfilm reel)

A1969   Roster of male inmates in the institution, 1869-1873.
.1 cu. ft.

A1902   Indenture agreements, 1851-1860.
.3 cu. ft. (1 volume) (1 microfilm reel)

A3145   Registers of inmates approved for parole, 1897-1912.
.1 cu. ft. (2 volumes)

A3119   Register of new and paroled inmates, 1919-1924.
.1 cu. ft. (1 volume)

A3150   Lists of paroled inmates compiled by chaplains, 1888-1895.
.1 cu. ft.

A3141   Chaplain's rough notes on parole and religious instruction of inmates, 1890-1905.
.1 cu. ft. (1 volume)

A3142   Catholic Parole Agent's record of employment and conduct of paroled inmates, 1887-1906.
.1 cu. ft. (1 volume)

A3144   Parole agents' registers of occupation and conduct of paroled inmates, 1888-1908.
1 cu. ft. (5 volumes)

A3147   Protestant parole officer's directory of contacts in various cities and rough notes on visits to paroled inmates, 1893-1902.
.1 cu. ft. (1 volume)

A3149   Register of inmates approved for discharge, 1874-1876.
.1 cu. ft. (1 volume)

A3067   Registers of outgoing inmates, 1901-1945.
1 cu. ft. (9 volumes)

A3250   Parole badge book, 1889-1897.
.1 cu. ft. (1 volume)

A3148   Register of addresses of discharged female inmates, 1899-1904.
.1 cu. ft. (1 volume)

A3137   Unidentified indexes to institution records, ca. 1870-1890.
.5 cu. ft. (3 volumes)

Inmate Case and Behavior Records

A1906   Male inmate case history books, 1849-1939.
16 cu. ft. (48 volumes) (25 microfilm reels) R

A3063　Name index to male inmate case history books, 1849-1867, 1891-1949.
2 cu. ft. (5 volumes) (1 microfilm reel)

A1907　Female inmate case history books, 1876-1904.
2 cu. ft. (4 volumes) (2 microfilm reels)

A3118　Index to case files of female inmates, 1876-1904.
.2 cu. ft. (1 volume)

A1960　Supplementary case files for male inmates, 1876-1913.
44 cu. ft. (36 microfilm reels)

A1961　Supplementary case files for paroled female inmates, 1879-1905.
4 cu. ft. (6 microfilm reels)

A3139　Brief case histories of male inmates, 1853-1860.
.3 cu. ft. (3 volumes)

A3140　Rough notes for Chaplains' registers of inmate case histories, 1886-1898.
.1 cu. ft. (1 volume)

A3143　Catholic Parole Agent's records of interviews with and institutional histories of inmates, 1887-1891.
.1 cu. ft. (1 volume)

A3146　Chaplains' registers of inmate case histories, 1881-1907.
6 cu. ft. (16 volumes)

A3153　Indexes to Chaplains' registers of inmate case histories and parole agents' registers of occupation and conduct of paroled inmates, 1881-1904.
.3 cu. ft. (3 volumes)

A3073　Inmate misconduct book, 1876-1880.
.3 cu. ft. (1 volume) (1 microfilm reel)

A3136　Reports of inmate conduct and punishments for offenses, 1882-1897.
2.5 cu. ft. (7 volumes)

A3116　Weekly record of female inmates' behavior and badges earned, 1889-1900, bulk 1889-1895.
.2 cu. ft. (1 volume)

A3059　Daily record of escapes, 1919-1930.
.1 cu. ft. (1 volume)

A3054   Registers of escapes from farm colonies, 1908-1940, bulk 1908-1935.
.6 cu. ft. (2 volumes)

A1968   Registers of male inmates' educational level, 1849-1893.
1 cu. ft. (3 volumes) (1 microfilm reel)

A3012   Male inmate school records, 1890-1892.
1 cu. ft. (2 volumes) (1 microfilm reel)

Photographs and Printed Material

A1975   Photographs of inmates, staff, and facilities, ca. 1904-1930.
2.5 cu. ft. (1 microfilm reel)

A3120   Glass plate negatives of new facility, 1905-1920.
7 cu. ft. (71 negatives) (1 microfilm reel)

A3138   Newspapers published by inmates, 1917-1948.
.3 cu. ft.

A3163   Printed items concerning school operations, ca. 1875-1939.
.2 cu. ft. (4 items)

A3125   Scrapbook of printed material concerning the State Industrial School, 1888-1905, bulk 1893-1894.
.3 cu. ft. (1 volume)

[End of Executive Department Subdivision entries]

Department of Agriculture and Markets

Current Functions. The Department of Agriculture and Markets has the responsibility to regulate, conduct research on, and promote agriculture in New York State. In order to regulate agriculture, the department monitors and inspects production, processing, and distribution of agricultural products and enforces related laws. The department conducts research on conditions of rural life, the quality of farm land, and improving techniques for production and marketing. The department promotes agriculture by publicizing agricultural products and business, assisting in the organization and operation of cooperative associations among producers and consumers, and sponsoring the New York State Fair.

Organizational History. This department evolved from a series of State agencies beginning with the establishment of the Dairy Commission in 1884 (Chapter 202). The commission, headed by a commissioner appointed by the governor, was empowered to regulate agriculture by inspecting dairy production and sales facilities in order to ensure product quality.

An 1893 law (Chapter 338) abolished the Dairy Commission and merged its functions with a new Department of Agriculture headed by a commissioner appointed by the governor. The law also transferred the State Meteorology Bureau and Weather Service to the department. The new department had responsibility to regulate agriculture by investigating methods to ensure product quality, setting standards for product quality, and inspecting production, to support research by State agricultural experimental stations and meteorological and weather observation stations, and to promote agriculture through the distribution of State funds granted to the State and county agricultural societies. In 1913, the commissioner of agriculture was granted the power to issue subpoenas and hold hearings on violations.

In 1914 (Chapter 245), a separate Department of Foods and Markets was created. Headed by a commissioner chosen by the governor, this department regulated agriculture by investigating food production and marketing costs; establishing standards for grading, handling, storing, and selling of foodstuffs; supervising auction markets; publishing bulletins on daily prices and production and marketing methods; and investigating facilities for transporting produce within the State.

A major reorganization occurred in 1917 (Chapter 802) when a Department of Farms and Markets was established, consolidating the Departments of Agriculture and Foods and Markets, the office of the state superintendent of weights and measures (created in 1851), and certain responsibilities of the Department of Health relating to food. The new department was headed by a Council of Farms and Markets, the original members of which were appointed by the governor. Upon expiration of their terms, new council members were elected by the legislature. The department consisted of a Division of Agriculture and a Division of Foods and Markets, each headed by a commissioner appointed by the council. In addition to the powers and functions of the previously mentioned agencies, the department was responsible for ensuring a sufficient supply of milk for urban centers, regulating the conduct of agriculture exchanges and boards of trade, and mediating controversies between producers and distributors.

In 1926 (Chapter 646), the current Department of Agriculture and Markets was established as part of the reorganized State government. It assumed all the functions and powers of the Department of Farms and Markets, which was abolished. A Council of Agriculture and Markets became the executive body with the power to appoint a chief administrative officer known as the commissioner of agriculture and markets. The State Fair Commission, created in 1909, was also transferred to the new department. In 1935 (Chapter 16), an amendment to the agricultural law provided for the appointment of the commissioner by the governor and abolished the Council of Agriculture and Markets.

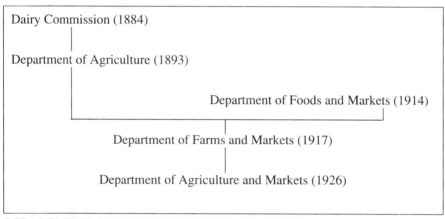

Dairy Commission (1884)

Department of Agriculture (1893)

Department of Foods and Markets (1914)

Department of Farms and Markets (1917)

Department of Agriculture and Markets (1926)

DEPARTMENT OF AGRICULTURE AND MARKETS

General Agency-level Records

A4265   Long Island duck promotion program files, 1960-1970.
2 cu. ft.

A4269   Correspondence with federal and state offices of economic opportunity, 1964-1969.
1 cu. ft.

A0511   Applications for migrant labor registration certificates, 1971-1973.
1 cu. ft.

A4268   Migrant child care program files, 1971-1974.
1 cu. ft.

A4267   Applications for individual services to migrant children, 1975.
.3 cu. ft.

Division of Agricultural Promotion Services

    14457   Publicity photographs, 1913-1975, bulk 1964-1975.
                   1 cu. ft.

Division of Marketing

    A4266   Administrative files, 1932-1976.
                   4 cu. ft.

    A0702   Directors subject and project files, 1959-1971.
                   7 cu. ft.

    A0717   Buffalo regional produce market reports, 1940-1975.
                   4.3 cu. ft.

    A0721   Central New York snap bean volume and price reports, 1962-1967.
                   .5 cu. ft.

    A0718   Central New York regional produce market reports, 1966-1973.
                   1 cu. ft.

    A0722   Utica regional produce market reports, 1963-1971.
                   1 cu. ft.

    13565   Marketing order ballot and voter registration files, ca. 1958-1959.
                   3 cu. ft.

Market and Consumer Information Service

    A0720   Utica regional livestock market reports, 1971.
                   .3 cu. ft.

Milk Control Board

    A3276   Public hearing minutes, 1933.
                   .2 cu. ft.

Department of Audit and Control

Current Functions. Under the direction of the state comptroller, chief fiscal officer of the State, the Department of Audit and Control is responsible for administering the accounts of the State. The department carries out this responsibility by: paying the State's bills and payrolls; auditing all revenues, receipts, and claims against the State; auditing the records, accounts, and financial and management practices of all State agencies and institutions; supervising the fiscal affairs of all units of local government in the State; reviewing the financial plans and fiscal and management practices of New York City; investing State funds and issuing bonds and notes; administering the State's retirement and social security agencies; administering the State's cash flow; and providing fiscal legal advice for State and local government agencies.

Organizational History. This department traces its origin to 1625 when New Netherland authorities appointed a schout-fiscal to examine the accounts at New Amsterdam. In 1658, a Board of Audit consisting of the director general, receiver general, and a council member assumed auditing responsibilities. After the English took control in 1664, the auditing function was carried out by an auditor general appointed by royal authorities. However, the colonial assembly, established in 1683, gradually asserted greater control over fiscal matters. The responsibility for fiscal matters continued to be divided between royal officials and the elected assembly until the American Revolution.

During the early days of the Revolution, the Provincial Congress chose auditors from among its own members and in mid-1776 appointed an auditor general. The first State constitution of 1777 created an Office of State Treasurer to collect and disburse revenues as authorized by the legislature but did not mention an auditor. However, an auditor general was appointed under a clause providing for the appointment of "other officers."

In 1782 (Chapter 21, Fifth Session), the legislature established the office of auditor to assume responsibility for settling the State's accounts. In 1787, the auditor assumed the duties relating to collection and commutation of quit rents previously carried out by the treasurer. In 1788, the auditor was directed to settle accounts with the United States and certain other states.

To avoid conflicts between the auditor and the treasurer, the legislature established the Office of Comptroller in 1797 (Chapter 21), combining the auditor's power to audit and the treasurer's power to pay into one chief fiscal officer. The comptroller assumed all duties of the auditor and certain powers of the treasurer, including drawing up payment warrants, investing the State's funds, and borrowing money on the credit of the State. The comptroller was appointed by the Council of Appointment until the 1821 constitution provided for election of the comptroller by the legislature. Under the 1846 and subsequent constitutions, the comptroller was elected in a general election.

The comptroller was designated a member of the Board of Commissioners of the Land Office in 1801 and was directed to sell lands for payment of delinquent State taxes. When construction of the canal system began in 1817, the comptroller was appointed to the Board of Commissioners of the Canal Fund and later to the Canal Board. The commissioners of the Canal Fund were responsible for managing the debts and funds of the State's canals. The Canal Board, comprised of the commissioners of the Canal Fund and the canal commissioners (responsible for canal construction and repair), exercised overall supervision over the State's canal system. The comptroller remained a member of the Land Board until it was reorganized in 1926, and of the Canal Boards until they were abolished in 1926.

The comptroller examined the financial affairs of banks from 1843 until the creation of the Banking Department in 1851. From 1849 until the creation of the Insurance Department a decade later, the comptroller regulated the organization and operation of insurance companies. Beginning in 1865, State-supported hospitals and charitable institutions were required to report on their financial condition to the comptroller, and in 1873 the comptroller was empowered to examine the financial affairs of prisons and various other State institutions. In 1880, the comptroller was authorized to initiate a system of collecting taxes on corporations. The comptroller assumed the duties of the former office of canal auditor in 1883. Beginning in 1905, municipal divisions of the State were required to adopt uniform fiscal reporting systems and to file annual reports subject to examination by the Comptroller's Office.

In 1910 (Chapter 149), State agencies were required annually to submit a proposed expenditure plan to the comptroller, who then forwarded recommendations to the Assembly Ways and Means and the Senate Finance committees. This was the forerunner of New York State's executive budget process. In 1913, the comptroller's auditing powers were strengthened by a law (Chapter 342) requiring agencies to adopt a uniform system of accounting and fiscal reporting, to verify purchases and services, and to obtain the comptroller's prior approval of all contracts over one thousand dollars. In 1920 (Chapter 741), a State employees retirement system was established under the administrative control of the comptroller.

The 1925 constitutional amendment reorganizing State government placed the elected comptroller at the head of a new Department of Audit and Control and assigned the office the duties of auditing all vouchers before payment, auditing the accrual and collection of all revenues and receipts, and prescribing accounting methods necessary to perform these activities. The 1926 law establishing the Department of Audit and Control (Chapter 614) transferred responsibility for the canal debt sinking fund from the commissioners of the canal fund to the comptroller. The comptroller's responsibility for licensing private detectives, auctioneers, steamship ticket agents, and theater ticket brokers was transferred to the Department of State. The new Department of Taxation and Finance, which absorbed the duties of the former state treasurer, was given the comptroller's former responsibility for administering revenue-collecting activities. This responsibility included activities under any law related to direct State taxes; duties of the comptroller concerning land taxes and land sales for payment of delinquent taxes; and custody of State employee retirement funds.

In 1975 (Chapter 219), the duties of the welfare inspector general, relating to investigation of complaints of abuses, fraud, or violations of the welfare system, were transferred to the Department of Audit and Control. Another law that year (Chapter 868) directed the comptroller to assist the Emergency Financial Control Board in carrying out its responsibilities relating to New York City revenues, expenditures, and indebtedness. In that year, the new office of the State Deputy Comptroller for New York City was established as a part of the department to fulfill this mission.

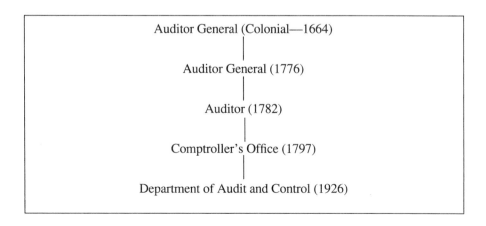

Auditor General (Colonial—1664)

|

Auditor General (1776)

|

Auditor (1782)

|

Comptroller's Office (1797)

|

Department of Audit and Control (1926)

DEPARTMENT OF AUDIT AND CONTROL (1927-)

First Deputy Comptroller

14131   Comptroller's speeches, 1960-1974.
4 cu. ft.

Division of Municipal Affairs

– Bureau of Municipal Affairs-Examinations

13100   Municipal audit examination reports, ca. 1919-1953.
4 cu. ft.

– Bureau of Municipal Research and Statistics

12464   Annual village constitutional tax margin statements, 1947-1986.
64 cu. ft.

13333   Annual city constitutional tax margin statements, 1947-1986.
9.5 cu. ft.

13332   Annual county constitutional tax margin statements, 1953-1985.
20.5 cu. ft.

B1215   Annual constitutional tax margin statements of school districts, ca. 1948-1959.
6 cu. ft.

13314   Annual financial reports of regional Off-Track Betting corporations, 1974-1983.
2.5 cu. ft.

13315   Annual financial reports of urban renewal agencies, 1963-1983, 1986-1987.
3.6 cu. ft.

13316   Annual financial reports of public authorities, 1951-1983, 1987.
5.8 cu. ft.

13317   Annual financial reports of industrial development agencies, 1975-1983, 1987.
3.1 cu. ft.

13318   Annual financial reports of consolidated health districts, 1954-1983.
2.6 cu. ft.

13319   Annual financial reports of soil and water conservation districts, 1969-1983.
3.7 cu. ft.

13320   Annual financial reports of regional planning boards, 1976-1983.
.8 cu. ft.

13321   Annual financial reports of fire districts, 1956-1987.
32.5 cu. ft.

13323   Annual financial reports of counties, 1961-1987.
42 cu. ft.

13324   Annual financial reports of cities, 1961-1987.
45 cu. ft.

13325   Annual financial reports of villages, 1956-1988.
208 cu. ft.

13326   Annual financial reports of towns, 1956-1987.
339 cu. ft.

11166   Annual financial reports of school districts, BOCES, community
colleges, libraries, and vocational extension boards, 1986-1988.
8 cu. ft.

14493   Annual financial reports of public libraries, 1978-1987.
5.1 cu. ft.

14494   Annual financial reports of municipalities' joint activities, 1984-
1987.
5 cu. ft.

B1258   Annual financial reports of community development agencies,
1977-1978.
.2 cu. ft.

13322   Annual schedules of real property taxes levied by county boards of
supervisors/legislators, 1958-1987.
30 cu. ft.

Office of Unclaimed Funds

A0836   Closed U.S. Deposit Fund mortgages and farm loan mortgages,
1837-1975.
22 cu. ft.

B0991   U.S. Deposit Fund reports and correspondence, 1910-1975, bulk
1901-1930.
3 cu. ft.

Comptroller's Committee on Constitutional Tax and Debit Limitations and City-School Fiscal Relations

A0948   Proceedings and draft legislation, 1948-1949.
.2 cu. ft.

Canal Records

B0602   Canal damage awards by Canal Appraisers, Board of Claims, and Court of Claims, 1835-1953.
46 cu. ft.

A1055   Accounts relating to construction and operation of Barge Canal, 1920-1938.
1 cu. ft.

A1403   General and Canal Fund bond register, ca. 1931-1935.
.5 cu. ft.

B0605   Requisitions for Barge Canal materials and equipment, 1934-1938.
4.5 cu. ft.

B0921   Abstracts and vouchers for Barge Canal and canal terminal expenses, 1936.
1 cu. ft.

Land Tax Records

B0931   Affidavits of publication of tax sale and redemption notices, 1814-1927.
5 cu. ft.

B0918   Certificates of sale of land for unpaid taxes, 1815-1928.
82 cu. ft.

B0847   Applications to redeem property from tax sales, 1828-1927.
20.5 cu. ft.

B0935   Notices to and from mortgagees of lands sold for taxes, 1853-1930.
2 cu. ft.

B0988   Affidavits of non-occupancy of lands purchased at comptroller's tax sales, 1869-1927, bulk 1869-1918.
.3 cu. ft.

B1261   Opinions of the attorney general and court decisions concerning the sale of lands for unpaid taxes, 1876-1937.
.5 cu. ft.

B0603 Accounts of taxes on State lands, 1886-1961.
53.5 cu. ft. (100 volumes)

A1349 Register of mortgage tax receipts, 1915-1933.
.3 cu. ft. (1 volume)

A1348 Daybook relating to mortgage taxation, 1916-1940.
.2 cu. ft. (1 volume)

A1384 Correspondence relating to the publication of notices of lands sold for taxes and unredeemed, ca. 1923-1927.
.5 cu. ft.

A1378 Statements of taxes assessed on Allegany State Park lands, 1926-1928.
.3 cu. ft.

Other Records

A0802 Audited accounts, 1780-1938.
21.1 cu. ft.

A1340 List of assignments and satisfactions of mortgages, 1911-1931.
.3 cu. ft. (1 volume)

A1379 Comptroller's consents to local governments to issue bonds, 1920-1931.
.5 cu. ft.

A1402 Check register, income tax account, 1925-1940.
.3 cu. ft. (1 volume)

A1237 Mortgage tax bonds given a surety by county clerks and treasurers, 1926-1936.
.2 cu. ft.

B0604 Railroad grade crossing elimination payment registers, 1927-1960.
3 cu. ft. (7 volumes)

A1355 Licensing receipts account book, 1928-1932.
.5 cu. ft.

A1406 Tables showing distribution of tax monies to various counties, 1929-1942.
.3 cu. ft. (1 volume)

A0821 Contract between III Olympic Winter Games Committee and Leo A. Malone, 1930.
.2 cu. ft.

A1459   Vouchers and correspondence submitted by the State Roosevelt Memorial Commission, 1932.
.2 cu. ft.

A1350   Case file of securities deposited in the comptroller's office, 1933.
1 cu. ft. (2 volumes)

A1347   Request to comptroller by Corporation Tax Bureau to issue refund checks to corporations, 1938.
.5 cu. ft. (1 volume)

A1408   Cash and earned income statement submitted by Corporation Tax Bureau, 1940-1943.
.1 cu. ft. (1 volume)

B0994   U.S. Deposit Fund day books, 1941-1976.
1 cu. ft.

A0944   Draft manual, "Uniform system of accounting for villages," 1953.
.3 cu. ft.

A0796   Annual debt statements of municipalities, fire districts, and school districts, 1967-1969.
3 cu. ft.

A0837   Computer-produced appropriation ledger abstracts for state agencies, 1968-1969.
9 cu. ft.

A0797   Annual and supplemental debt statements of housing and urban renewal authorities, 1968-1969.
.4 cu. ft.

A0838   Computer-produced accounting reports for State agencies, 1971-1972.
37 cu. ft.

AUDITOR GENERAL

A1261   Entry documentation concerning the estate of Abraham De Peyster, ca. 1771-1774.
.5 cu. ft.

A1208   List of Loan Office Certificates from the United States to the State of New York, 1777-1781.
.1 cu. ft.

A1240   Accounts of monies paid into treasuries of Albany and Dutchess counties, 1779-1782.
.5 cu. ft.

A0893   Index to certificates and accounts for purchase of forage and account of hay pasture and grain supplied to the Continental Army, 1780-1782.
.3 cu. ft. (1 volume)

A0808   Register of land bounty rights, ca. 1782.
.5 cu. ft.

AUDITOR

A1065   Lists of certificates of payments by the Treasurer, ca. 1776-1786.
1 cu. ft. (10 volumes)

A0174   Certificates submitted by disabled Revolutionary War veterans claiming pensions and audited accounts of pensions, 1779-1789.
5.3 cu. ft. (9 volumes)

A0870   Copies of accounts audited by the Auditor-General for bills presented to the State, 1780-1794.
4 cu. ft. (9 volumes)

A0809   Paymaster returns for service in New York Line, 1780.
.5 cu. ft.

A0892   List of pay certificates issued to New York Continental soldiers by the U.S. Paymaster General ("Pierce's Certificates"), 1783-1787.
.3 cu. ft.

A1257   Inventories of items sold at public auctions, 1785-1786.
.5 cu. ft.

A0973   Tax accounts of the treasurer of the City and County of New York, 1785-1787.
.1 cu. ft.

A1212   List of receipts relating to land patents, 1786.
.25 cu. ft.

A1211   Certificates of exemption from quitrents, 1786-1787.
.5 cu. ft.

A1228   Certificates of remission from quitrents, 1786-1790.
.3 cu. ft.

A0969   Warrants to sheriff of Ulster County to levy arrears of taxes, 1788.
.2 cu. ft. (12 items)

A1262   Accounts of debt subscription certificates, 1793.
.2 cu. ft.

COMPTROLLER'S OFFICE (1797-1926)

Bureau of Canal Affairs

A3240   Ledger accounts for leases of surplus canal water, salaries of canal officials, and canal loans, 1826-1931.
.3 cu. ft. (1 volume)

A1439   Lists of awards made by Board of Claims, 1892-1894.
.2 cu. ft.

A1270   Engineers' accounts, 1899-1920.
.3 cu. ft. (1 volume)

Canal Appraisers

A1441   Documents relating to canal claims, ca. 1830-1880.
2.5 cu. ft.

Canal Board

A0868   Minutes, 1833-1855.
1 cu. ft. (4 volumes)

A0856   Rough minutes, 1832-1926.
82 cu. ft.

A1140   Petitions and appeals to the Canal Board, 1828-1926.
70 cu. ft. (110 microfilm reels)

A0859   Index to Canal Board rough minutes, petitions, and appeals, 1845-1925.
2.7 cu. ft. (16 volumes) (3 microfilm reels)

A1434   Index to petitions and appeals to the Canal Board, 1828-1832.
.1 cu. ft. (1 volume) (1 microfilm reel)

A1086   Account of expenditures for constructing Champlain Canal, 1818-1824.
.5 cu. ft.

A1438   Canal operating and administrative files, 1827-1833.
.2 cu. ft. (1 microfilm reel)

A1160   Financial and legal records filed with the Canal Department, 1841-1885.
.5 cu. ft.

A1088   Sample form book compiled by Canal Department, 1850-1883.
.3 cu. ft. (1 volume)

A1468   Testimony and brief in case of Black River claims heard by Canal Appraisers, 1869-1871.
.2 cu. ft. (2 volumes)

A1278   Register of dates of occupation on lands appropriated for the Barge Canal, 1906-1916.
.2 cu. ft. (1 volume)

A1274   Barge Canal construction monthly reports, 1910-1916.
.3 cu. ft. (2 volumes)

Canal Commissioners

A1440   Incoming correspondence relating to canals, ca. 1830-1880.
3 cu. ft.

A1899   Contract documents for canal enlargement and repairs, ca. 1836-1900.
60 cu. ft.

A1125   Contracts and accounts for construction and repair, ca. 1817-1828.
10 cu. ft.

A0810   Canvass of proposals for Erie Canal Enlargement, 1851.
.3 cu. ft. (1 volume)

A1268   Index to contracts for Erie Canal improvements, ca. 1840-1860.
.3 cu. ft.

A0819   Canal financial and administrative records, 1838-1880.
.5 cu. ft.

A1316   Comptroller's register of checks drawn for Canal Commissioners, 1817-1824.
.2 cu. ft. (1 volume)

A1006   Western Island Lock Navigation Company damage assessments and reimbursements, 1820.
.2 cu. ft.

A0828   Entry documentation for canal-related expenses, 1827-1901.
.5 cu. ft.

A1126   Abstracts and vouchers of expenditures, ca. 1831-1869.
17 cu. ft.

A1132   Superintendents of Repairs' reports of expenditures for repairs, 1835-1878.
12 cu. ft.

A1131   Superintendents of Repairs' estimate of expenditures for repairs, 1835-1905.
11 cu. ft.

A3131   Vouchers for expenditures on enlargement of the Erie Canal, 1837-1848, bulk 1848.
3 cu. ft.

A1129   Resident and division engineers' monthly estimates, 1850-1868, 1875.
4 cu. ft.

A1098   Estimates of work done and material delivered on Erie, Champlain, and Black River canals, 1867-1868.
.1 cu. ft.

A0954   Vouchers for repair of Ox Bow break, Erie Canal, 1871.
.3 cu. ft.

A0392   Engineers' drafts and vouchers for general fund, 1895-1896.
.5 cu. ft.

A0851   Original maps of surveys for the Erie Canal, 1817.
1 cu. ft. (1 volume)

A0800   Survey maps and plans for projected canal alterations, ca. 1830-1851.
64 maps.

A0852   Survey map of Susquehanna and Chemung rivers, 1830.
.5 cu. ft. (1 volume)

A0848   Canal system survey maps, 1832-1843.
19 cu. ft. (4 microfilm reels)

A1058   Designs for Watervliet Arsenal Bridge, 1851.
1 sheet.

A0854   Survey map of extension of Genesee Valley Canal from Olean to Mill Grove Pond, 1857.
.3 cu. ft. (1 map)

A1195   Calendar of petitions, 1849-1854.
.2 cu. ft. (1 volume)

A0815   Impeachment trial subpoenas and subpoena tickets for Canal Commissioner, 1853.
.5 cu. ft.

A0879   Scrapbooks of newspaper articles relating to the canals, 1817-1826.
.5 cu. ft. (2 volumes)

Canal Department

A0881   Expense accounts related to Commissioners for Inland Navigation Between the Great Lakes and the Hudson River, 1810-1814.
.3 cu. ft.

A1093   Accounts and returns of canal tolls by railroads, 1844-1851.
1 cu. ft. (4 volumes)

A0923   Register of canal boats, 1859.
.3 cu. ft.

– Auditor of the Canal Department

A1144   Incoming correspondence, ca. 1846-1883.
9 cu. ft.

A1135   Lock tenders' monthly reports of lockages, 1858-1881.
2 cu. ft.

A1138   Boat inspectors' weekly reports, 1862-1881.
3 cu. ft.

A1136   Weigh Masters' annual statements and inventory and weekly abstracts, 1860-1882.
2 cu. ft.

A1172   Weekly statements of canal shipments to or from tide water, 1863.
.2 cu. ft.

A1171   Weekly statements of canal shipments through Buffalo to or from other states, 1877, 1879.
.2 cu. ft.

A1389   Report of A.J. Davis on irregularities in performance of repair of Chemung Canal Feeder, submitted to Commission to Investigate Canal Frauds, 1871.
.5 cu. ft.

A1095   Statement of work done under contract on the Erie Canal
Enlargement, 1847-1849.
.3 cu ft. (1 volume)

A0988   Abstracts of bids received for work on canals, 1854-1857.
.3 cu. ft.

A1039   Contract for constructing bridge over Cattaraugus Creek at Irving,
1868.
.1 cu. ft. (1 contract)

A0817   Contract for protection of Albany Basin, 1869.
.1 cu. ft. (2 items)

A1139   Bills of lading and clearances for cargoes, 1830-1855, 1869, 1881.
1 cu. ft.

A1137   Certificates of registry of canal boats, 1837-1880.
2 cu. ft.

A1034   Lists of freight on Baxter Steam Canal Boats, ca. 1840-1870.
.5 cu. ft.

A0818   Register of tolls paid by railroads on canals, 1849-1851.
.5 cu. ft.

A1141   Documents relating to refund of overpaid tolls, 1851-1882.
18 cu. ft.

A1437   Sample forms for canal tolls paid by railroads, ca. 1851.
.2 cu. ft.

A1267   Accounts of monies paid to contractors and others for construction, repair, and enlargement of Erie and Champlain canals, 1817-
1871.
1.5 cu. ft. (3 volumes)

A1435   List of expenditures for work done on the Erie Canal, ca. 1829-
1857.
.1 cu. ft.

A1130   Resident and division engineers' abstracts and vouchers of expenditures, 1833-1874.
7 cu. ft.

A1099   Register of appointments, 1848-1861.
.3 cu. ft. (1 volume)

A1134 Inventories of canal property, 1835-1876.
2 cu. ft.

A1380 Releases upon commutation for farm bridges over canals, with related correspondence and documents, 1835-1876.
.5 cu. ft.

A1167 Miscellaneous documents relating to canals, ca. 1825-1875.
2 cu. ft.

– Chief Clerk of the Canal Department

A1080 Canal Toll Collector's book, 1847.
.1 cu. ft. (1 volume)

– Western Division Engineer

A1469 Historical abstracts concerning lands of Western Division, Erie Canal, ca. 1860-1880.
.1 cu. ft.

Commissioners of the Canal Fund

A1077 Engrossed minutes and index, 1817-1855.
.6 cu. ft. (3 volumes)

B0316 Index to minutes, 1817-1854.
.3 cu. ft. (1 volume)

A1076 Rough minutes, 1827-1926.
3 cu. ft. (11 volumes)

A0905 Resolutions and reports of the Commissioners, 1818, 1825, 1874.
.5 cu. ft.

A1038 Canal Fund loan proposals, 1817-1857.
.5 cu. ft.

A0883 Lists of stockholders of Million Dollar Loan and canal loans, 1815-1823.
.5 cu. ft.

A1012 Schedule of Erie and Champlain Canal stock redeemed by the Commissioners of the Canal Fund, 1838.
.1 cu. ft. (1 item)

A1395 Statements of proceeds from sales of Canal Fund lands, 1826-1833.
.5 cu. ft.

A1388 Legal documentation relating to lands conveyed to Commissioners of the Canal Fund, 1861-1881.
.5 cu. ft.

A1163   Documents relating to deposit of Canal Funds in banks, ca. 1831-1901.
8 cu. ft.

A1094   List of contracts with banks for interest on canal money, 1831-1834.
.1 cu. ft.

A1097   Monthly balances of canal monies in banks, 1834-1844.
.5 cu. ft.

A1170   Bonds of banks holding deposits of Canal Fund monies, 1855-1867.
.2 cu. ft.

Canal Investigating Commission

A0834   Printed material, correspondence and photographs from the Canal Investigating Commission, 1888-1912.
6 cu. ft.

Contracting Board

A1127   Proposals and bonds for canal enlargement and repairs, 1848-1869.
12 cu. ft.

Other Canal Records

A0872   Engrossed minutes of the Canal Commissioners, 1849-1857.
.5 cu. ft. (1 volume)

A1081   Canal fund accounts (receipt and disbursement book), 1824-1832.
.3 cu. ft. (1 volume)

A1145   Vouchers for expenditures on account of canal fund, 1833-1900, bulk 1853-1900.
34 cu. ft.

A1096   Monthly bank balances of Canal Fund, 1833-1835.
.2 cu. ft.

A1085   Canal Fund account book, 1835-1840.
.3 cu. ft. (1 volume)

A0826   Entry documentation submitted by the Commissioners of Navigation to the comptroller, 1794-1828.
1 cu. ft.

A1089   Canal stock transfer receipt book, 1820-1824.
.3 cu. ft. (1 volume)

A1087   Accounts of Canal Commissioners for expenditures on branch canals, 1825-1837.
.3 cu. ft.

A1158   Engineers' abstracts and vouchers for survey of canal routes, 1825-1835.
.3 cu. ft.

A0013   Abstracts, check rolls, and vouchers for canal expenditures, 1827-1880.
247 cu. ft.

A1142   Bonds of canal employees, contractors, and boards, 1827-1876.
3 cu. ft.

A1265   Accounts for enlargement and improvement of the Erie Canal, 1835-1849.
.5 cu. ft.

A1092   Account book for cash paid out for Black River, Genesee Valley, and other branch canals, 1840-1859.
.3 cu. ft.

A1179   Superintendent of Repairs' unpaid accounts, 1846-1875.
.3 cu. ft.

A0857   Canal superintendents' accounts, 1852-1858.
.3 cu. ft. (1 volume)

A1399   Canvasses of proposals for enlargement of Erie Canal and completion of Genesee Valley Canal, 1854-1857.
2 cu. ft. (7 volumes)

A1082   Canal auditor's decisions, 1854-1882.
.3 cu. ft. (1 volume)

A1442   Maps and plans of canal structures, ca. 1830-1900.
.3 cu. ft.

A1091   Measurements, calculations, and estimates for construction of Chenango Canal, 1833-1837.
1 cu. ft. (3 volumes)

A1078   Canal engineer's field notes for Erie Canal, 1834.
.5 cu. ft. (5 volumes)

A1133   Superintendents of Repairs' annual reports of structures or work completed or repaired, 1841-1875.
1 cu. ft.

A1190   Field notes of canal engineers, 1841-1851.
.1 cu. ft. (3 volumes)

A1177   Superintendent of Repairs' reports of inspection of materials and tools, 1849-1852.
.1 cu. ft.

A1176   Superintendent of Repairs' reports of locktenders employed by contractors for repairs, 1863-1864.
.3 cu. ft.

A1266   Canal Commissioners' estimates of work done and materials delivered on Erie, Champlain, and Black River canals, 1867-1868.
.3 cu. ft.

A0890   Canaseraga Creek Improvement records, 1906-1915.
.3 cu. ft.

A1273   Monthly reports on Barge Canal terminal construction, 1913-1920.
.3 cu. ft. (2 volumes)

A1264   Accounts of taxes paid on passengers of steamboats, 1817-1819.
.3 cu. ft.

A0814   Register of canal boat name changes, 1817-1852.
.1 cu. ft. (1 volume)

A1198   Cash account of Toll Collector at Rochester, 1826.
.3 cu. ft. (2 volumes)

A1064   Reports of canal tolls received, 1826.
.1 cu. ft.

A1057   Lists of passengers on boats on the Erie Canal, 1827-1829.
2.5 cu. ft.

A1175   Annual statistical reports of cargoes cleared in 1830 at various canal ports, 1832.
.2 cu. ft.

A1178   Agreements for commutation of passenger tolls on freight boats carrying passengers, 1834.
.1 cu. ft.

A1079   Passenger list and freight account book of steamboat "Red Jacket," 1838-1839.
.3 cu. ft. (2 volumes)

A1448 Leases of toll collectors' offices, 1849-1882.
.3 cu. ft.

A1157 Toll collectors' annual accounts, 1853, 1878-1879.
.3 cu. ft.

Corporation Tax Bureau

B0976 Accounts of cash received, 1901-1921.
4 cu. ft. (12 volumes)

Commissioners of the Land Office

A0903 Register of Canal Fund land sold by the Surveyor General, 1843-1847.
.5 cu. ft.

A0850 State Engineer and Surveyor's maps of the Onondaga Salt Springs Reservation, 1891.
.5 cu. ft. (1 volume)

Land Tax Bureau

– *Tax Sales and Foreclosures*

A0972 Corrected proofs of advertisement for redemption of lands sold for non-payment of U.S. Direct Tax, 1804.
.1 cu. ft. (7 items)

A0895 Payments for land sold for taxes, 1821.
.1 cu. ft. (1 volume)

A1338 List of lands advertised to be sold for arrears of quitrents, 1815.
.3 cu. ft. (1 volume)

A1332 Deeds to lands sold for non-payment of taxes, 1833-1894.
.1 cu. ft.

A1286 Ledger of accounts of property acquired through foreclosure, 1839-1884.
1 cu. ft. (1 volume)

A1411 Applications for cancellation of tax sales, 1841-1925.
.3 cu. ft.

A1387 Legal documentation relating to comptroller's sales of land for taxes, ca. 1870-1910.
1 cu. ft.

A1396 Newspaper notices of tax sales, 1878-1911.
.3 cu. ft.

A1409 Indexes to applications for redemption of lands from tax sales, 1889-1895.
.3 cu. ft. (8 volumes)

A1342 Proceedings on applications to redeem land from tax sales, 1895-1918.
.3 cu. ft. (1 volume)

A1407 Abstracts of applications to redeem land from tax sale of 1920, 1921-1923.
.3 cu. ft. (1 volume)

– *Taxes and Quitrents*

A1377 Statement of valuations and taxes on State lands, 1923.
.5 cu. ft.

A1351 List of quitrents, 1820.
.3 cu. ft. (1 volume)

A1214 Delivery receipts for distribution of quitrents, ca. 1820-1824.
.25 cu. ft.

– *Assessment Records*

A0830 County assessments of real and personal property, 1786-1910.
1 cu. ft.

A0976 Accounts of town assessors and commissioners of taxes, 1799-1801.
.6 cu. ft.

A1210 County summaries of tax assessment rolls, ca. 1838.
.1 cu. ft. (43 items)

A1382 Town assessor's statements of assessed value of forest and improved lands, 1884.
.5 cu. ft.

A1341 Notices of local assessments of State property for local improvements, 1904-1906.
.3 cu. ft. (1 volume)

– *Land Grants, Sales, and Titles*

A1352 Receipt book of land grants from Gerrit Smith to "colored and poor white slaves from the South", 1846.
.3 cu. ft. (1 volume)

A0823 Legal documentation for sale of unappropriated land, 1731-1883.
4 cu. ft.

A1218   Bonds for the sale of unappropriated lands, ca. 1803-1815.
.5 cu. ft.

A1335   List of buyers of State lands, 1818-1834.
1 cu. ft. (1 volume)

A1337   Register of lands sold by the Surveyor General, 1835-1881.
1 cu. ft. (3 volumes)

A1381   Applications to purchase State lands, 1859-1913.
.5 cu. ft.

A1297   Resolution, agreements, and purchase list of the sale of college land scrip, 1864-1870.
.5 cu. ft. (1 volume)

A1383   Notices from Forest Commission and Commissioners of the Land Office approving sale of State lands, 1894.
.5 cu. ft.

A1346   Conservation Commission recommendations to the Commissioners of the Land Office relating to lands to purchase for new State parks, 1917-1923.
1 cu. ft. (3 volumes)

A1323   Lists of bonds and mortgages on State lands delivered to the attorney general, 1811-1817.
.3 cu. ft. (1 volume)

A1299   Copies of deeds from comptroller, 1889-1923.
1 cu. ft. (1 volume)

A0971   Certificates of searches of judgment dockets and mortgage records, 1813-1819, 1838-1843, 1859.
.25 cu. ft.

A0820   Certified search of land in Township 41 of Totten and Crossfield's Patent, 1897.
.3 cu. ft. (1 volume)

– *U.S. Deposit Fund*

A0983   County commissioners' annual reports of the U.S. Deposit Fund, 1837-1909.
30 cu. ft.

A1282   County commissioners' minute and account books of the U.S. Deposit Fund, 1837-1911.
24 cu. ft. (41 volumes)

A1281   County commissioners' ledgers of mortgage loans of the U.S. Deposit Fund, 1837-1911.
13 cu. ft. (16 volumes)

A1284   Ledger of general accounts with county commissioners of the U.S. Deposit Fund, 1837-1911.
2 cu. ft. (2 volumes)

A0865   U.S. Deposit Fund county commissioners' ledger of accounts, 1840-1911.
.5 cu. ft. (1 volume)

A1287   County commissioners' accounts relating to interest on the U.S. Deposit Fund, 1839-1866.
.3 cu. ft. (2 volumes)

A1285   Mortgage statements of county commissioners of the U.S. Deposit Fund, 1838.
1 cu. ft. (1 volume)

B1062   U.S. Deposit Fund foreclosed mortgage files, 1843-1910.
2 cu. ft.

14469   U.S. Deposit Fund appraisal reports on mortgaged property, 1909-1910.
4 cu. ft.

B0992   U.S. Deposit Fund title searches, 1880-1920.
2 cu. ft.

B0993   U.S. Deposit Fund county commissioners' bonds, 1902-1909.
1 cu. ft.

A1288   Register of County Treasurers and Commissioners of the U.S. Deposit Fund, 1873-1906.
1 cu. ft. (1 volume)

B1063   U.S. Deposit Fund reports and lists, ca. 1890-1960, bulk 1902-1911.
2 cu. ft.

Other Land and Land Tax Records

B0966   Index to lands sales for unpaid quitrents (sale of 1808), 1808-1814.
.2 cu. ft. (1 volume)

A1234   Report of the joint committee of the Senate and Assembly on the subject of quitrents, 1821.
.2 cu. ft.

B0964   Minutes of Commissioners to Extinguish Claims Against Lands Sold by the State, 1799-1831.
.2 cu. ft. (1 volume)

A0217   Certificates of lands sold at public sales for which deeds were given, ca. 1800-1830.
1 cu. ft.

A1052   Bonds from purchasers of lands in old military tract, 1805-1813.
.3 cu. ft.

B0968   Register of lands sold by Surveyor General, 1830-1834.
.2 cu. ft. (1 volume)

B0950   Tax assessment rolls of real and personal estates, 1799-1804.
20 cu. ft. (26 microfilm reels)

B0990   Copies of tax assessment rolls for towns in Hamilton and Warren Counties, 1843-1876, bulk 1857-1876.
.3 cu. ft. (33 items)

B0958   Tax assessment rolls for Town of Gravesend, Kings County, 1885-1892.
.5 cu. ft. (8 volumes)

B0959   Tax assessment roll for Town of Rochester, Ulster County, 1909.
.2 cu. ft. (1 volume)

B0960   Tax assessment rolls for Union Free School District No. 1, Town of Ossining, Westchester County, 1916-1917.
.5 cu. ft. (2 volumes)

B0961   Tax assessors' atlases of Kings and Richmond county towns, ca. 1871-1896.
ca. 7 cu. ft. (15 volumes)

B0963   Index to tax maps for Kings and Richmond counties, n.d.
.2 cu. ft. (1 volume)

B0315   Abstracts of property valuations made for State taxes, 1799-1800.
.4 cu. ft.

B0951   Registers of arrears of taxes, 1801-1804.
.5 cu. ft. (3 volumes)

A1071   Geographical registers of comptroller's tax deeds, 1815-1845, 1895, 1900, 1924-1926.
9.3 cu. ft. (8 volumes)

B0956   Register of comptroller's deeds, 1873-1896.
         .2 cu. ft. (1 volume)

B0957   Register of tax relevied, 1887-1890.
         .2 cu. ft. (1 volume)

B0952   Accounts of rejected taxes in Forest Preserve Counties, 1912.
         .2 cu. ft. (1 volume)

B0849   Registers of rejected property descriptions, 1807-1865.
         7 cu. ft. (52 volumes)

B0954   Statement of lands sold for taxes, 1808-1821.
         .2 cu. ft. (1 volume)

11276   Accounts of unpaid taxes assessed on non-resident lands, 1805-1926.
         136 cu. ft.

B0953   Registers of non-resident lands sold in tax sales of 1808 and 1814,
         ca. 1812-1818.
         1.5 cu. ft. (5 volumes)

B0934   Lists of non-resident lands with unpaid taxes, ca. 1810-1850.
         1.3 cu. ft.

B0848   Registers of non-resident lands sold for unpaid taxes, 1818-1836,
         1839.
         20 cu. ft. (20 volumes)

B1259   Maps of non-resident lands sold for unpaid taxes, ca. 1820-1910.
         3 cu. ft.

B0945   Tax sale notices to occupants of lands sold, 1821-1926.
         11 cu. ft.

B0846   Published notices of lands sold for unpaid taxes and unredeemed,
         1826-1905, bulk 1843-1905.
         3 cu. ft. (13 volumes)

B0851   Index to applications to redeem property from tax sales, 1828-
         1903.
         1 cu. ft. (11 volumes)

B0929   Documents supporting orders for cancellation of tax sales, 1829-
         1926.
         18 cu. ft.

B0845   Register of bids and payments for land sold for unpaid taxes, 1830-1926.
5 cu. ft. (20 volumes)

A1181   Schedule of lands of John Hone sold for taxes, 1831.
.2 cu. ft.

B0941   County treasurers' returns of unpaid taxes on non-resident lands, 1849-1851.
3 cu. ft.

B0940   County treasurers' statements of non-resident lands sold for unpaid taxes, 1849-1854.
1 cu. ft.

B0937   County treasurers' tax sales records, ca. 1850-1856.
.5 cu. ft.

B0938   County treasurers' statements of conveyance and redemptions of non-resident land sold for unpaid taxes, 1852-1854.
1 cu. ft.

B0932   Affidavits of publication of county treasurers' notices of tax sales, 1852-1855.
3 cu. ft.

A1258   Treasurer's receipts for payments of land purchased at comptroller's tax sale, 1853.
.5 cu. ft.

B0930   Payment receipts for lands purchased at tax sales, 1859-1926.
3 cu. ft.

A1412   Tax sale certificates, 1859.
.3 cu. ft.

B1260   Copies of documentation establishing ownership of lands sold for unpaid taxes, 1873-1923.
.5 cu. ft.

B0985   Cancelled certificates of sale of land for unpaid taxes, 1877.
.3 cu. ft.

B0936   County treasurer's lists of non-resident lands to be sold for unpaid taxes, 1887-1904.
1.3 cu. ft.

A0849   Entry documentation relating to escheats, ca. 1901-1903.
.3 cu. ft.

B0943 Reports of occupancy of lands purchased by the State in tax sales, 1902-1912.
.3 cu. ft.

A0807 Accounts and receipts of Commission for Settling Claims for Land Ceded to Vermont, 1797-1800.
.2 cu. ft.

A0878 Records of the Albany City lottery to dispose of public lands, 1822.
.2 cu. ft.

A1241 Legal documentation relating to college landscrip fund, 1865-1874.
.3 cu. ft.

B0987 Lists of State lands, ca. 1865-1905.
.4 cu. ft. (13 items)

B0942 Letters from agents appointed to serve notice on illegal occupants of State lands, 1881-1893.
1 cu. ft.

B1262 Reports by county clerks and treasurers of land owned by counties and mortgaged to loan commissioners, 1881.
.5 cu. ft.

A1446 Documents relating to charges against Louis F. Haffen, Bronx Borough President, 1908-1909.
1 cu. ft.

B1263 Proof of publication of list of wild, vacant and forest lands owned by the State, 1895.
.2 cu. ft.

B0955 Register of decedent estates paying transfer taxes, 1900.
.1 cu. ft. (1 volume)

Correspondence and Reports

A0847 Incoming correspondence, 1777-1890.
92 cu. ft.

A1075 Outgoing correspondence, 1807-1909.
34 cu. ft. (172 volumes)

A1269 Outgoing correspondence relating to the canals and canal fund, 1826-1886.
34 cu. ft. (34 volumes)

A1358 Outgoing correspondence relating to taxation and sale of State land, 1891-1910.
2 cu. ft. (10 volumes)

A1357 Outgoing correspondence relating to land taxes, 1897-1910.
5 cu. ft. (32 volumes)

A1283 Outgoing correspondence relating to audits and vouchers and State expenses, 1893-1909.
2 cu. ft. (14 volumes)

A1051 Incoming correspondence from county treasurers, 1816-1825, 1852.
.3 cu. ft.

A1249 Correspondence relating to the payment of interest on loans from the Common School Fund, 1845, 1896-1897.
.25 cu. ft. (46 items)

A1364 Outgoing correspondence from the Clerk of the Contracting Board, 1857-1861.
.3 cu. ft. (1 volume)

A1370 Copies of outgoing telegrams, 1872-1885.
.3 cu. ft. (1 volume)

A1361 Incoming correspondence from the Chief Tax Clerk, 1878-1900.
.3 cu. ft. (1 volume)

A1359 Outgoing correspondence relating to prisons, the Onondaga Salt Springs, and the U.S. Deposit Fund, 1890-1903.
1.3 cu. ft. (10 volumes)

A1165 Correspondence concerning prisons, 1892-1895.
.3 cu. ft.

A1238 Incoming correspondence from clerks of boards of supervisors regarding the assessment of taxes, 1893-1894, 1897-1898.
.25 cu. ft.

A1326 Outgoing correspondence relating to tax searches, 1893-1895.
.5 cu. ft. (1 volume)

A1368 Outgoing correspondence relating to legislative accounts, 1895-1903.
.3 cu. ft. (1 volume)

A1365   Outgoing general correspondence from the deputy comptroller, 1897-1900.
.3 cu. ft. (1 volume)

A1360   Outgoing correspondence authorizing the execution of enclosed drafts, 1902-1911.
1.3 cu. ft. (7 volumes)

A1362   Outgoing correspondence relating to Civil Service and appointments, 1903-1920.
.6 cu. ft. (3 volumes)

A1363   Outgoing correspondence replying to inquires about records of soldiers of the Revolutionary War, 1904-1909.
.6 cu. ft. (3 volumes)

A0931   Incoming correspondence regarding State franchise tax, 1917-1918.
2 cu. ft.

A0979   Comptroller's reports to the legislature, 1789-1843.
1.3 cu. ft.

A1188   Index to comptroller's reports to the legislature, 1797-1820.
.2 cu. ft.

Railroads and Highways

A0907   Entry documentation for Utica and Schenectady Railroad and Schenectady and Troy Railroad, 1804-1849.
.3 cu. ft.

A1046   Auburn and Syracuse Railroad waybills, 1839.
.2 cu. ft.

A1405   Statements and receipts for interest due to holders of New York State stock issued to aid the Hudson and Berkshire Railroad Company, 1840-1865.
.3 cu. ft. (1 volume)

A1474   Ledger for State stock issued for construction of Long Island Railroad, 1841-1876.
.3 cu. ft. (1 volume)

A0896   List of shareholders in the Hudson River Railroad Company at Hudson and Rhinebeck, 1847.
.1 cu. ft.

A0912   Records regarding bonds for the New York and Erie Railroad Company, 1847-1848.
.1 cu. ft. (7 items)

A0987 Lists of tax assessments on railroads, 1900-1901, 1903-1904.
.1 cu. ft.

A1229 Accounts for road improvement, ca. 1806-1819.
.5 cu. ft.

A1290 Comptroller's accounts of taxes due for various State roads, 1811-1815.
.5 cu. ft. (1 volume)

A1043 Minutes of commissioners of highways of Town of Clarksville, 1836.
.3 cu. ft.

B0989 Assessment rolls for construction of roads from Lewis County to Brown's Tract in Herkimer County, 1853-1868.
.3 cu. ft. (16 items)

A1339 List of taxes paid to road districts, 1868-1876.
.3 cu. ft. (1 volume)

A1374 County Clerks' reports (statements) on the highway money system, 1902, 1905.
.3 cu. ft.

A1061 Registers and correspondence relating to highway maintenance and repair, 1902-1909.
.2 cu. ft.

A1391 Documents relating to acquisition of lands for highway purposes, ca. 1902-1908.
.5 cu. ft.

A1398 State Engineer's maps of highway rights of way and estimates of value, ca. 1906.
1.5 cu. ft.

A0936 Vouchers, payment orders, and payrolls for highway maintenance and repair, 1909-1916.
1.2 cu. ft.

A1386 Notices to State regarding cutting of brush along highways on State land, 1909-1912, 1922-1924.
.5 cu. ft.

A1375 Highway money system reports by county boards, 1911-1913.
.25 cu. ft.

Military Finances

A0200   Revolutionary War accounts and claims, 1775-1808, bulk 1782-1799.
25 cu. ft. (42 microfilm reels)

B1182   Correspondence and claims for war services from Adjutant-General's Office, 1813-1915.
.3 cu. ft.

A1193   Index to invalid pensioners, ca. 1850.
.2 cu. ft.

A1302   Abstract of claims of the New York Militia, 1812.
.2 cu. ft. (1 volume)

A1182   Index to War of 1812 claim certificates, ca. 1860.
.3 cu. ft. (1 volume)

A1303   Record of certificates and affidavits of veterans of the War of 1812, 1869-1870.
.3 cu. ft. (1 volume)

A1183   Opinion of State agent for War of 1812 claims, 1905.
.1 cu. ft.

A1320   Register of abstracts of audited accounts for governor's military expenses, 1819.
.2 cu. ft. (1 volume)

A0925   Circular regarding court martial records, 1819.
.5 cu. ft.

A1251   Compensation claims of former Commissary General, 1844-1871.
.1 cu. ft. (12 items)

A1254   Entry documentation relating to pension claims, First N.Y. Regiment Volunteers, Mexican War, 1878-1882.
.2 cu. ft.

A1252   Bonds and correspondence regarding public defense, 1861-1862.
.2 cu. ft.

A1253   Entry documentation relating to the cost of raising troops, 1861-1863.
.2 cu. ft.

A0806   Index to claims for the war account, 1862-1868.
.5 cu. ft.

A1328   Abstracts of payments of New York State bounty by the Paymaster General, 1863-1864.
.5 cu. ft.

A1458   Summary account of bounties paid out by Paymaster General, 1865.
.1 cu. ft.

A0910   Claims examined by the Auditors Board, 1864-1866.
.5 cu. ft.

A1460   Vouchers and bills submitted by the Andersonville Monument Dedication Commission, 1914.
.2 cu. ft.

A1255   Claims of Spanish-American War volunteers, 1899.
.1 cu. ft.

State Agencies, Employees, and Facilities

A0978   Receipts and accounts for State expenses, ca. 1765-1907.
.3 cu. ft.

A1331   Register of bonds of State and local officials, 1768-1873.
.2 cu. ft. (1 volume)

A0824   Entry documentation for State agency expenses, 1784-1909.
3.5 cu. ft.

A0825   Entry documentation for building and maintenance of government facilities, 1785-1855.
1.5 cu. ft.

A1037   Register of appointments, petitions, and resignations of appointed officials, ca. 1800-1864.
.5 cu. ft.

A1321   Payment book to State agencies and officials, 1819-1840.
.1 cu. ft. (1 volume)

A0840   Account book of salary payments to government officials and employees, 1829-1832.
.2 cu. ft. (1 volume)

A0959   Certificates of employee salaries, 1833-1889.
.1 cu. ft. (20 items)

A1245   Coal and wood bids from dealers for provision of fuel for State buildings, 1856.
.2 cu. ft.

A0984   Monthly statements of monies received by State agencies and institutions, 1899-1918.
4.5 cu. ft.

A0199   Blueprints of State buildings and county courthouses, ca. 1900-1920.
2 cu. ft.

A0835   Summary of appropriations requested by State government agencies, 1910.
.2 cu. ft. (2 volumes)

A0801   Employee position and salary roster of State agencies, 1910.
.3 cu. ft. (1 volume)

A1207   Appropriations requested by State departments and the legislature, 1912, 1914.
.1 cu. ft. (1 item)

A1279   Ledger of salaries and expenses for State agencies, 1923-1924.
.1 cu. ft. (1 volume)

A0949   Personal service histories of State employees, 1926.
.5 cu. ft.

A0831   Warrants for payments to government officials and legislators, 1799-1836.
2.5 cu. ft.

A0846   Vouchers for Senate and Assembly expenses, ca. 1802-1915.
12 cu. ft.

A1305   Payroll for Assembly members, 1834-1843.
.1 cu. ft. (1 volume)

A3241   Ledger accounts of Senate members, officers, and employees, 1883-1885.
.5 cu. ft.

A1353   Accounts of Senate and Assembly expenses, 1911-1917.
.2 cu. ft. (1 volume)

A1069   Accounts of salaries of assessors for towns, counties and corporations, 1799-1801, 1823-1825.
.5 cu. ft.

A0964   Audited accounts of Onondaga Commissioners, 1801-1892.
.1 cu. ft.

A1247   Bills and receipts of the superintendent of the Onondaga Salt Springs, 1841-1842.
.5 cu. ft.

A1324   Weekly returns of deposits for salt duties, Onondaga Salt Springs, 1843-1848.
.3 cu. ft. (1 volume)

A1334   Accounts of the County Loan Commissioners, 1802-1807, 1827-1851.
.5 cu. ft. (2 volumes)

A1230   Accounts of comptroller's office expenses, 1808-1815.
.25 cu. ft.

A1463   Journal of Surveyor General's accounts, 1810-1824.
.2 cu. ft. (1 volume)

A1319   Abstract of statement of monies received by the Clerk of the Supreme Court in the City of New York, 1839-1840.
.2 cu. ft.

A1242   Annual reports of inspector of gas meters, 1883-1889.
.2 cu. ft.

A1156   Abstracts and vouchers for fighting fires submitted by the Fisheries, Game and Forest Commission, ca. 1901-1908.
5 cu. ft.

A0932   Receipts of New York State Fair Commission, 1903, 1905.
.3 cu. ft.

A1028   Vouchers and accounts of Commissioners of Quarantine, New York City, 1904-1905, 1924.
.2 cu. ft.

A1155   Vouchers for expenses submitted by Board of Barber Examiners, 1905.
.5 cu. ft.

A1031   Minutes of hearing by the Commission to Investigate the Public Service Commission, First District, 1911.
.25 cu. ft.

A1184   Report of treasurer of Lake Champlain Tercentenary Commission, 1911.
.2 cu. ft.

A1372   Minutes of the New York State Athletic Commission, 1911-1917.
.3 cu. ft. (3 volumes)

A1373   Minutes of meetings of the Board of Commissioners of the Mohansic Lake Reservation, 1919-1920.
.3 cu. ft. (1 volume)

A0937   General specifications of purchasing committee for State institutions reporting to the fiscal supervisor of State Charities, ca. 1919-1920.
.3 cu. ft.

A1018   Specifications of tax forms to be used between State Tax Commission and comptroller, ca. 1921.
.1 cu. ft. (1 volume)

A0873   Bills, receipts, and warrants for the proposed State prison at Albany, 1796-1803.
.3 cu. ft.

A1149   New York State Prison financial records, 1800-1828.
6.3 cu. ft.

A0860   Accounts of prison factory work, 1802-1803.
.3 cu. ft.

A1294   Minutes of meetings of the Commissioners for Building a State Prison in the First or Second Senate District, ca. 1825-1829.
.5 cu. ft.

A1231   Statements of expenditures for building and repair of State prisons and normal schools, 1896.
.1 cu. ft.

A1166   Superintendent of Prisons' vouchers for services and expenses of engineers for prison highway construction, ca. 1919-1922.
.3 cu. ft.

A1150   Accounts, vouchers, and reports on building and maintenance of Auburn Prison, 1816-1825.
3 cu. ft.

A1293   Payroll for construction of Auburn Prison, 1818-1819.
.2 cu. ft. (2 volumes)

A1151   Auburn Prison accounts and vouchers of agent and warden, 1869-1876.
2 cu. ft.

A1062   Accounts of monies expended at Auburn Prison, 1871-1873.
.1 cu. ft.

A1152   Sing Sing ("Mount Pleasant") Prison financial records, 1825-1847.
2 cu. ft.

A1292   Account book of expenses for building Sing Sing Prison (Mt. Pleasant), 1825-1829.
.1 cu. ft.

A1153   Financial records relating to maintenance of Clinton Prison, 1845-1868.
1 cu. ft.

A1213   Entry documentation for construction of Reformatory for Women at Bedford, 1893-1896.
.2 cu. ft.

A1162   Prisoners' deposit vouchers from Institution for Defective Delinquents, Napanoch, 1925.
.2 cu. ft.

A1203   Register of apportionment of monies for schools, academies, hospitals, and orphan asylums, 1826-1868.
.4 cu. ft. (2 volumes)

A1226   Entry documentation for State asylums, 1870-1905.
.5 cu. ft.

A1450   Accounts for construction of New York State Lunatic Asylum, Utica, 1839-1840.
.3 cu. ft. (11 volumes)

A1225   Entry documentation for construction of State Tuberculosis Hospital, Raybrook, New York, 1902-1905.
.5 cu. ft.

A1404   Craig Colony at Sonyea treasurer's report, 1921.
.3 cu. ft. (1 volume)

A1330   Journal of expenses for building State Hall, 1834-1839.
.5 cu. ft.

A1295   Payroll for workers employed in building State Hall, 1839-1841.
.2 cu. ft. (2 volumes)

A1169   Minutes and working papers of the board to supervise the repairs upon the State Hall, 1897-1898.
.3 cu. ft.

A1209   Bill for goods procured for the Executive Mansion, Dec. 26, 1868.
.1 cu. ft. (1 folder)

A1296   Account book pertaining to cleaning ladies in the State Capitol, 1875.
.2 cu. ft. (1 volume)

Banks and Corporations

A1390   Statement of bank failures, 1845-1876, 1876.
.2 cu. ft.

A0957   Accounts of bank note impressions, 1856-1857.
.1 cu. ft. (3 items)

A0975   Letter to Superintendent of Banking Department with memorial protesting illegal practices of savings banks in Buffalo, 1859.
.1 cu. ft. (3 items)

A1291   List of companies chartered in New York State, ca. 1798-1837.
.5 cu. ft.

A0833   Financial reports of corporations, 1805-1922.
1 cu. ft.

A1301   Ledger of taxes on corporations, 1824-1829.
.5 cu. ft. (1 volume)

A0829   Insurance company bonds and reports of agents, 1825-1880.
.3 cu. ft.

A0965   Accounts of taxes on incorporations, 1825-1827.
.1 cu. ft. (5 items)

A1204   Register of incorporated companies, ca. 1827-1828.
.3 cu. ft. (1 volume)

A1220   Records of the East Boston Timber Company, ca. 1833-1840.
4.2 cu. ft.

A1325   Abstracts of corporation reports, 1834-1841.
.5 cu. ft. (1 volume)

A1289   Register of incorporated companies, 1866.
.1 cu. ft.

A1248   Reports by stock corporations, 1868.
.2 cu. ft.

A1472   Examination of accounts of Battle Island Paper Company, 1915.
.1 cu. ft.

Tax Accounts

B0965   Returns of arrears of United States direct tax, 1815.
.1 cu. ft. (1 volume)

A1315   Comptroller's accounts with county treasurers for taxes due the
State, 1816-1829.
.3 cu. ft. (1 volume)

A1189   Index to direct tax books, ca. 1820.
.2 cu. ft.

B0973   Accounts of property transfer taxes, 1885-1910.
15 cu. ft. (25 volumes)

A1345   Accounts of tax monies received, 1897, 1900, 1904-1907.
1 cu. ft. (4 volumes)

B0974   Accounts of adjusted estate transfer taxes, 1909-1913.
.5 cu. ft. (3 volumes)

A1356   Register of tax monies received, 1910-1912, 1917.
.3 cu. ft.

A0934   Accounts of receipts and taxes paid by athletic clubs, 1911-1914.
.1 cu. ft. (10 items)

Securities, Loans, and Debts

A1449   Cancelled State stock certificates, 1815-1920.
14.5 cu. ft.

A1307   Statement of interest due to holders of New York State stock (various issues), 1815-1831.
1 cu. ft. (6 volumes)

A1465   Ledgers for State stock, 1815-1818.
.5 cu. ft. (2 volumes)

A1310   Stock transfer book, 1815-1838.
.6 cu. ft. (3 volumes)

A1300   Ledger for State and private stock sale, 1842-1848.
.3 cu. ft. (1 volume)

A1197   Lists of powers of attorney under which transfers of stock were
made, 1850-1876.
.2 cu. ft.

A1244   List of interest due on State stock, 1855-1871.
.2 cu. ft.

A1354   Register of individual and depository bonds guaranteed by surety companies, 1901-1917.
.3 cu. ft. (1 volume)

A1343   Accounts of municipal securities held in various State funds, 1906-1912.
.3 cu. ft. (1 volume)

A1074   Ledger of the repayment of the loan of 1792, ca. 1792-1849.
.3 cu. ft.

A1044   Ledger of the repayment of the loan of 1808, ca. 1808-1850.
.1 cu. ft.

A0909   Loan to College of Physicians and Surgeons of the City of New York, 1817.
.1 cu. ft. (1 item)

A1196   Receipt books for redemption of "Million Dollar Loan," 1824-1845.
.3 cu. ft. (2 volumes)

A1256   Proposals and awards made for State loans regarding the general fund debt sinking fund, 1859-1862, 1875.
.5 cu. ft.

A1233   Entry documentation pertaining to the new emission of bills of credit, 1786-1797.
.1 cu. ft. (30 items)

A1048   Report of indebtedness of cities and villages, 1856.
.3 cu. ft.

Auctions and Lotteries

A1304   Ledger of duties paid by auctioneers, 1827-1840.
.5 cu. ft. (1 volume)

A0874   Register of auctioneers, 1830-1848.
.5 cu. ft. (3 volumes)

A1443   Auctioneers' statements of sales, ca. 1838-1844.
1 cu. ft.

A1322   Accounts of State lotteries, 1817-1819.
.1 cu. ft. (1 volume)

Printing and Publishing

A0875   Draft of index to first volume of "Laws of New York 1777-1786," 1819.
.3 cu. ft. (1 volume)

A0945   List of newspapers for publishing proposals for printing 1862 Session Laws, 1862.
.1 cu. ft.

A0952   Vouchers submitted for publishing session laws of 1893, 1893.
.2 cu. ft.

A1029   List of newspapers designated to publish concurrent resolutions of the legislature of 1861, 1861.
.1 cu. ft.

A0974   Affidavits of publication of comptroller's notices, 1798-1885.
.1 cu. ft.

A0902   Lists of newspapers selected to publish official notices, 1837-1860.
.2 cu. ft.

A1223   Bills for State printing, 1840-1842.
.2 cu. ft.

A0915   Newspaper receipt for printing notice, 1853.
.1 cu. ft.

General Accounting Records

A0269   General account ledgers, 1775-1918.
50 cu. ft.

A1280   Ledgers for bonds and mortgages held by the State of New York, 1796-1910.
26 cu. ft. (41 volumes)

A1309   Comptroller's subordinate ledgers, 1796-1827.
.5 cu. ft. (2 volumes)

B0995   Ledger of accounts with county treasurers, 1799-1810.
.3 cu. ft. (1 volume)

B0850   Ledgers of accounts with county treasurers, 1848-1912.
2 cu. ft. (4 volumes)

A1333   Ledger of deposits and withdrawals in bank accounts, 1806-1820.
.1 cu. ft. (2 volumes)

A1263   Ledger of State treasurer, 1812-1816.
.1 cu. ft. (1 volume)

A1306   Ledger of State funds, 1831-1851.
.1 cu. ft. (1 volume)

A1298   Comptroller's ledger of accounts with county agricultural societies, 1841-1854.
.3 cu. ft. (1 volume)

A1317   Comptroller's ledger "K", 1879-1890.
.3 cu. ft. (1 volume)

A0966   Daily journal, 1797-1802.
.3 cu. ft. (1 volume)

A1314   Treasurer's journal of receipts and expenditures, 1802-1812.
.2 cu. ft. (2 volumes)

A1318   Daily journals of receipts and disbursements, 1803-1843.
2 cu. ft. (9 volumes)

A1329   Daily journal, 1838-1841.
.3 cu. ft. (1 volume)

A0862   Daybooks, 1801-1890.
ca. 20 cu. ft. (71 volumes)

B0975   Appropriations cash book, 1866-1868.
.3 cu. ft. (1 volume)

A0827   Audited accounts of payments made by overseers of the poor for support of children born to slaves, 1799-1820.
.2 cu. ft.

A1308   Comptroller's accounts with individuals, 1812-1817.
.5 cu. ft. (2 volumes)

A1260   Accounts of non-current bank notes deposited in the Treasury and other banks, 1817, 1819-1822.
.2 cu. ft.

A1312   Warrant and check register for various accounts, 1828-1836.
.5 cu. ft.

A0841   Account book for lumber business, 1837-1840.
.1 cu. ft. (1 volume)

A1453   Accounts of bank deposits and withdrawals, 1838-1850.
.1 cu. ft. (1 volume)

A1327 Accounts of apportionment of State monies, 1868-1920.
.1 cu. ft. (1 volume)

A1164 Monthly schedules of accounts and balances in bank, 1899-1904.
.1 cu. ft.

A1259 Treasurer's certificates of money paid into the treasury, 1788, 1798-1799, 1803-1806.
.5 cu. ft.

A1236 Warrants issued, 1798-1802, 1861-1863.
.1 cu. ft.

A0839 Payment authorization to Treasurer, 1799.
.1 cu. ft. (1 item)

B0967 Register of interest payments, 1802-1815.
.1 cu. ft. (1 volume)

A0863 Warrants for payment, 1890-1894.
6 cu. ft. (3 volumes)

A0864 Payment records, 1894-1916.
72 cu. ft. (37 volumes)

A0866 Treasurer's receipts, 1914-1916.
2 cu. ft. (1 volume)

A0822 Entry documentation submitted by the collector for the Port of New York, 1723-1838.
.5 cu. ft.

A0832 Entry documentation submitted by the Indian Commissioner for annuities paid to Indians, 1796-1925.
3.5 cu. ft.

A0961 Reports, correspondence and entry documentation relating to inspection of potash, 1816-1839.
.1 cu. ft. (20 items)

A1394 Entry documentation relating to draining of the Cayuga Marshes, 1825-1841, 1853-1861.
.25 cu. ft.

A1447 Cancelled checks, 1835-1900.
1.4 cu. ft.

A1200 William Beard estate records, 1918.
.5 cu. ft.

A1366   Certificates for deputy comptroller to sign warrants and audit accounts, 1902-1910.
.1 cu. ft. (1 volume)

A1401   Statements of court and trust funds in New York City banks, 1892-1901.
.3 cu. ft.

A1400   Statement of bonds and mortgages taken by City Chamberlain, New York County, on account of court and trust funds, 1899-1900.
.3 cu. ft.

A1397   Statements of court-administered trust funds (New York and Kings counties) transferred to National Bank of Commerce in New York, ca. 1900-1915.
.5 cu. ft.

A1344   Register of court cases relating to trust funds, 1907-1908.
.3 cu. ft. (1 volume)

A3312   Quarterly statements of fees collected, 1850-1856.
.1 cu. ft.

Other Records

A0977   Map and assessments prepared by commissioners for draining the swamp and marsh lands in the Town of Salina, 1824.
.3 cu. ft.

A1186   Inventory of documents stored in State Hall, ca. 1830.
.3 cu. ft.

A0962   Comptroller's blank forms, ca. 1835.
.3 cu. ft.

A1199   Form for engineers' field notes to be filed with comptroller, 1842.
.1 cu. ft. (1 item)

A1187   Index to comptroller's miscellaneous papers, ca. 1860.
.2 cu. ft.

A1235   Records relating to the purchase of firearms, 1861.
.2 cu. ft.

A1466   Field notes of the surveys of Brant Lake tract, 1884.
.3 cu. ft. (1 volume)

A1063   Copies of certificates of appointment of notaries public, 1887-1888.
         .3 cu. ft.

A1222   Bear bounty affidavits, 1892-1894.
         .5 cu. ft.

A1224   Applications and correspondence relating to liquor licenses for steamboats and railroad cars, 1892-1896.
         .2 cu. ft.

A1367   Comptroller's opinion on bills introduced in the legislature, 1897-1909.
         .3 cu. ft. (1 volume)

A0938   Certificates and correspondence relating to fish net bounties, 1898-1900.
         .3 cu. ft.

A1371   Transcript of hearing before the Assembly Committee on Privileges and Elections, 1903.
         .2 cu. ft. (1 volume)

A1154   Barbers' applications for certificate of qualification, 1904-1905.
         .3 cu. ft.

A1054   Schedule of bids for improvement bonds for canals, highways, and parks, 1905-1917.
         .3 cu. ft.

A1022   Applications and resignations for the office of notary public, 1908-1911.
         12 cu. ft.

A1232   Maps and assessment for the draining of Cayuga Marshes, 1925.
         .25 cu. ft.

Banking Department

Current Functions. The function of the Banking Department is to protect the public interest by regulating and supervising the business of State chartered commercial banks, trust companies, bank holding companies, savings banks, savings and loan associations, credit unions, investment companies, mortgage bankers, and other financial intermediaries operating within the State. In addition to its supervisory role the department attempts to educate consumers and resolve complaints.

In its supervisory role the department is responsible for examining the practices of banks and other financial institutions; approving acquisitions, branch expansions, mergers, and other forms of consolidation; in certain circumstances levying fines and ordering discontinuance of unsound financial practices; and replacing management, and taking possession of failing institutions and operating or liquidating them for the benefit of depositors and creditors.

Organizational History. State banking policy began with an act in 1782 prohibiting the operation of any bank within the State except for the Federal Bank of North America. In 1791, the legislature authorized a charter for the first State bank, the Bank of New York, and thereafter chartered other banks by special acts. A law in 1829 (Chapter 94) set up the Bank Fund, later renamed the Safety Fund, to guarantee the payment of debts of insolvent banks. All State-chartered banks were required to make an annual contribution to the fund, which was managed by the State treasurer. The same law provided for the appointment of three bank commissioners to examine the financial status of banks and to report annually to the legislature.

State regulation of banks was altered by the Banking Law of 1838 (Chapter 260), which required banks to file certificates of incorporation with the secretary of state and report annually to the comptroller. In 1843, the Safety Fund and the bank commissioner positions were abolished, and bank examination responsibilities were transferred to the comptroller. Bank regulatory functions of the comptroller and secretary of state were subsequently transferred to the Banking Department headed by a superintendent of banking, established in 1851 (Chapter 164). No major alteration of banking policy occurred for the next seventy-five years, and the Banking Department was continued (Laws of 1926, Chapter 352) after the 1925-26 constitutional reorganization of State government.

In 1932 (Chapter 118), the Banking Board was created to advise and cooperate with the Banking Department in the formulation of banking standards and to exercise power to approve or disapprove the issuance of bank charters and licenses and the establishment of branch banks. The superintendent of banking is chairperson and ex officio member of the board, which consists of twelve other members appointed by the governor for three-year terms.

BANKING DEPARTMENT

General Agency-level Records

14272	Inactive institution files, 1838-1967. 125 cu. ft.
13858	Bank liquidation case files, 1929-1959. 83.8 cu. ft. R
B1115	Registers of account books relative to the circulation of bank notes, 1835-1843. .5 cu. ft.
B1116	Register of bank note plates by banks, 1838-1842. .5 cu. ft.
B1119	Note register (received and delivered), 1838-1842, 1848-1854. .5 cu. ft.
B1120	Registry ledger (notes in circulation), 1838-1846. .5 cu. ft.
B1121	Note register (notes in circulation), 1838-1851. .5 cu. ft.
B1136	Bank note circulation ledger, 1844. .5 cu. ft.
B1135	Note register (received and disposed of), 1844. .5 cu. ft.
B1134	Note register (notes delivered), 1844-1847. .5 cu. ft.
B1122	Note register (bank certificates and orders), 1838-1847. .5 cu. ft.
B1124	Book of orders for bank notes, 1839-1849. .5 cu. ft.
B1126	Ledger of protested bank notes, 1840-1870. .5 cu. ft.
B1138	Daybooks relating to sealing and burning of notes, 1844-1881. 12 cu. ft.
B1141	Diary of bank notes, 1847-1874. 15 cu. ft.

166

B1142   Register of sealing and burning of notes, 1848-1850.
.5 cu. ft.

B1143   Ledger of bank notes in circulation, 1850-1858.
.5 cu. ft.

B1149   Ledger of notes in circulation, 1852-1929.
4 cu. ft.

B1158   Register of notes, 1859-1873.
.5 cu. ft.

B0607   List of securities considered legal investments for New York savings banks, 1921-1968.
1 cu. ft.

B1118   Note register (securities deposited for circulating notes), 1838-1840.
.5 cu. ft.

B1145   Register of securities, 1851-1868.
1 cu. ft.

B1155   Register of securities held in trust for banks, 1857-1916.
7 cu. ft.

B1157   Register of securities, 1858-1873.
.5 cu. ft.

B1193   Certificates of securities held in trust for banks, 1857-1878.
2 cu. ft. (16 volumes)

B1128   Registers of stock, 1841-1868.
.5 cu. ft.

B1129   Day book of interest on stocks at banks, 1843-1870.
4 cu. ft.

B1140   Schedule of bank fund stock, 1845.
.5 cu. ft.

B1159   Register of stocks and mortgages, 1862-1867.
1 cu. ft.

B1173   Journals of transactions relative to stocks, 1910-1943.
5 cu. ft.

B1117   Ledger of paper money in circulation, 1838-1854.
.5 cu. ft.

B1123   Register's receipts of impressions, 1839-1866.
1 cu. ft.

B1132   Register of plates, 1843-1844.
.5 cu. ft.

B1137   Circulation journal, 1844-1850.
.5 cu. ft.

B1144   Register of checks issued from bank funds, 1851-1865.
.5 cu. ft.

B1150   Register of mutilated impressions burned, 1852-1865.
.5 cu. ft.

B1153   Register of stocks, bonds, and mortgages transferred, 1857-1880.
1 cu. ft.

B1154   Journal of bank notes, stocks, and bonds, 1857-1907.
33 cu. ft.

B1160   Register of plates, ca. 1863.
.5 cu. ft.

B1163   Accounts of savings bank expenses, 1870-1909.
.5 cu. ft.

B1166   Register of out-of-state investments and mortgages, 1890-1891.
.5 cu. ft.

B1125   Roster of corporations, ca. 1840-1930.
.5 cu. ft.

B1127   Register of bank redemption agents, 1840-1867.
.5 cu. ft.

B1130   Comptroller's ledger (Incorporated Bank Department: letters), 1843-1847.
.5 cu. ft.

B1131   Comptroller's ledger of general transactions, 1843-1849.
.5 cu. ft.

B1133   Ledger of expenses for examinations, 1844-1895.
.5 cu. ft.

B1139   Register containing Articles of Association and list of officers for the Long Island Bank, 1845.
.5 cu. ft.

B1146   Bank fund ledger, 1851-1873.
.5 cu. ft.

B1147   Bank fund day book and journal, 1851-1873.
.5 cu. ft.

B1148   Register of power of attorney, 1852-1906.
1 cu. ft.

B1151   Account book of interest paid on bank notes, stocks, and mortgages, 1854-1865.
1 cu. ft.

B1152   Register of quarterly balances book, 1856-1888.
.5 cu. ft.

B1156   Circulation day book for incorporated banks, 1858-1870.
1 cu. ft.

B1161   Order book: American Bank Note Company, 1865.
.5 cu. ft.

B1162   Day book of transactions with individuals, 1870-1873.
.5 cu. ft.

B1164   Journal of expense for special examination, 1884-1904.
1 cu. ft.

B1165   Register of examinations of Building & Loan Association, 1887-1923.
1 cu. ft.

B1167   Certificates of association of banks of deposit and discount, 1892-1916.
1 cu. ft.

B1168   Register of affidavit of publication of orders or changes of names of banks, 1896-1921.
.5 cu. ft.

B1169   Abstracts of disciplinary letters to banks, 1897-1908.
9 cu. ft.

B1170   Ledger of accounts, 1898-1924.
1 cu. ft.

B1171   Register of oaths filed by banks, trust companies and savings and loan associations, 1901-1903.
.5 cu. ft.

B1172   Certificates of organization and authorization of private banks, private bankers, personal loan brokers and credit unions, 1902-1922.
1 cu. ft.

B1174   Register of oaths of directors of savings and loan associations, 1911.
.5 cu. ft.

B1175   Certificates of association of banks of deposit and discount, mortgage companies and miscellaneous corporations, 1916-1919.
.5 cu. ft.

B1176   Certificates of authorization and organization of banks of deposit and discount trust companies, investment companies, miscellaneous corporations and savings and loan associations, 1919-1921.
15 cu. ft.

B1177   Register of application certificates of banks for authorization of fiduciary powers, 1921-1923.
.5 cu. ft.

B1178   Ledger of general transactions, 1924-1929.
.5 cu. ft.

B1179   Cash receipts journal, 1930-1946.
1 cu. ft.

B1180   General ledger of the Banking Department, 1930-1957.
.5 cu. ft.

B1181   Bills and correspondence of the Auburn and Syracuse Railroad, 1839-1840.
.3 cu. ft.

B1183   Appointment of harbor master of Port of New York, 1819.
.3 cu. ft.

B1185   Appointments of coroners, 1818-1819.
.3 cu. ft.

B1186   Legal and entry documentation relating to Court of Appeals, 1841-1869.
.3 cu. ft.

B1187   Legal documentation relating to land from County Clerks, 1820-1880.
.3 cu. ft.

B1189   Legal documentation relating to appointments to State offices, ca. 1800-1863.
         1 cu. ft.

B1190   Entry documentation from New York and Erie Railroad, 1824-1842.
         .3 cu. ft.

B1191   Legal documentation relating to land from attorney general's office, 1801-1883.
         .3 cu. ft.

B1192   Register of certificates of organization and association of individual banks, 1884.
         .5 cu. ft.

B1194   Diary, 1854-1857.
         .5 cu. ft.

B1195   Comptroller and register's account book with index, 1838-1841.
         .5 cu. ft.

B1196   Statements of condition of banking institutions, 1922-1926, 1939-1968.
         2.4 cu. ft.

B1197   Law bulletins, 1929-1946.
         1 cu. ft.

B1198   Annual reports, 1920-1964.
         2 cu. ft.

Department of Civil Service

Current Functions. The Department of Civil Service is the central personnel agency for New York State government. It provides a wide range of services to ensure that State agencies meet their human resources needs in a timely manner. The department determines salaries for State positions, classifies job titles, recruits and tests prospective employees, and certifies eligibility lists. It also develops and analyzes the State's work force plan, administers State employee insurance, provides technical assistance and information service to support the affirmative action efforts of State agencies, administers training, and provides examination and consultant services to local government.

The Civil Service Commission is a bipartisan body comprised of three members who are appointed by the governor and confirmed by the State senate. The president of the commission is the executive head of the Department of Civil Service. The commission is responsible for overseeing the merit system of employment mandated by the State constitution. The commission approves rules and regulations of local government civil service commissions and personnel officers. In addition, the commission hears and makes determinations on appeals on a variety of civil service matters, including classification, examination, disqualification, salary, and title.

Organizational History. New York State's first civil service law, enacted in 1883 (Chapter 354) provided for a merit system of competitive examinations for the appointment and promotion of State government employees. It established a Civil Service Commission, consisting of three persons appointed by the governor with advice and consent of the senate, to administer the law. In 1884 civil service provisions were extended to some local governments; municipal civil services commissions were established and supervised by the State commission. In 1894 the principle of the merit system was embodied in the new State constitution.

Following the 1925-26 reorganization of State government, the Department of Civil Service was created, and the Civil Service Commission was designated as the head of the department (Laws of 1926, Chapter 354). In 1953 (Chapter 19) the governor was authorized to designate one commissioner as president of the commission and chief administrator of the department.

DEPARTMENT OF CIVIL SERVICE
Executive Office of President

> B0537   Subject and correspondence files, ca. 1938-1974.
> 11 cu. ft.

Public Relations Office

> B0510   Photographs, press releases, and press clipping files, 1945-1971.
> 5.5 cu. ft.

Division of Affirmative Career Programs

> – Monitoring Bureau

> B0545   Affirmative action plans and monitoring files, 1976-1982.
> 13 cu. ft.

Classification and Compensation Board

14099   Minutes and memoranda, 1949-1960.
.8 cu. ft.

Classification and Compensation Division

14080   Classification Division and Classification Board working files and minutes, 1930-1949.
2.4 cu. ft.

B0544   Classification and Compensation hearing transcripts, 1963, 1966-1968.
1 cu. ft.

14081   Chapter 307 salary conversion, salary reports and position specifications files, 1949-1965, bulk 1954-1956.
2.5 cu. ft.

Classification and Compensation Appeals Board

B0514   Appeals case files, 1949-1960.
12 cu. ft.

Examination and Staffing Services Division

14109   State administered Civil Service examinations, 1908-1952, 1960-1961.
89 cu. ft.

14103   Municipal examination administration files, 1922-1952.
2 cu. ft.

Grievance Appeals Board

14094   Grievance policies, procedures and decisions, 1920-1970, bulk 1950-1970.
2 cu. ft.

B0515   Appeals hearing transcripts, 1966-1968.
.4 cu. ft. R

Merit System Affirmative Action Office

B0546   Subject, correspondence, and project files, 1977-1981.
4.4 cu. ft. R

Municipal Services Division

B0541   Division director's and assistant director's files, ca. 1938-1970.
2 cu. ft.

B0504   Municipal civil service examinations, 1944-1953.
37 cu. ft. (159 volumes)

B0543   Rules and plans of municipal and county civil service commissions, ca. 1899-1975.
29 cu. ft.

14083   Manuals and publications, ca. 1934-1970.
2 cu. ft.

Municipal Survey Section

B0505   Management surveys of municipal civil service commissions, 1938-1979.
10 cu. ft.

Personnel Council

14078   Meeting minutes, 1945-1972.
3 cu. ft.

B0513   Subject and correspondence files, 1945-1972.
3 cu. ft.

B0512   Transcripts of Personnel Council conferences of departmental representatives, 1945-1954.
2.7 cu. ft.

Division of Personnel Research

14082   Research reports, 1948-1954.
1.4 cu. ft.

Personnel Services Division

– Training Section

14084   Training reports, manuals and miscellaneous files, 1940-1975.
3 cu. ft.

14098   Internship and traineeship programs files, 1947-ca.1968.
1.4 cu. ft.

Personnel Services and Development Division

B0518   Performance evaluation administrative files, 1937-1979.
2 cu. ft.

Planning Section

14104   Project files and reports, ca. 1955-1972.
2 cu. ft.

Other Records

15029   State employee history cards, ca. 1894-1950.
259.3 cu. ft.

14087   Comparative appraisal report, 1915-1916.
           .5 cu. ft. (2 volumes)

B1106   Professional activities files, 1933-1958.
           1.6 cu. ft.

14089   State Commission on Extension of the Civil Service secretary's
           files, 1939-1942.
           1 cu. ft.

14090   Files relating to the Joint Legislative Committee on the Admin-
           istration of the Civil Service System, 1942-1943.
           1 cu. ft.

14096   Department publication file, 1948-ca. 1970.
           2 cu. ft.

14095   Statistical and special reports on State employment, 1949-1969.
           4 cu. ft.

14088   Files relating to the Temporary State Commission on Coordination
           of State Activities and Department Reorganization, 1950-1959.
           1 cu. ft.

14100   Alfred E. Smith Fellows Program files, 1969-1971.
           .4 cu. ft. R

CIVIL SERVICE COMMISSION

B0500   Commission meeting minutes, 1883-1968.
           21.2 cu. ft. (98 volumes)

14105   Commission meeting calendars, 1930-1970.
           11 cu. ft. (70 volumes)

A0557   Correspondence, 1894-1930.
           275 cu. ft.

14102   Memoranda of letters received, 1883-1888.
           .5 cu. ft. (1 volume)

14092   Outgoing correspondence, 1887, 1899-1900, 1906, 1909.
           1 cu. ft. (6 volumes)

14106   Amendments to State Civil Service rules and regulations:
           approved and disapproved, 1901-1968.
           5 cu. ft. (26 volumes)

B0501   Disciplinary appeals case files, ca. 1950-1979.
4 cu. ft. R

B0547   Classification and compensation appeals case files, 1960-1979.
10.4 cu. ft.

14101   Files and hearing transcripts of investigations of the Buffalo and Niagara Falls Civil Service Commissions, 1912, 1914, 1938.
.4 cu. ft.

B0507   Minutes and report of investigation of New York City Municipal Civil Service Commission's practices, 1914-1915.
2 cu. ft. (11 volumes)

B0509   Files of the investigation of the Lackawanna Civil Service Commission, 1942-1949.
4 cu. ft.

B0539   Report and supporting documents of investigation of Public Service Commission with respect to the policies and practices of Milo Maltbie, 1948.
.8 cu. ft.

14097   Eligibility lists and reports of examinations, ca. 1884-1920.
4 cu. ft. (9 volumes)

B0508   Amendments to Municipal Civil Service Commission rules, 1901-1942.
4 cu. ft.

B0506   Security risk program files, 1951-1960.
2 cu. ft. R

14091   Transcripts of conferences on possible constitutional change in civil service, 1966.
2 cu. ft. (includes 38 audio tapes)

COMMISSION ON PENSIONS

14093   Minutes and memoranda, 1954-1960.
1 cu. ft. (6 volumes)

NEW YORK STATE EMPLOYEES MERIT AWARD BOARD

14085   Minutes and scrapbooks, 1946-1961.
2.4 cu. ft.

TEMPORARY HEALTH INSURANCE BOARD

    B0511   Minutes, working files, and insurance specifications and proposals, 1956-1961.
               3 cu. ft.

Public Employment Relations Board

Current Functions. The Public Employment Relations Board (PERB) is responsible for assisting in resolving labor-relations disputes between public-employee organizations and agencies of State and local government and school districts. PERB provides mediation, fact-finding, and arbitration services in disputes over contract agreements; settles questions of union representation; and hears charges of improper practices by public employers, employees, and employee organizations.

Organizational History. During the first half of the 20th century, public-employee organizations were established to seek job security and other benefits for government employees. Although strikes by public employees were proscribed by common law, a series of municipal employee strikes after World War II led to enactment of the Condon-Wadlin Act in 1947 (Chapter 391), establishing penalties for striking public employees. Three years later an executive order was issued that guaranteed State employees the right to join employee organizations and created a grievance procedure.

In the early 1960s, the continuing incidence of government labor-management confrontation and the concomitant growing labor activity among school teachers, especially in New York City, demonstrated the need for systematic conciliation and employee representation procedures. However it was not until 1967 (Chapter 392) that the Public Employees' Fair Employment Act (also known as the Taylor Law) was enacted. This law continued the prohibition against strikes by public employees and included penalties, granted public employees the right of organization and representation, imposed upon public employers the duty to recognize and negotiate with employee organizations, required public employers to enter into written agreements with unions, and created the Public Employment Relations Board to resolve disputes.

The board, which consists of three gubernatorial appointees, is placed administratively within the Department of Civil Service but is not subject to its control. The board appoints an executive director and appropriate staff to carry out its business.

PUBLIC EMPLOYMENT RELATIONS BOARD

Legal Section

11378   Case files for board decisions challenged in court, ca. 1977-1984. 29 cu. ft.

Department of Correctional Services

Current Functions. The Department of Correctional Services is responsible for the confinement and habilitation of approximately 52,000 inmates held at sixty-two State correctional facilities. The department confines offenders at appropriate security levels and maintains order through disciplinary action when necessary; fulfills the basic daily needs of inmates and provides necessary medical and dental care, and offers habilitation opportunities through academic, vocational, maintenance, and industrial programs. In addition, the department administers programs for inmates who require protective custody or specialized treatment for mental or physical handicaps or who have drug, alcohol, or emotional problems. Finally, the department helps inmates adjust to their eventual return to the community by allowing the release of qualified inmates on a temporary basis.

Organizational History. From the opening of the first State prison in 1797 until the present day, New York State's correctional system has had a wide influence on the direction of criminology and penology in the United States. Among the important early institutions established in New York State were: Newgate Prison (1797), Auburn Prison (1818), New York House of Refuge (1824), Sing Sing Prison (1828), Dannemora Prison (1845), Western House of Refuge (1849), Elmira Reformatory (1876), and Bedford Hills Reformatory for Women (1901). Newgate, Auburn, Sing Sing, and Dannemora were instrumental in the development of the 19th-century penitentiary movement throughout the country. In particular, the Auburn system of discipline — congregate work by day, solitary separation in cells at night, enforced silence, lockstep formations, and severe corporal punishment — served as a model for similar institutions elsewhere. Elmira Reformatory was the first adult reformatory in the country and precipitated a national reformatory movement. Elmira's innovative, highly publicized program included indefinite sentences based on conduct and performance, individualized treatment of inmates, and the extensive use of parole. In the development of reformatories for women, Bedford Hills was extremely important and its programs were emulated at many other institutions. Most influential were Bedford's programs for the scientific study of "feeblemindedness" and "defective-delinquency" as causes of crime.

Until 1846, the State's corrections system was administered by a board of inspectors that in turn appointed wardens for each prison. The State constitution of 1846 established a single Board of Prisons to oversee all State prisons, and in 1876 this board was replaced by the Office of Superintendent of State Prisons.

The reorganization of State government in 1925-26 abolished the Office of Superintendent of State Prisons and created a Department of Correction headed by a commissioner appointed by the governor (Laws of 1926, Chapter 606). In addition to continuing the work of the superintendent of state prisons, the Department of Correction also assumed the functions of the State Board of Charities relating to correctional institutions. Since 1867, the State Board of Charities and its predecessor, the Board of State Commissioners of Public Charities, had been responsible for supervising correctional institutions (except prisons) and reformatories in the State.

The new department was comprised of four divisions: a Division of Administration, responsible for custody of inmates and maintenance of institutions; a Division of Prison Industries, supervising prison and reformatory production shops and farm work; a Division of Parole; and a Division of Probation. In 1930 (Chapter 824), the Division of Parole was transferred from the Department of Correction to the Executive Department.

In 1970 (Chapter 475), the present Department of Correctional Services was created. It consolidated the previous Department of Correction, the State Commission of Correction (established in 1926), and the Division of Parole. A companion 1970 law (Chapter 476) changed the designation of most institutions to a "correctional facility." Another 1970 law (Chapter 479) removed the Division of Probation from the new department and transferred it to the Executive Department. In 1972 (Chapter 399), the department's Division of Criminal Investigation was transferred to the newly formed Division of Criminal Justice Services in the Executive Department. In 1973 (Chapter 398), the Commission of Correction was also separated from the department and made an independent agency within the Executive Department. In 1977, administration of hospitals for mentally ill inmates was transferred to the Department of Mental Hygiene (Chapter 978) and the Division of Parole was again removed from the department and made an independent Executive Department agency (Chapter 904).

Board of Inspectors
(each State prison)

Board of Prisons (1846)

Superintendent of State Prisons (1876)

Department of Correction (1926)

Department of Correctional Services (1970)

SUPERINTENDENT OF STATE PRISONS

A3265   Engineers' reports to the State commissioner of highways on highway construction with prison labor, 1916-1921.
.2 cu. ft.

DEPARTMENT OF CORRECTION

A0620   Prison financial operating reports, 1924-1933.
2 cu. ft. (6 volumes)

A0429   Opinions and correspondence of the attorney general interpreting criminal and prison laws, 1892-1957.
3 cu. ft. (11 volumes)

DEPARTMENT OF CORRECTIONAL SERVICES

Bureau of Records and Statistical Analysis

B1342 Inmate characteristics statistical files, 1956-1975.
4 magnetic tapes.

Division of Administration

14610 Inmate case files, 1894-1970.
2,654.5 cu. ft. R

Includes inmate case files from the following correctional institutions:

Albion State Training School, 1894-1968.
167 cu. ft.

Attica Prison, 1940-1956.
49 cu. ft.

Auburn Prison, 1914-1956.
161 cu. ft.

Clinton Prison, 1930-1956.
70 cu. ft.

Elmira Reformatory, 1916-1956.
408 cu. ft.

Great Meadow Prison, 1915-1956.
320 cu. ft.

Green Haven Prison, 1930-1964.
10 cu. ft.

Institution for Male Defective Delinquents (Napanoch), 1920-1956.
251 cu. ft.

New York State Vocational Institution (Coxsackie), 1930-1965.
392 cu. ft.

Wallkill Prison, 1920-1965.
254 cu. ft.

Westfield State Farm, 1915-1930, 1955-1965.
12 cu. ft.

Woodbourne Correctional Institution, 1930-1970.
315 cu. ft.

ADIRONDACK CORRECTIONAL TREATMENT AND EVALUATION CENTER
(Adirondack Correctional Facility)

    B0151   Executive office files, 1966-1975.
                24 cu. ft.

    B0150   Principal keeper's discipline summary card file, ca. 1966-1975.
                2 cu. ft. R

ALBION STATE TRAINING SCHOOL (Albion Correctional Facility)

    B0088   Daily census of inmate population, 1933-1945.
                1 cu. ft. (1 volume)

    B1255   Inmate ledgers, 1894-ca. 1935.
                6 cu. ft. (12 volumes)

    B0093   Principal keeper's daily journal of infractions and complaints, 1938-1969.
                4.5 cu. ft.

    B0090   Psychological evaluation tests and reference information, 1952-1966.
                1 cu. ft. R

    B1008   Photographic negatives, ca. 1940.
                .5 cu. ft.

AUBURN CORRECTIONAL FACILITY

    B0077   Warden's office files, 1901-1973.
                8 cu. ft. R

    B0030   Annual reports of Auburn Prison and Prison for Women, 1919-1974.
                5 cu. ft.

    B1222   Inmate record cards, ca. 1880-1970.
                48 cu. ft.

    B1224   Weekly reports of disciplinary action, 1934-1972.
                15 cu. ft.

    B0028   Correctional Volunteer Services office files, 1970-1974.
                1 cu. ft.

AUBURN PRISON (Auburn Correctional Facility)

B0066	Registers of indefinite and definite sentences, 1897-1932. 1.2 cu. ft. (6 volumes)
B0067	Registers of male inmates received, 1870-1953. 6 cu. ft. (6 volumes)
B0068	Registers of male inmates discharged, 1817-1949. 6 cu. ft. (6 volumes)
B1007	Annual report, 1962-1963. .1 cu. ft. (1 volume)
B0062	Daily reports of male population, 1879-1952. 1 cu. ft. (4 volumes)
B1223	Inmate punishment ledger, 1873-1948. 3 cu. ft. (6 volumes)
B0031	Register of commutations, 1889-1912. 1 cu. ft. (4 volumes)
B1225	Case files relating to capture of escaped inmates, ca. 1910-1930. 1 cu. ft.
B0029	Case files of inmates discharged by death, ca. 1933-1963. 5 cu. ft.
A0780	Punishment record, 1836-1846. .3 cu. ft. (1 volume)
A1103	Daybook of financial transactions, 1821-1825. .3 cu. ft. (1 volume)
B1230	General accounts journal, 1874-1893. 1 cu. ft. (2 volumes)
B1231	Accounts journal, 1866-1873. .3 cu. ft. (1 volume)
B0069	Daily attendance reports of institution personnel, 1941-1942, 1951-1952. .5 cu. ft.
B0071	Daily journal of inspector in charge, 1860-1871. .3 cu. ft. (1 volume)
B0074	Monthly sales journal, 1932-1938. 1 cu. ft. (1 volume)

B1226 Contract files relating to prison purchases of food, supplies, and equipment, 1930-1940.
3 cu. ft.

B0072 Expenditures for broom, hollow ware, and iron castings industries, 1893-1897.
.3 cu. ft. (1 volume)

B0073 Daily report of moneys received by prisoners, 1907-1909.
.3 cu. ft. (1 volume)

B0059 Male inmate identification file, 1921-1936.
2 cu. ft. (2 volumes) R

B0065 Psychological evaluation reports, ca. 1935-1942.
1.5 cu. ft. R

B0085 Psychological evaluation tests, 1938-1961.
4.5 cu. ft. R

B0010 Psychological examination reports, 1955-1962.
3 cu. ft. R

B0052 Physician's office files, 1915-1968.
5 cu. ft. R

B0057 Physician's registers of inmates admitted, 1900-1905, 1909-1938.
6 cu. ft. (8 volumes) R

B0051 Physician's register of inmates discharged, 1909-1948.
1.5 cu. ft. (3 volumes) R

B0058 Hospital daily statistical summary, 1904-1919.
.3 cu. ft. (1 volume)

B0056 Register of deaths, 1888-1937.
.3 cu. ft. (1 volume) R

B1006 Inmate scrapbook, ca. 1962-1970, bulk ca. 1967-1970.
.2 cu. ft., (1 volume)

STATE PRISON FOR WOMEN (Auburn Correctional Facility)

B0054 Female inmate identification file, 1909-1933.
.5 cu. ft. (1 volume) R

B0053 Registers of female inmates received, 1893-1933.
1 cu. ft. (2 volumes)

B0055 Register of female inmates discharged, 1893-1919.
1.5 cu. ft. (1 volume)

B0063　　　Daily reports of female population, 1893-1906.
　　　　　.3 cu. ft. (1 volume)

B0060　　　Register of commutations for female inmates, 1920-1930.
　　　　　.3 cu. ft. (1 volume)

BEDFORD HILLS CORRECTIONAL FACILITY

B1013　　　Daily report books, 1960-1973, bulk 1960-1965.
　　　　　2 cu. ft. (13 volumes)

B1011　　　Inmate misbehavior case files, ca. 1964-1974.
　　　　　6 cu. ft. R

B1010　　　Inmate work release case files, ca. 1973-1974.
　　　　　2 cu. ft. R

Superintendent's Office

B1018　　　Subject files, ca. 1962-1974.
　　　　　4 cu. ft.

CLINTON PRISON (Clinton Correctional Facility)

B0120　　　Correspondence and subject files of the warden, 1932-1951.
　　　　　1.5 cu. ft.

B0117　　　Warden's daily journal, 1904-1909, 1912-1913.
　　　　　.5 cu. ft. (3 volumes)

B0118　　　Outgoing correspondence of agent and warden, 1845-1912.
　　　　　.5 cu. ft. (3 volumes)

B0121　　　Office files of deputy warden and deputy superintendent, ca. 1964-
　　　　　1974.
　　　　　1.5 cu. ft. R

B0115　　　Diary of the principal keeper, 1868-1884.
　　　　　.3 cu. ft. (2 volumes)

B0116　　　Record book of prison inspectors, 1848-1864.
　　　　　.3 cu. ft. (2 volumes)

B0142　　　Alphabetical register of inmates, ca. 1905-1907, 1910.
　　　　　1 cu. ft. (3 volumes)

B0098　　　Inmate admission ledgers, 1846, 1851-1866, 1926-1948.
　　　　　2 cu. ft. (10 volumes) R

B0097   Inmate record cards, 1914-1964.
2 cu. ft. R

B0096   Daily inmate population census journals, 1920-1942.
4 cu. ft. (16 volumes)

B0094   Daily disciplinary record, 1895-1896, 1929-1946, 1969-1976.
2 cu. ft. (2 volumes) R

B0119   Annual reports, 1922-1953.
1.3 cu. ft. (20 volumes)

B0095   Photographs of Clinton Prison, ca. 1900-1969.
4 cu. ft.

B0107   Hall keeper's daily record, 1929-1969.
.3 cu. ft. (1 volume)

B0105   Chaplain's Office statistical register, ca. 1889-1897.
.5 cu. ft. (1 volume)

B0103   Ledgers of appropriations and disbursements, 1844-1854, 1859-1873, 1876.
.5 cu. ft. (1 volume)

B0104   Journal of receipts and disbursements, 1846-1854.
.5 cu. ft. (1 volume)

B1246   General ledger of financial transactions, 1899-1910.
1 cu. ft. (1 volume)

B1252   Profit and loss journal, 1870-1875.
.5 cu. ft. (1 volume)

B1248   Cash book, 1910-1915.
1 cu. ft. (1 volume)

B1253   Prison inventory and journal of financial accounts, 1871-1873.
.2 cu. ft. (1 volume)

B1247   Voucher register, 1848-1873.
1 cu. ft. (2 volumes)

B0106   Keeper's time book for convict labor, 1849-1856.
.3 cu. ft.

B0109   Agent's book of contracts, 1853-1864.
.3 cu. ft. (1 volume)

B0110   Book of general and special orders, 1873-1874.
.3 cu. ft. (1 volume)

B0108   Record of ores mined by prison labor, 1871-1877.
.3 cu. ft. (1 volume)

B0112   Journal of expenditures for shirt industry, 1891-1892.
.3 cu. ft. (1 volume)

B0113   Travel expense account of prison employees, 1911-1915.
.3 cu. ft. (1 volume)

B0114   Manufacturing department inmate employees time book, 1910-1917.
.3 cu. ft. (1 volume)

B0123   Medical and psychiatric diagnostic files, 1934-1967.
132 cu. ft. R

B0100   Physician's register of inmates admitted, 1890-1918.
1 cu. ft. (2 volumes) R

B0102   Hospital admission and treatment registers, 1901-1911.
1 cu. ft. (2 volumes)

B1249   Physician's daily log of inmates received, treated, and discharged, 1898-1901.
.2 cu. ft. (1 volume)

B1250   Daily log of morning clinic, hospital, and tuberculosis treatments, 1914-1938.
1 cu. ft. (2 volumes)

B0099   Register of hospital admissions (tubercular patients), ca. 1902-1903.
.3 cu. ft. (1 volume)

B0101   Register of surgical cases, 1897-1918.
.3 cu. ft. (1 volume) R

DANNEMORA STATE HOSPITAL (Adirondack Correctional Facility)

A1505   Inmate data cards, 1900-1972.
5.3 cu. ft. R

A1502   Inmate commitment files, ca. 1900-1961.
5 cu. ft. R

B0149   Psychiatric examination case files, ca. 1968-1971.
1.5 cu. ft. R

A1503   Protestant chaplain interview files from Dannemora State Hospital and State prisons, ca. 1940-1973.
.5 cu. ft. R

EASTERN NEW YORK REFORMATORY (Eastern New York Correctional Facility)

    B0133   Admission register, 1900-1908.
                    .3 cu. ft. (1 volume)

    B0132   Discharge register, 1900-1909.
                    .3 cu. ft. (1 volume)

    B0127   Biographical register of men returned for parole violations, 1916-1920.
                    1 cu. ft. (1 volume)

NEW YORK STATE REFORMATORY AT ELMIRA (Elmira Correctional and Reception Center)

    B0125   Daily register of inmates received, transferred, paroled, and discharged, 1877-1883.
                    .3 cu. ft. (1 volume)

    B0135   Ledger of monthly and cumulative statistics on the inmate population, 1915-1923.
                    .3 cu. ft. (1 volume)

    B0140   Ledgers relating to inmate education, labor, and conduct, 1886-1905.
                    21 cu. ft. (40 volumes)

    B0126   Register of new inmates of Italian citizenry, 1915-1930.
                    .2 cu. ft. (1 volume) R

    B0134   Examining physicians' memoranda file, 1918-1928.
                    1 cu. ft. (1 volume) R

    B1000   Inmate nationality register, ca. 1908-1915.
                    .2 cu. ft. (1 volume)

    A0636   Annual reports and inmate publications, ca. 1870-1925.
                    2 cu. ft.

ELMIRA REFORMATORY (Elmira Correctional and Reception Center)

    B0131   Admission register, 1877-1950.
                    6 cu. ft. (11 volumes) R

    B1111   Inmate receiving register, 1940-1948.
                    .3 cu. ft. (1 volume)

    B0139   Index to inmate consecutive numbers, 1877-1947.
                    16 cu. ft. (21 volumes)

B0141   Biographical registers and receiving blotters, 1879-1957.
         210 cu. ft (169 volumes) R

B1110   Registers of new inmates received by county of sentencing, 1935-
         1940.
         .5 cu. ft. (2 volumes)

B0129   Biographical register of federal prisoners, 1902-1934.
         2 cu. ft. (2 volumes) R

B0137   Daily log of morning and afternoon inmate counts, 1928-1952.
         12 cu. ft. (12 volumes)

B0138   Daily log relating to evening and night guard duty, 1945-1957.
         4 cu. ft. (4 volumes) R

B0130   Register of men returned for violation of parole, 1907-1948.
         2 cu. ft. (2 volumes) R

B0136   Biographical register of men returned for parole violations, 1913-1937.
         10 cu. ft. (10 volumes) R

B0128   Inmate nickname register, ca. 1940.
         1 cu. ft. (1 volume) R

B1001   Inmate newspaper (The Summary), 1956-1958.
         .2 cu. ft.

Classification Clinic

B1270   Inmate receiving register, 1936-1949.
         .3 cu. ft. (1 volume) R

FISHKILL CORRECTIONAL FACILITY

A1525   Admission and discharge registers, 1949-1977.
         .3 cu. ft. (2 volumes)

A1523   Inmate transfer register, 1973-1977.
         2 volumes.

A1526   Correction officers' observation log, 1975-1976.
         .2 cu. ft. (1 volume) R

A1527   Security check registers, 1974-1977.
         .3 cu. ft. (3 volumes)

A1506   Daily ward log report books, 1972-1977.
         2 cu. ft. (18 volumes) R

A1514   Physical examination and ward transfer registers, 1957-1977.
         .2 cu. ft. (2 volumes) R

A1511   Nurse's register, 1975-1977.
.2 cu. ft. (2 volumes) R

A1513   Log of inmate visits to physicians, 1974.
.1 cu. ft. (1 volume) R

A1508   Assault registers, 1965-1977.
.2 cu. ft. (3 volumes) R

A1515   Search logs, 1977.
.4 cu. ft. (4 volumes)

A1518   Special watch logs, 1976-1977.
.2 cu. ft. (11 volumes) R

A1509   Suicide attempt register, 1967-1976.
.2 cu. ft. (1 volume) R

A1507   Visitor log books, 1959-1977.
1 cu. ft. (6 volumes)

A1510   Yard visitor log, 1976-1977.
.2 cu. ft. (1 volume)

A1519   Requisition log, 1976.
.2 cu. ft. (1 volume)

A1516   Inmate clothing registers, 1964-1977.
.6 cu. ft. (6 volumes)

A1520   Clothing room log, 1975.
.1 cu. ft. (1 volume)

A1517   Packages received registers, 1969-1976.
.3 cu. ft. (3 volumes)

A1528   Inmate trip register, 1975-1976.
.1 cu. ft. (1 volume)

A1512   Certificates of search from Matteawan State Hospital and Fishkill
Correctional Facility, 1971-1975.
.1 cu. ft.

MATTEAWAN STATE HOSPITAL (Fishkill Correctional Facility)

A1504   Inmate identification cards, ca. 1938-1956.
2 cu. ft. R

A1501   Inmate identification files, 1934-1974.
36 cu. ft. R

A1500   Inmate case files from Matteawan and Dannemora State hospitals, ca. 1880-1960.
273 cu. ft. R

A1522   Commissary register, 1963-1965.
.1 cu. ft. (1 volume)

A1524   Inmate medical prescription registers, 1964-1967.
.3 cu. ft. (2 volumes) R

NEW YORK HOUSE OF REFUGE

A2051   Minutes of the Board of Managers, 1857-1935.
4 cu. ft. (13 volumes) (4 microfilm reels)

A2053   Committee reports to the Board of Managers, 1857-1889.
.3 cu. ft. (2 volumes) (1 microfilm reel)

A2091   Minutes of the Visiting Committee, 1844-1893.
.3 cu. ft. (1 volume) (1 microfilm reel)

A2057   Ladies' Committee minutes, 1825-1831 and 1855-1893.
1 cu. ft. (2 volumes) (1 microfilm reel)

A2059   Building Committee minutes, 1851-1861.
.1 cu. ft. (1 volume) (1 microfilm reel)

A2058   School Committee minutes, 1855-1916.
.1 cu. ft. (3 volumes) (1 microfilm reel)

A2092   Indenturing Committee meeting minutes, 1827-1839 and 1861-1913.
4 cu. ft. (12 volumes) (3 microfilm reels)

A2071   Chaplain's reports to the Indenturing Committee, 1863-1874, 1892.
3 cu. ft. (1 volume) (1 microfilm reel)

A2093   Special reports to the Executive Committee, 1901-1909.
2 cu. ft. (5 volumes)

A2060   Minutes of Reception and Parole Committee, 1921-1929.
.3 cu. ft. (3 volumes)

A2061   Managers' facility inspection reports, 1897-1902.
.2 cu. ft. (2 volumes)

A2052   Minutes of the Acting Committee, 1824-1935.
4 cu. ft. (13 volumes)

A2063   Register of honorary members of the Society for the Reformation of Juvenile Delinquents, 1874-1885.
.1 cu. ft. (1 volume)

A2081   Proceedings relating to the dissolution of the Society for the Reformation of Juvenile Delinquents in the City of New York, 1935.
.1 cu. ft.

A2054   Superintendent's daily journals, 1825-1841, 1844-1935.
9 cu. ft. (29 volumes) (12 microfilm reels)

A2055   Daily journal of the city office, 1876-1880.
.3 cu. ft. (1 volume) (1 microfilm reel)

A2075   Visitors' registers, 1864-1883, 1901-1935.
1 cu. ft. (2 volumes)

A2076   Testimony and reports relating to special investigations, 1902-1911.
1 cu. ft.

A2078   Scrapbooks, 1892-1925.
1 cu. ft. (5 volumes)

A2079   Receipt book for employees' wages, 1844-1869.
.1 cu. ft. (1 volume)

A3188   Payroll register, 1905-1917.
.2 cu. ft. (1 volume)

A3186   Registers of audited bills, 1909-1933.
.7 cu. ft. (3 volumes)

A2083   Instructions for inmates working in offices, 1908.
.1 cu. ft. (1 volume)

A3187   Hospital admission registers, 1855-1865, 1911-1935.
2 cu. ft. (7 volumes) R

A2073   Industrial Department cash book, 1888-1900.
.2 cu. ft. (1 volume)

A2072   Registers of Industrial Department audited bills, 1888-1900.
.4 cu. ft. (2 volumes)

A2080   Dispensary record, 1915-1934.
1.3 cu. ft. (8 volumes) R

A2074   Steward's record of receipts and disbursements of supplies, 1920-1931.
1 cu. ft. (1 volume)

A2070   Parole agents' daily reports, 1894-1915.
4 cu. ft. (22 volumes)

A2085   Contracts for labor, goods, and services, 1826-1895.
.2 cu. ft. (1 volume)

A2077   Annual inventories of property, 1911-1934.
.7 cu. ft. (13 volumes)

A2082   Receipt book for construction of new House of Refuge on Randall's Island, 1852-1855.
.1 cu. ft. (1 volume)

A2090   Annual reports and miscellaneous publications, 1829, 1831, 1834-1932.
2 cu. ft. (35 volumes)

A2089   Miscellaneous published material, 1826-1921.
17 cu. ft. (109 volumes)

A2087   Register of inmates admitted and discharged, 1859-1882.
.2 cu. ft. (1 volume) (1 microfilm reel)

A2088   Inmate admission registers, 1882-1932.
1 cu. ft. (3 volumes) (1 microfilm reel)

A2064   Inmate case histories, 1824-1935.
70 cu. ft. (106 volumes) (47 microfilm reels) R

A2084   Daily census of inmates, 1860-1935.
2 cu. ft. (9 volumes)

A2056   Girls' Division daily journals, 1861-1866, 1873-1896.
1.3 cu. ft. (4 volumes) (1 microfilm reel)

A2086   Pupils' record cards, 1928-1935.
1.7 cu. ft. (1890 cards)

A2067   Register of masters of indentured inmates, 1825-1845, 1860-1903.
.4 cu. ft. (3 volumes) (1 microfilm reel)

A2066   Indenture agreements, 1825-1904.
15 cu. ft. (39 volumes) (14 microfilm reels)

A2068   Register of deferred applications for parole, 1860-1891.
.3 cu. ft. (1 volume) (1 microfilm reel)

A2069   Parole registers, 1882-1933.
1 cu. ft. (3 volumes) (2 microfilm reels)

A2065   School admission and discharge registers, 1882-1925.
1 cu. ft. (6 volumes)

A2062   Register of employees, 1851-1918.
        .1 cu. ft. (1 volume)

A3255   Intercepted letters to an inmate, 1924.
        .1 cu. ft. R

A3254   Audited accounts for new construction, 1861-1862.
        .1 cu. ft. (1 volume)

SING SING PRISON (Sing Sing Correctional Facility)

B0143   Inmate admission registers, 1865-1971.
        76 cu. ft. (148 volumes)

B1238   Principal keeper's daily journal, 1917-1918, 1938.
        1 cu. ft. (2 volumes)

B1239   Daily report to the warden, 1927-1928.
        .3 cu. ft. (1 volume)

B0148   Inmate admission register for federal prisoners, 1896-1908.
        .2 cu. ft. (2 volumes)

B0147   Admission registers for prisoners to be executed, 1891-1946.
        .5 cu. ft. (2 volumes)

B0145   Case files of inmates sentenced to electrocution, 1939-1963.
        15 cu. ft.

B1244   Log of actions relating to inmates scheduled for execution, 1915-
        1967.
        .4 cu. ft. (2 volumes)

B1242   Log of electrocutions and notes of death chamber, 1892-1907.
        .3 cu. ft. (1 volume)

B1243   File of governor's commutations of sentence, 1917-1923.
        .3 cu. ft. (1 volume)

B1241   Night watch journal, 1931-1953.
        .3 cu. ft. (2 volumes)

B1240   Record of escapes, 1911-1919.
        .3 cu. ft. (1 volume)

B0146   List of foreign born prisoners, 1944.
        .1 cu. ft.

B0144   Inmate newspaper (Star of Hope), 1901-1902, 1905-1906.
        .4 cu. ft. (2 volumes)

STATE PRISON OF THE CITY OF NEW YORK (Newgate)

A0775   Register of prisoners received, 1797-1810.
.3 cu. ft. (1 volume)

WESTERN REFORMATORY FOR WOMEN (Albion Correctional Facility)

B1257   Office files of the warden, ca. 1903-1963.
4 cu. ft.

B0092   Daily activity notebooks, 1960-1967.
4 cu. ft.

B0089   Psychiatric and psychological statistical reports, 1959-1971.
1 cu. ft. R

B0091   Psychological evaluation reports, ca. 1960-1970.
4 cu. ft. R

B1256   Employee personnel files, ca. 1950-1965.
7 cu. ft.

WESTFIELD STATE FARM (Bedford Hills Correctional Facility)

B1012   Ward daily log books, 1957-1968, bulk 1957-1959.
3.5 cu. ft.

B1022   Inmate psychiatric and medical history cards, ca. 1931-1939.
1 cu. ft. R

B1017   Ledger of miscellaneous expenses and appropriations, 1935-1945.
.3 cu. ft. (1 volume)

Prison Section

B1014   Receiving blotters, 1933-1952.
2 cu. ft. (4 volumes) R

B1016   Register of parole applicants, ca. 1945-1955.
1 cu. ft. R

Reformatory Branch

B1015   Receiving blotters, 1931-1952.
3 cu. ft. (4 volumes) R

Department of Economic Development

Current Functions. The Department of Economic Development is responsible for promoting business development in order to create private-sector jobs and generate additional tax revenues. It works with public and private development agencies to encourage the expansion of existing businesses, to attract new industries, and to increase foreign investment and trade. The department also assists minority businesses and actively promotes tourism.

Organizational History. The department evolved from two separate organizations created in 1935: the Division of State Planning, in the Executive Department, and the Bureau of State Publicity, in the Conservation Department. The Division of State Planning (Laws of 1935, Chapter 304) was established to coordinate plans for State economic development. It was headed by the State Planning Council, which consisted of five members appointed by the governor. The Conservation Department's Bureau of State Publicity was established to undertake advertising and promotion of tourism (Laws of 1935, Chapter 808).

Following a recommendation of the Joint Legislative Commission on Labor and Industrial Relations, these two organizations were combined into a Division of Commerce in the Executive Department (Laws of 1941, Chapter 216). In 1943 the Division of Commerce was made into a department, charged with promoting the economic development of the State. In 1987, the Department of Commerce was renamed the Department of Economic Development. This act reorganized the State's economic development activities under a director of economic development.

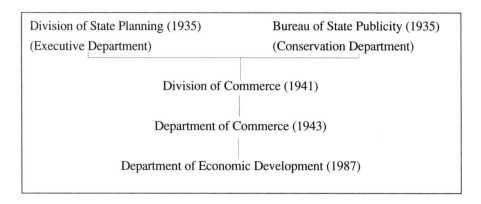

DEPARTMENT OF COMMERCE

General Agency-level Records

> 14221   Publicity files regarding the 1980 Winter Olympics, 1972-1980.
> 2 cu. ft.

Business Advisory Council

> B0920   Meeting and correspondence files, 1955-1958.
> .5 cu. ft.

Central File Division

> 10181   Legislative files, 1945-1970.
> 20 cu. ft.

Division of Industrial Sciences and Technologies

> 14141   Subject files, ca. 1967-1983.
> 35 cu. ft.

Economic Development Board

> 14220   Subject and correspondence files, ca. 1975-1979.
> 20 cu. ft.

> B1107   Land Use and Natural Resources Inventory and Land Related
> Information System research, planning, and use files, 1966-1982.
> 26 cu. ft.

> B1109   Land Use and Natural Resources Inventory and Land Related
> Information System land use overlay maps, 1968-1977.
> 25 cu. ft.

Office of Planning Services

> B1052   Land Use and Natural Resources Inventory and Land Related
> Information System aerial photographs, 1967-1974.
> 25 cu. ft.

State Education Department

Current Functions. The State Education Department is responsible for general supervision of all educational institutions in the State, for operating certain educational and cultural institutions, and for certifying teachers and certifying or licensing practitioners of 31 professions. The department's supervisory activities include chartering all educational institutions in the State, including schools, libraries, and historical societies; developing and approving school curricula; accrediting college and university programs; allocating State and federal financial aid to schools; and providing and coordinating vocational rehabilitation services. In addition, the commissioner exercises a quasi-judicial authority to review, upon appeal, the actions of any local school official or board. The department operates the New York State School for the Blind at Batavia and the New York State School for the Deaf at Rome. The Office of Cultural Education includes the State Museum and Science Service, State Library, State Archives and Records Administration and the Public Broadcasting Program, which maintain scientific and cultural research collections and provide services to State government and the public.

Organizational History. New York State's education system has antecedents in both English and Dutch colonial education. The Dutch, concerned with providing widespread general education, established tax-supported common schools under church and state control in most of New Netherland's communities. Under the English, who established a system of private or church-supported academies, emphasis was placed on advanced education of the elite, and the common school system of the Dutch all but disappeared. In 1754, the first college in the colony, King's College, was founded in New York City under a royal charter and was ruled by a board of governors designated by the colonial government.

In 1784 (Chapter 51), the legislature enacted the first education bill in the State's history, creating the Board of Regents of The University of the State of New York to act as governing body of King's College, which was renamed Columbia College. This board was also authorized to found and endow additional colleges in the State. This act designated the governor, lieutenant governor, president of the senate, speaker of the assembly, mayors of Albany and New York, attorney general, secretary of state, and twenty-four other persons as the Board of Regents. Three years later (Laws of 1787, Chapter 82) board membership was changed to the governor, lieutenant governor, and 19 members appointed by the legislature, and the functions of the Board were significantly altered. Relieved of direct operating responsibility for Columbia College, the board was authorized to charter new colleges and to exercise general supervision over Columbia and any new colleges. At the same time the board was charged with supervision of all academies, authorized to charter new ones, and empowered to make monetary grants to colleges and academies.

During its first year of operation the reorganized Board of Regents recommended State support for public schools. However, no action was taken until 1795 (Chapter 75), when the legislature appropriated $100,000 a year for each of the next five years to encourage the establishment of common schools under the supervision of town commissioners.

Further action to encourage public education was taken in 1805 (Chapter 66) when the comptroller was authorized to sell certain State lands and use the proceeds to establish a "permanent fund for the support of public schools." In 1812 (Chapter 242), the Common School Act provided the basis for a statewide system of public elementary schools. The act created a superintendent of common schools, appointed by the Council of Appointment, to "prepare plans for the improvement and management of the common school fund, and for the better organization of common schools."

The office of superintendent was abolished in 1821 (Chapter 240) and its duties transferred to the secretary of state, who served ex officio as superintendent of common schools. The following year (Chapter 256), the ex officio superintendent was given the authority to hear and decide appeals from the decisions of local school officials and boards. In 1854 (Chapter 97), the superintendent's responsibilities were transferred to a newly created Department of Public Instruction under a superintendent of public instruction who was elected by the legislature and also served as an ex officio regent. This department exercised steadily increasing advisory and supervisory powers over public elementary schools and teacher-training programs while the Board of Regents continued general control of colleges and universities and private academies. Meanwhile, the Union Free School Act of 1853 (Chapter 433) permitted common school districts to consolidate for the purpose of organizing tax-supported public schools. These union free school districts could include "academical departments" for secondary-level instruction. The superintendent of public instruction supervised these new union free schools, but there was overlap with the authority of the Regents because the 1853 law provided that all "academical departments" established in union free schools were subject to the supervision of the Board of Regents.

The State's educational system, which had expanded rapidly in the second half of the 19th century, was given a constitutional foundation in 1894. Article IX of the new consititution stipulated that "the Legislature shall provide for the maintenance and support of a system of free common schools, wherein all of the children of this state may be educated," and it also provided for the continuation of the Board of Regents of The University of the State of New York, with powers to be defined by the legislature.

Dual administrative responsibility for education continued until enactment of the so-called Unification Act of 1904 (Chapter 40). This law abolished the Department of Public Instruction and created the State Education Department, headed by a commissioner who was also the chief executive officer of the Board of Regents. The first commissioner was elected by the legislature for a six-year term, and thereafter the commissioner was selected by the Board of Regents. Although the language of the Unification Act left some doubt as to the relationship between the Board of Regents and the commissioner, actual practice followed the intent of the law to establish the Board of Regents as a policy-making body and the commissioner as chief administrative officer. The State Education Department was continued after the State government reorganization of 1925-26. A constitutional amendment in 1925 clarified the role of the commissioner as chief administrative officer of the department serving at the pleasure of the Board of Regents.

During the 19th and early 20th centuries the Board of Regents was given responsibility for several cultural and scientific activities. In 1844 (Chapter 255) the New York State Library, created in 1818 (Chapter 276), was placed under control of the Regents, and in 1889 (Chapter 529) the Regents were empowered to charter local libraries and museums. The scientific collections of the New York State Geological and Natural History Survey, established in 1836 (Chapter 142), were placed under the Regents in 1845 (Chapter 179) and known as the State Cabinet of Natural History. Several later laws added or removed the work of various State scientists to the purview of the Regents until the Unification Act of 1904 finally brought them all together in the New York State Museum under the Regents. The state historian, whose position was first created in 1895 (Chapter 393) as a gubernatorial appointee in the Executive Department charged with publishing public records, was placed in the Education Department in 1911 (Chapter 380). At the same time, the department was given responsibility for supervising the condition of public records in local government offices. In 1971 (Chapter 869), a State Archives was created in the department as the official repository for historically valuable State government records and to continue the State's responsibilities relating to local government records. The State's records management program was transferred to the Education Department from the Office of General Services in 1987 (Chapter 42), and combined with the archives to form the State Archives and Records Administration.

Beginning with the Medical Board in 1872, a number of newly created and existing professional examining boards were placed under the supervision of the Board of Regents. These boards now issue licenses or certificates and discipline practitioners in the following professions: architecture, certified shorthand reporting, chiropractics, dentistry, engineering, land surveying, landscape architecture, massage, medicine, nursing, occupational therapy, ophthalmic dispensing, optometry, pharmacy, physical therapy, podiatry, psychology, public accountancy, social work, speech-language pathology and audiology, and veterinary medicine.

The State Education Department is governed by a Board of Regents consisting of 16 members elected by the legislature. The board is also head of The University of the State of New York (different from the State University of New York, under a separate heading in this guide) consisting of all public and private schools, colleges and universities, and chartered libraries, museums, historical societies, and other educational institutions in the State. The department's chief executive officer is the commissioner of education and president of the university, who is appointed by the Board of Regents.

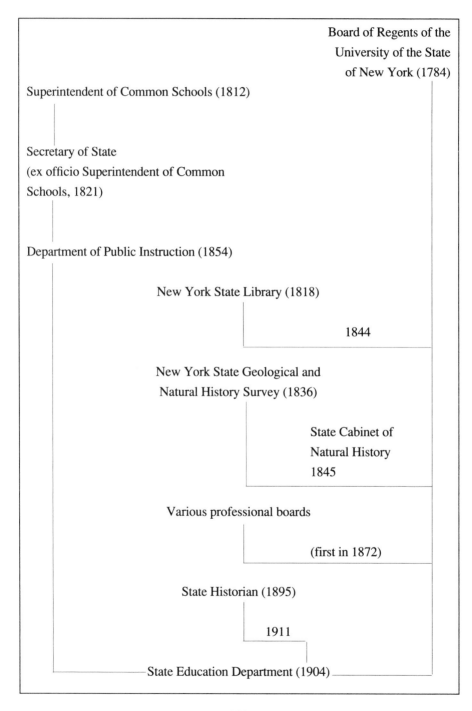

Board of Regents of the
University of the State
of New York (1784)

Superintendent of Common Schools (1812)

Secretary of State
(ex officio Superintendent of Common
Schools, 1821)

Department of Public Instruction (1854)

New York State Library (1818)

1844

New York State Geological and
Natural History Survey (1836)

State Cabinet of
Natural History
1845

Various professional boards

(first in 1872)

State Historian (1895)

1911

State Education Department (1904)

STATE EDUCATION DEPARTMENT

Board of Regents

B0946   Minutes of meetings of the Board of Regents, 1784-1859.
.1 cu.ft. (2 microfilm rolls)

A2017   Reports of academies, 1846-1848, 1884-1888.
9.2 cu. ft.

A2027   Reports of the Regents Inquiry into the Character and Cost of Public Education, 1936-1937, 1948.
13 cu. ft.

A2028   Correspondence and working files from Study 7 of the Regents' Inquiry into the Character and Cost of Public Education, 1935-1941, bulk 1936-1937.
5 cu. ft.

A0346   Reports of meteorological observations made at academies, 1826-1859.
41.5 cu. ft.

A2020   Account of Literature Fund and other moneys for the use of colleges and academies, ca. 1832-1880.
.5 cu. ft. (1 volume)

A2019   Minutes and accounts of Standing Committee on the State Library, 1848-1851, 1883-1890.
.5 cu. ft.

A2024   Accounts ledger, 1857-1888.
1 cu. ft. (3 volumes)

A2023   Expense journal, 1883-1884.
.5 cu. ft. (1 volume)

A2021   Expense invoices, 1867-1879.
2.5 cu. ft. (6 volumes)

A2026   Financial records, 1853-1862.
.5 cu. ft.

A2034   Registers of pupils in the LeRoy Academic Institute, 1874-1891.
.5 cu. ft. (2 volumes)

A2035   Record of Regents academic examinations given at LeRoy Academic Institute, 1866-1891.
.5 cu. ft. (1 volume)

B0313   Charters of educational corporations returned to the State Education Department, 1932-1958.
.5 cu. ft.

A2040   Pawling School charters, 1908, 1914.
.5 cu. ft.

A2046   Commissioner's election certificates, 1904, 1910.
.2 cu. ft. (2 items)

A0490   Governor's proclamation and concurrent resolution of the Senate and Assembly concerning the 175th anniversary of the Board of Regents, 1959.
.1 cu. ft.

– Chancellor

B0620   Letter of Winston S. Churchill to Chancellor John P. Myers, 1951.
.1 cu. ft. (1 item)

– Secretary

B0442   Convocations files, 1958-1977, bulk 1974, 1977.
2 cu. ft.

A2022   Incoming correspondence regarding convocations, 1866-1872.
.5 cu. ft. (1 volume)

B0443   Audiotapes of convocations and Education Department functions, 1952-1970.
4 cu. ft.

– High School Department

A2018   Principals' reports of Regents examinations, 1898-1899.
4 cu. ft.

Commissioner's Office

15080   Commissioner's subject files, 1942-1986.
266 cu. ft.

B0444   Commissioner's interim subject files, 1956-1969, bulk 1967-1969.
18 cu. ft.

B0466   Outgoing correspondence, 1956-1977.
14 cu. ft.

A2097   Commissioner's correspondence relating to Liberty Bond purchases by the Board of Regents, 1917.
.2 cu. ft.

A2098   Commissioner's addresses and articles, ca. 1872-1913.
         2 cu. ft.

A2043   Commissioner's addresses, press releases, and proclamations,
         1946-1950.
         2 cu. ft.

B1060   Commissioner's speech files, 1951-1977.
         38 cu. ft.

B0469   Cabinet meeting minutes, 1948-1955, 1971-1974.
         .6 cu. ft.

B0460   Commissioner's history file, 1955-1969.
         2 cu. ft.

B0464   Commissioner's Constitutional Convention files, 1958-1968, bulk
         1967.
         1 cu. ft.

B0465   Commissioner's files on Joint Legislative Committee to Revise
         and Simplify the Education Law hearing, 1964.
         .4 cu. ft.

B0467   Commissioner's files on Regents meetings, 1970-1977.
         13 cu. ft.

A2042   Records of commissioner's visit to France, 1917.
         1 cu. ft.

A2045   Films of Commissioner's speeches, 1964.
         1 cu. ft. (8 films)

B1054   Photographic prints and negatives of Commissioner Gordon M.
         Ambach and Education Department staff, 1987.
         .1 cu. ft.

B0563   Audio tapes of speeches and interviews of Commissioner Gordon
         M. Ambach, 1979.
         2 tapes.

B1057   Transcripts of minutes of meetings of the Board of Regents, 1784-
         1787, 1852-1853.
         .2 cu. ft.

A2041   Scrapbooks of newspaper clippings, 1911-1916, 1955-1965.
         4 cu. ft. (13 volumes and 3 boxes)

B0468 Executive assistant's subject files, 1943-1950.
1 cu. ft.

B0470 Executive assistant's administrative files, 1960-1975.
12 cu. ft.

B0471 Administrative assistant's subject files, 1966-1969.
6 cu. ft.

Deputy Commissioner's Office

B0459 Deputy commissioners's subject files, 1941-1955, 1958-1970.
57 cu. ft.

A2095 Correspondence and subject files relating to State War Council activities, 1941-1946.
2 cu. ft.

A2096 Postwar planning files, 1943-1949.
2 cu. ft.

Office of Counsel

B0496 Appeals case files, 1842-1904, 1969-1975.
105.6 cu. ft.

B1104 School district centralization files, 1944-1962.
14 cu. ft.

Law Division

A4212 Letterpress copies of decisions in appeals to the commissioner, 1910-1937.
2 cu. ft.

Office of Higher and Professional Education

– Deputy Commissioner's Office

14288 Subject and correspondence files, 1969-1984.
123 cu. ft.

– Board of Pharmacy

B0481 Registers of licensed druggists and prescription clerks in New York City, 1871-1872.
1 cu. ft. (2 volumes)

B0486 New York City Board of Pharmacy registers of licensed pharmacists, 1872-1900.
2 cu. ft. (8 volumes)

B0484   New York City Board of Pharmacy registers of licensed assistant pharmacists, 1872-1897.
1 cu. ft. (3 volumes)

B0487   New York City Board of Pharmacy examination register, 1898-1900.
.2 cu. ft. (1 volume)

B0489   New York City Board of Pharmacy licensing index, ca. 1872-1900.
.4 cu. ft. (1 volume)

B0483   Kings County Board of Pharmacy registers of licensed pharmacists, 1879-1897.
1 cu. ft. (3 volumes)

B0485   Erie County Board of Pharmacy registers of applications, 1884-1900.
.8 cu. ft. (4 volumes)

B0488   Registers of applicants examined and licensed, 1884-1900.
.4 cu. ft. (3 volumes)

B0493   Pharmacist and druggist licenses registers, 1901-1910.
2.4 cu. ft. (11 volumes and 3 boxes)

B0490   Registers of apprentices, ca. 1901-1923.
1 cu. ft. (7 volumes)

B0491   Registers of pharmacies and drug stores, 1901-1950.
9.8 cu. ft. (27 volumes)

B0492   Registers of storekeepers permits, 1901-1962.
2.4 cu. ft. (7 volumes)

Office of Cultural Education

– Associate Commissioner's Office

B0457   Subject files, 1956-1970, bulk 1960-1970.
12 cu. ft.

A2048   Plans of the Cultural Education Center in the Empire State Plaza, Albany, 1966-1968.
3 cu. ft.

A2049   Photographs of the Empire State Plaza, Albany, 1966.
.2 cu. ft.

– New York State Museum

– – Assistant Commissioner/Director

11843	Assistant commissioner's correspondence and subject files, 1954-1968, bulk 1962-1968. 39 cu. ft.
B0561	State Museum director's, State geologist's, and State paleontologist's correspondence files, 1828-1944. 59.8 cu. ft.
B0579	State Museum director's, State geologist's, and State paleontologist's correspondence, drafts of publications, and photographs, 1844-1900. 2 cu. ft.
A4208	Incoming correspondence of the assistant State paleontologist, State paleontologist, State geologist, and State Museum director, 1804-1919, bulk 1881-1915. 4 cu. ft.
A0260	State Museum director's, State geologist's, and State paleontologist's incoming correspondence relating to research on the Gaspe Peninsula, Quebec, 1901-1913. .4 cu. ft.
B0583	Correspondence and subject files of the director of the New York State Science Service, 1970-1972. 1 cu. ft.
B0584	Assistant director's correspondence file, 1931-1963, bulk 1931, 1953-1963. 2 cu. ft.
B0585	Assistant commissioner's files relating to the Commissioner's Committee on Museum Resources, 1961-1964. 1 cu. ft.
A4214	Speeches, articles, and essays of the director of the Division of Science and State Museum, ca. 1910-1925. .2 cu. ft.
A3294	State Museum director's, State geologist's, and State paleontologist's lecture files, ca. 1910-1925. .4 cu. ft.

A0128   State Museum director's, State geologist's, and State paleontologist's album of diplomas and certificates, 1832-1896.
.3 cu. ft. (1 volume)

– – Geology

B0571   State geologist's and assistant State geologist's correspondence files, 1905-1968.
61.2 cu. ft.

A4210   Correspondence and research files concerning the oil and natural gas industries in New York State, 1885-1961, bulk 1905-1961.
4 cu. ft.

B0570   Mineralogist's correspondence file, 1902-1928, bulk 1902-1922.
1 cu. ft.

A0225   Geology field notes, ca. 1832-1939, bulk ca. 1832-1845, 1885-1939.
3.5 cu. ft. (88 volumes)

B0948   Geologic maps and drawings, ca. 1892-1971.
5 cu. ft. (ca. 500 maps/drawings)

A4213   Negatives and photographs of mineral producing facilities and geologic features, ca. 1890-1954.
3 cu. ft. (ca. 300 negatives and prints)

B0581   Financial statements, bills, and receipts relating to geological and paleontological research, 1890-1909.
1 cu. ft.

B0574   Mineral producers' annual reports, 1910-1946, 1961-1968.
20 cu. ft.

A3159   Photograph album of geologic features in Great Britain, ca. 1890-1900.
.2 cu. ft. (1 volume)

– – Paleontology

B0575   State paleontologist's correspondence files, 1899-1954.
10.4 cu. ft.

A4211   Correspondence and lists concerning fossils borrowed, loaned, or exchanged by the State paleontologist, 1855-1899.
.5 cu. ft.

A3158   State paleontologist's journal, 1899-1900.
.2 cu. ft. (1 volume)

B0582 State paleontologist's publications and professional meetings file, 1913-1951.
1 cu. ft.

B0576 State paleontologist's reports, 1927-1954.
.2 cu. ft.

A4193 Original drawings for Volume V of the Natural History of New York: Paleontology, 1874.
.2 cu. ft. (1 volume)

B1061 Original drawings of fossil graptolites, ca. 1900-1940.
2 cu. ft.

B0577 State paleontologist's photographs, ca. 1900-1960.
5.5 cu. ft. (ca. 400 photographs and negatives)

– – Biology

B0572 State entomologist's correspondence file, ca. 1856-1952, bulk 1874-1952.
48 cu. ft.

B0573 State entomologist's topical file, 1894-1934.
5.4 cu. ft.

B0569 Zoologist's correspondence files, 1898-1932.
4 cu. ft.

A3157 Correspondence relating to research on the song of the wood pewee, 1926-1943.
.4 cu. ft.

A0560 Biology field notes, ca. 1890-1937.
1 cu. ft. (20 volumes)

A4215 Bibliographies of entomological writings, ca. 1825-1910.
.5 cu. ft. (2 volumes)

A3160 Constitution and minutes of meetings of the Entomological Society of Albany, 1899-1907.
.2 cu. ft. (1 volume)

A3161 Accession data for the Benjamin W. Arnold Oological (Bird's Egg) Collection, ca. 1880-1917.
1 cu. ft. (39 photographs)

– – Archeology

15513   State archeologist's office correspondence files, 1904-1979.
23 cu. ft.

A3288   State archeologist's correspondence files on the Society for American Archaeology, 1949-1956.
.4 cu. ft.

A3291   State archeologist's correspondence files on the Eastern States Archeological Federation, 1943-1954.
.4 cu. ft.

A3289   State archeologist's correspondence files on the New York State Archeological Association, 1925-1949.
.2 cu. ft.

A3290   State archeologist's correspondence files on the New York Archaeological Council, 1969-1974.
.4 cu. ft.

B0580   Manuscripts and museum director's correspondence files concerning archeological work of Max Schrabisch, 1918-1938.
.5 cu. ft.

A3292   Hudson Valley Archaeological Survey director's correspondence files, 1939-1940.
.4 cu. ft.

A3293   State archeologist's research and publications files, ca. 1905-1943.
1 cu. ft.

– – Other Records

A4209   Vouchers for payment of expenses of the geological and natural history survey, the geological survey, and the agricultural survey, 1837-1848.
.5 cu. ft.

B0578   Pre-publication texts and illustrations for State Museum publications, 1840-1948.
9.9 cu. ft.

B0949   Plans and drawings of museum facilities and exhibit cases, ca. 1870s-1948.
1 cu. ft. (79 plans and drawings)

A0182   Register of visitors to the Geological and Agricultural Hall, 1873-1874.
.3 cu. ft. (1 volume)

A0492   Original bill of sale and record of the action of the Council of the Onondaga Indians whereby the University of the State of New York became Wampum Keeper of the Six Nations, 1898.
.2 cu. ft. (1 item)

A3279   Photographs and printed documents concerning Joseph Henry Memorial, 1914-1928.
.2 cu. ft.

A3164   Files relating to the commissioner's Museum Inquiry Committee and proposed State Museum building, 1928-1944, bulk 1930-1934.
1 cu. ft.

A3295   Draft of "The State Museum 1904-1944," 1947.
.2 cu. ft.

B0586   News release and public relations files, 1966-1968.
1 cu. ft.

B0587   Departmental long range plan, 1967.
.5 cu. ft.

– New York State Library

A3285   Plans and subject files concerning the Education Building, 1908-1962.
1.5 cu. ft.

A3266   Transcripts and translations of New York colonial manuscripts, ca. 1850-1918.
4 cu. ft.

A0126   Manuscript/typescript of "Early records of the city and county of Albany and colony of Rensselaerswyck," 1658-1765.
1 cu. ft.

13911   Unpublished manuscript of "The ministry and churches of all denominations in the Middle Colonies from the first settlements until the year 1800," by Edward T. Corwin, ca. 1914.
.4 cu. ft.

B0928   Plans, photographs, and working files of the Planning Committee for the Shrine for the Emancipation Proclamation, 1961-1963.
3 cu. ft. (2 oversize folders, 2 boxes)

A2025   Book and document exchange record, ca. 1857-1887.
.5 cu. ft. (2 volumes)

– New York State Archives and Records Administration

– – Local Government Records Bureau

15745   Local government records correspondence files, 1911-1984.
41 cu. ft.

State Historian

13913   Manuscript copy of Volume 25 of the New York Colonial Council Papers, 1675-1676 (compiled ca. 1910).
.2 cu. ft.

A0131   Unpublished typescript, galleys, and page proofs of "Military Papers of General Peter Gansevoort", 1763-1818 (compiled ca. 1906-1907).
1 cu. ft.

A3168   Unpublished annual report and typescripts of "Mexican War Papers" and State historian's correspondence, 1846-1904, bulk 1846-1850, 1897-1904 (compiled 1897-1904).
.2 cu. ft.

A0257   Transcriptions of Civil War records, 1861-1897, bulk 1861-1865.
2 cu. ft.

A4170   Memorial album of the second New York Veteran Cavalry, 1863-1909, bulk 1863-1865.
.3 cu. ft. (1 volume)

Division of History

A0071   Unpublished typescript of "Papers of Colonel Israel Keith", 1767-1800 (compiled ca. 1912-1916).
.2 cu. ft.

Division of Archives and History

A0224   State historian's teaching and research notes, 1890-1916, bulk 1890-1901, 1916.
1.5 cu. ft.

A0061   State historian's speeches, 1940-1944.
.4 cu. ft.

A3113   Files on local historic sites and monuments, 1922-1928.
2 cu. ft.

11890   Historic sites bronze marker file, 1926-1942.
3 cu. ft.

A0245   Photographs of historic sites and structures, 1936-1963.
7 cu. ft.

A0060   Files relating to the Martin Van Buren Historic Site ("Lindenwald"), 1927-1938.
.5 cu. ft.

A3262   Subject files relating to State and federal records programs, 1938-1951.
1 cu. ft.

A3165   Inventory of local school records, 1936.
.4 cu. ft.

A4194   Correspondence and research files for Saratoga County Historical Survey, 1935.
.4 cu. ft.

A3271   Transliterations of New York colonial manuscripts, ca. 1942-1943.
3 cu. ft.

13914   File relating to the purchase of photostatic copies of New York Colonial Council Minutes from the British Public Record Office, 1921.
.1 cu. ft.

A3167   Historical research files, ca. 1795-1945.
7 cu. ft.

13917   Historical information subject files, ca. 1905-1966.
2 cu. ft.

A3272   Biographical history cards on prominent New Yorkers, ca. 1940-1942.
.3 cu. ft.

A3166   Background files for a publication on New York in World War I, 1917-1925.
1.4 cu. ft.

A0412   Data and photograph files on World War I veterans, 1919-1924.
39 cu. ft.

B0568   Correspondence files of the executive secretary of the Executive Committee on the 150th Anniversary of the American Revolution, 1926-1929.
3 cu. ft.

B0566   Correspondence files of the supervisor of Public Records and the secretary of the Advisory Committee on the Commemoration of the Sullivan Campaign, 1928-1936.
6 cu. ft.

13912   General files relating to observances of the 150th anniversary of the American Revolution and other events, 1923-1939.
3 cu. ft.

B0567   Photographs of observances of the 150th Anniversary of the American Revolution, 1926-1927.
1 cu. ft. (ca. 300 negatives and photographs)

13918   Celebrations file, 1954-1959.
1 cu. ft.

13915   Calendars and minutes of meetings of the State Council of Parks, 1925-1933.
1 cu. ft.

A4195   Unpublished lists and monographs submitted to the State historian, ca. 1911-1928.
.4 cu. ft.

A3313   Publicity photographs of State Historian Albert B. Corey, 1948-1959.
.1 cu. ft.

A0097   Photographs, ca. 1940.
.3 cu. ft.

– Works Progress Administration Projects

A4178   Manuals, bibliographies, and indexes published by the Works Progress Administration, 1935-1941.
2 cu. ft.

A4179   Works Progress Administration sponsored surveys and studies, 1936-1940.
7 cu. ft.

– – Historical Records Survey

A4173   Director's general correspondence files, 1935-1941.
3.2 cu. ft.

A4172   Director's correspondence concerning surveys, 1936-1942.
3.2 cu. ft.

A4176   District supervisors' correspondence and administrative files, 1936-1942.
13.9 cu. ft. R

A4171   Correspondence and reports of the church archives editor, 1936-1942.
.8 cu. ft.

A0550   Inventory of county records, 1936-1941.
35 cu. ft.

A4180   Inventory of town, village, and city records, 1936-1942.
50 cu. ft.

A4181   Inventory of church records, 1937-1942.
6 cu. ft.

A4183   American Imprints Inventory cards, ca. 1700-1876 (compiled 1941-1942).
22 cu. ft.

A4184   Survey of buildings housing State and local government records, 1936-1942.
9 cu. ft.

A0413   Biographical sketches of famous individuals, ca. 1930-1939.
1 cu. ft.

A4174   Abstracts of broadsides identified in western New York, ca. 1760-1875 (compiled 1942).
.2 cu. ft.

A4175   Polemic literature concerning unionism in the Works Progress Administration in New York City, 1935-1937.
.1 cu. ft.

A0137   Institution forms, ca. 1942.
.3 cu. ft.

A4182   Extracts from minutes of the annual sessions of the Buffalo Baptist Association, 1817-1940.
.2 cu. ft.

A4192   Maps, charts, and illustrations prepared by Historical Records Survey staff, ca. 1936-1942.
.1 cu. ft.

A4177 Work reports and personnel, travel, and purchasing files, 1936-
1941.
3 cu. ft. R

A4185 Biweekly payroll, 1936-1941.
2 cu. ft. (8 volumes)

– – Federal Writers' Project

A4188 State directors' correspondence and reports files, 1938-1941.
.5 cu. ft. R

A0551 State director's publications background files, 1936-1942.
60 cu. ft.

A4190 Correspondence and administrative files of the District 1
Supervisor's Office, 1936-1942.
9 cu. ft.

A4191 Administrative files of the District 2 Supervisor's Office, 1936-
1942.
5 cu. ft.

A4189 Correspondence and administrative files of the Long Island Office,
1936-1942.
6 cu. ft.

A4187 Correspondence and administrative files of the Schenectady
County Office, 1937-1942.
10 cu. ft.

11891 Research files for the Historical Album of New York State, 1941-
1944, bulk 1941-1942.
5 cu. ft.

A4186 Research files for a name and subject index to French's Gazetteer
of 1860, ca. 1939.
7 cu. ft.

Office of State History

13910 Correspondence and subject files, 1895-1976.
24.4 cu. ft.

13916 Files of the Board/Committee on Geographic Names, 1913-1977.
2 cu. ft.

Office of Vocational Rehabilitation

11649   Closed case reports and reviews, 1927-1961.
13 cu. ft. R

Motion Picture Division

A1429   Subject files, 1923-1965.
23 cu. ft.

A1427   Distributor and exchange correspondence files, 1929-1965.
2 cu. ft.

A1421   Distributor/exchange card file, 1921-1965.
4 cu. ft.

A1418   License application case files, 1921-1965.
1,135 cu. ft.

A1419   Index to case files, 1921-1965.
25 cu. ft.

A1420   License application summary books, 1921-1965.
20 cu. ft. (120 volumes)

A1433   License application summary books for films sent to Albany, 1927-1965.
2.6 cu. ft. (16 volumes)

A1422   Record of films rejected or approved with eliminations, 1921-1958.
5 cu. ft.

A1417   Eliminations bulletins, 1927-1964.
6 cu. ft.

A1428   Censorship files, 1927-1945.
3.5 cu. ft.

A1423   Alphabetical list of films rejected or approved with eliminations, 1921-1965.
.2 cu. ft. (1 volume)

A1424   Statistical summary of actions taken, 1929-1939.
.2 cu. ft. (3 volumes)

A1426   Daily schedules of films viewed, July 1942-November 1963.
1.5 cu. ft.

A1425   Monthly recapitulation books, July 1942-March 1962.
.3 cu. ft. (3 volumes)

A1415   Annual reports, 1922-1947.
.2 cu. ft.

A1416   Handbooks of laws, rules, and regulations, 1927-1963.
.2 cu. ft. (17 volumes)

A1432   Annual financial statements, 1959-1965.
.1 cu. ft.

A1431   Personnel files, 1930-1965, bulk 1950-1960.
2 cu. ft.

A1430   Eliminations bulletins from other states and countries, 1951-1965.
1 cu. ft.

Division of Visual Instruction

A3045   Instructional lantern slides, ca. 1856-1939, bulk 1911-1939.
ca. 24,350 lantern slides (portions on 18 microfilm reels)

A3134   Negatives and positive transparencies of instructional photographic images, ca. 1856-1939, bulk 1911-1939.
199 cu. ft. (12,000-15,000 glass plates and film negatives)

A3132   Subject card indexes to instructional photographic images, 1911-1939.
4 cu. ft. (ca. 18,000 cards) (93 microfiche)

A3133   Registers of accessioned and classified negatives, 1911-1939.
1 cu. ft. (2 volumes)

A4199   Special lantern slide sets, ca. 1880-1934.
166 slides

A4198   Negatives of portraits of delegates to the 1915 Constitutional Convention, 1915.
ca. 100 negatives

A3151   Caption notebooks for original negatives by Edward Raffius, 1923-1930.
.2 cu. ft.

A3135   Published study guides and lists of educational lantern slides, ca. 1906-1934.
2.4 cu. ft.

Office of District Organization and District Superintendents

   – Assistant Commissioner's Office

     B0482   County district administration and supervision files, 1962-1975.
6 cu. ft.

     B0314   Subject files, 1970-1979.
2 cu. ft.

Rural Education Bureau

     A3220   Tuition contracts between school districts, 1927-1932.
4.2 cu. ft.

     14214   Maps of central school districts proposed by district superinten-
dents, 1930-1932.
2 cu. ft.

Bureau of Rural Administrative Services

     B0480   Reference files, 1907-1958.
2 cu. ft.

     B0475   County Vocational Education and Extension Boards correspon-
dence and program files, 1948-1962.
1 cu. ft.

     A4216   Files relating to the New York State Council on Rural Education,
1943-1956.
1 cu. ft.

Bureau of School District Organization

     B0477   Subject and administrative files, 1923-1967, bulk 1957-1967.
7.4 cu. ft.

     11121   Correspondence with district superintendents, 1943-1979.
8 cu. ft.

     B0472   School district centralization and reorganization files, 1924-1974.
84 cu. ft.

     14219   Reference file of school district boundary maps, 1943-ca. 1969.
6 cu. ft. (4 volumes, ca. 300 maps)

     B0473   Boards of Cooperative Educational Services correspondence and
administrative files, 1948-1979.
15 cu. ft.

B0474   Boards of Cooperative Educational Services applications for shared services, 1948-1968.
8 cu. ft.

14209   Boards of Cooperative Educational Services new service proposals, 1975-1978.
2 cu. ft.

11120   Files of revised Master Plan studies, 1956-1959.
4 cu. ft.

B0476   Certification files regarding State aid and reorganization, 1962-1965.
3 cu. ft.

Bureau of Statistical Services

13638   Annual financial and statistical reports of school districts, 1904-1975, 1979.
324 cu. ft.

A3046   Abstracts of school district trustees reports, 1905-1951.
162 cu. ft. (489 volumes)

B0558   Annual census and enrollment reports of school districts, 1931-1965.
46 cu. ft.

B0555   Annual financial and statistical reports of private and parochial schools, 1904-1965.
33 cu. ft. (120 volumes)

B0557   Annual financial and statistical reports of universities, colleges, and junior colleges, 1901-1965.
19.4 cu. ft. (129 volumes)

A3049   Annual reports of vocational schools, 1911-1948.
8 cu. ft. (89 volumes)

A3048   Annual financial and statistical reports of normal schools, 1911-1924.
.2 cu. ft. (1 volume)

A3047   Annual reports of adult immigrant education (Americanization) classes, 1922-1937.
2 cu. ft. (15 volumes)

B0556   Annual financial and statistical reports of institutions and associations chartered by the Board of Regents, 1914-1955.
5 cu. ft. (26 volumes)

B0499   Annual statistical reports of nursing program graduates and enrollments, 1961-1962.
.2 cu. ft. (1 volume)

B0559   Annual survey of pupils, staff, and schoolhousing in school districts, 1962-1965.
2 cu. ft. (12 volumes)

B0560   Fall reports of private and parochial schools, 1965-1966.
2 cu. ft.

B0562   Higher Education Data System data collection forms, 1968-1969.
9 cu. ft.

Division of Vocational and Extension Education

  – Associate Commissioner's and Acting Assistant Commissioner's Office

A2050   Subject files, 1937-1941.
11 cu. ft.

A2094   Defense files, 1940-1941.
2 cu. ft.

  – Assistant Commissioner's Office

A2099   Reference file, 1913-1935, bulk 1922-1927.
2 cu. ft.

  – Other Records

A0409   Central correspondence files, 1911-1925, bulk 1921-1925.
35 cu. ft.

A3038   White House Conference on Child Health and Protection files, 1930-1931.
.8 cu. ft.

A2047   Temporary Emergency Relief Administration projects payroll records, 1935.
2.4 cu. ft.

A3039   Syracuse Collegiate Center files of the Emergency Adult Education Project, 1936-1937.
.2 cu. ft.

A3041   Federal Vocational Education Funds files, 1939-1946.
2.3 cu. ft.

Office of Elementary Education

– Assistant Commissioner's Office

A3042   Historical sketches and photographs of school systems in cities
and villages, ca. 1850-1920.
2.4 cu. ft.

– Bureau of Instructional Supervision

B1351   Indian schools land acquisition correspondence files, 1942-1957.
.2 cu. ft.

Office of Finance and School Administrative Services

– Assistant Commissioner's Office

B0478   School district reorganization studies files, 1947-1954.
1 cu. ft.

Division of Educational Finance

B0554   School district and vocational education and extension board
establishment and alteration legal files, ca. 1873-1971.
15 cu. ft.

13108   School district boundary alterations file, ca. 1914-1975.
3 cu. ft.

11000   Boards of cooperative educational services annual financial and
statistical reports, 1948-1966.
7 cu. ft.

Bureau of Apportionment

B0494   Register of school district establishment, consolidation, and centralization, ca. 1860-1954.
.4 cu. ft.

Bureau of Educational Management Services

11748   Native American education tuition and transportation files, 1952-
1979.
12 cu. ft. R

Office of Instructional Services

– Assistant Commissioner's Office

11501   Correspondence and administrative files of Project Redesign, 1970-1976.
21 cu. ft.

Office of Secondary Education

– Assistant Commissioner's Office

A3223   Assistant Commissioner's correspondence file, 1917-1922.
1 cu. ft.

Administration Division

A2014   Entry documentation for Emergency Fund (Capitol Fire), 1911-1912.
.5 cu. ft.

A2015   Entry documentation for dedication of Education Building fund, 1912-1914.
.5 cu. ft.

A3225   Lists of teachers employed in New York City schools, 1919-1920, bulk 1919.
.5 cu. ft.

Commissioner's Committee on Inquiry into Charges of Waste and Extravagance in the Construction of School Buildings in New York City

A2044   Correspondence and subject files, 1949-1959.
3.5 cu. ft. (4 boxes and 4 reels microfilm)

Center on Innovation in Education

14043   New York City school decentralization files, 1967-1977, bulk 1967-1969.
5 cu. ft.

Office of School District Employer-Employee Relations

15946   Tenured teacher disciplinary case hearing transcripts and exhibits, 1970-1990.
89 cu. ft. R

15953   Reference file of decisions in tenured teacher disciplinary cases, 1971-1986.
5 cu. ft. R

15400   School district collective bargaining files, 1967-1973.
5.2 cu. ft.

Division of Urban Education

14189   Correspondence and subject files, 1968-1974.
8 cu. ft.

14188   Urban Education Program correspondence and project files, 1968-1973.
128 cu. ft.

14238   New York City School-Community Interaction Umbrella Program correspondence and project files, 1971-1974.
6 cu. ft.

Office of Model Cities Program Services

14193   Model Cities Program files, 1967-1973.
12 cu. ft.

Bureau of Higher Education Opportunity Programs

13223   Program and audit case files, 1964-1986.
132.5 cu. ft. R

Native American Education Unit

13143   Subject and correspondence files, 1954-1983.
9 cu. ft.

A0729   Research files for Regents paper on Native American education, 1964-1975.
5 cu. ft.

A0728   Johnson-O'Malley Act project files, 1971-1982.
1.5 cu. ft.

Special Schools Bureau

A3222   Correspondence and subject files concerning schools for Native Americans, the deaf, the blind, and other special populations, 1906-1925, bulk 1915-1925.
5 cu. ft.

A3037   New York State Merchant Marine Academy supervision files, 1915-1930.
.8 cu. ft.

Division of Teacher Education and Certification

A4197   Registers of teaching certificates issued, 1908-1951.
6 cu. ft. (37 volumes)

Teacher Training and Certification Bureau

> A3224 Correspondence and reports concerning vocational teacher training and certification, 1919-1928.
> .5 cu. ft.

Teacher Training Division

> A3221 Teachers training school and training class attendance registers and annual reports, 1927-1933, bulk 1927-1928.
> 2 cu. ft.

Examinations Division

> A0073 Registers of University of the State of New York college degree applications, 1892-1917.
> .5 cu. ft. (3 volumes)

> A4203 Background statements of candidates for the position of District Superintendent of Schools, 1911.
> 1 cu. ft. (3 volumes)

Examinations and Inspections Division

> A4201 Reports of examinations for teaching certificates, 1904-1927.
> 8 cu. ft. (50 volumes)

> B0452 Regents College Scholarship candidate lists, 1922-1957.
> 1.5 cu. ft. (7 volumes) R

> B0447 Soldiers, Sailors, Marines and Nurses Scholarship candidate lists, 1930-1932.
> .5 cu. ft. (1 volume) R

Division of Examinations and Testing

> B0446 Cornell University Scholarship candidate lists, 1897, 1935-1951.
> 1 cu. ft. (16 volumes) R

Bureau of Examinations and Testing

> B0450 Candidate lists for children of deceased/disabled veterans scholarship, 1936-1961.
> .5 cu. ft. (3 volumes) R

> B0445 Applications for State scholarships for children of deceased or disabled veterans, 1954-1956.
> 1 cu. ft. R

> B0455 War Service Scholarship Examination scores list, 1950-1951.
> .5 cu. ft. R

B0449   Medicine and Dentistry Scholarship candidate lists, 1949-1959.
.5 cu. ft. (2 volumes) R

B0453   Medicine and Dentistry Scholarship Examination scores lists, 1951-1963.
.4 cu. ft. R

B0451   Basic Nursing Scholarship candidate lists, 1955-1957.
.5 cu. ft. (3 volumes) R

B0448   Science and Engineering Scholarship candidate lists, 1956-1957.
.5 cu. ft. (1 volume) R

03612   Regents College Scholarship information cards, 1954.
.4 cu. ft.

Regents Examination and Scholarship Center

B0454   War Service Scholarship candidate lists, 1944-1959.
3 cu. ft. (18 volumes) R

B0456   Scholarship winners lists, 1939-1965.
.5 cu. ft.

Division of Adult Education and Library Extension

A0055   Files of Regents literacy test forms, 1923-1947.
1 cu. ft.

A0063   Press clippings and background files concerning the Regents literacy test, 1916-1932, bulk 1922-1932.
.9 cu. ft.

A3112   Enlistment papers and reports of the New York State Boys' Working Reserve (Farm Cadet Program), 1918.
3 cu. ft.

A2012   Victory Book Campaign files, 1939-1943, bulk 1942-1943.
2.5 cu. ft.

A2013   Library War Bond Campaign files, 1944-1945.
.5 cu. ft.

Bureau of Adult Education

B0497   Correspondence and annual reports of adult education classes, 1921-1969, bulk 1941-1965.
21 cu. ft.

Bureau of School Registration

    B0594   Secondary school registration card file, ca. 1840-1985.
             .1 cu. ft. (1 microfilm roll)

Bureau of Secondary School Supervision

    14310   Register of Advance-in-grade certificates issued to secondary schools, 1906-1967.
             .3 cu. ft. (1 volume)

Division of School Buildings and Grounds

    A3050   School district enrollment reports, 1923-1933.
             1 cu. ft.

Division of Educational Facilities Planning

    B0916   Architectural drawings of additions and alterations to public schools, ca. 1935-1970.
             1 cu. ft. (54 microfilm rolls)

Division of Research

  – Assistant Commissioner's Office

    A3044   Files relating to the Advisory Committee on New York State's Records System, 1945-1948.
             .4 cu. ft.

  – Other Records

    A2029   Reports on action taken on Regents' Inquiry recommendations within the State Education Department, 1946.
             1 cu. ft.

Bureau of Business and Distributive Education

    10220   Application files for registration of private business schools, ca. 1923-1970.
             19 cu. ft. R

    B0549   Application files for approval of private business schools and courses for veteran training, 1945-1970.
             7 cu. ft.

    B0553   Circular letters and bulletins issued, 1937-1967.
             2 cu. ft.

    B0550   School surveys and studies files, 1939-1961.
             1 cu. ft.

B0552 Reports of field visits, 1946-1966.
1 cu. ft.

B0551 Course syllabi, 1900-1964.
.1 cu. ft.

Bureau of Home Economics Education

A3040 School supervision files, 1921-1935.
.4 cu. ft.

Bureau of Publications

A0471 Publicity photograph negatives, 1942-1971.
8 cu. ft. (ca. 6,000 film negatives)

A4196 Subject index to publicity photograph negatives, ca. 1971.
.4 cu. ft.

B0426 Photographs, ca. 1900-1920.
.5 cu. ft.

Bureau of Mass Communications

B0498 Audio tapes, video tapes, and guides, 1967-1975.
12 cu. ft.

B0947 Videocassette of NBC TV's "Bicentennial Salute to New York",
1976.
.5 cu. ft. (2 video cassettes)

New York State School for the Blind

B0440 General ledger accounts, 1884-1898.
.5 cu. ft.

B0431 Ledger accounts, 1866-1868.
.5 cu. ft.

B0439 Ledger accounts of students, 1868-1877.
.5 cu. ft.

B0436 Ledger accounts of counties, 1873-1880.
.5 cu. ft.

B0438 Ledger accounts of supplies and special appropriations, 1896-
1898.
.5 cu. ft.

B0427 Daybooks, 1877-1881.
.5 cu. ft.

B0435	Journal accounts of students, 1873-1876. .5 cu. ft.
B0434	Treasurer's cash book, 1882-1888. .5 cu. ft.
B0429	Balance sheets, 1877-1880. .5 cu. ft.
B0428	Stock book, 1875-1877. .5 cu. ft.
B0441	Analysis of provision account, 1877-1894. .2 cu. ft. (1 volume)
B0437	Statements sent to the comptroller, 1875-1882. .5 cu. ft.
B0433	Annual report of accounts, 1901-1902. .5 cu. ft.
B0430	Inventory lists, 1881, 1885. .5 cu. ft.
B0432	Book lists, ca. 1900. .5 cu. ft.

New York State College of Agriculture and Life Sciences

B0926	Photographs and plans of Roberts Hall, East Roberts Hall, and Stone Hall, 1905-1985, bulk 1985. 1 cu. ft. (2 volumes and 19 mylar plans)

New York State College of Forestry at Syracuse University

B1067	Photographic display panels of college activities, ca. 1928. 3 cu. ft. (19 items)

Other Records

A3308	List of employees of the State Education Department, 1909. .2 cu. ft.
A3226	Applications from school districts for reimbursement for classroom equipment purchased, 1916-1924. 2 cu. ft.
14196	Financial and statistical data tables, 1918-1919. .2 cu. ft.

A3264   Sample blank financial and statistical reports required to be filed
         by local school officials, ca. 1919-1935.
         1 cu. ft.

A3247   School district enumeration lists and maps, 1930-1934.
         .4 cu. ft.

A0246   Nassau County school study files, 1950-1956.
         .8 cu. ft.

DEPARTMENT OF PUBLIC INSTRUCTION

Office of the Superintendent

04340   Incoming correspondence, 1852-1894, bulk 1854-1886.
         15.8 cu. ft.

A2000   Outgoing correspondence, 1854-1904.
         74 cu. ft. (349 volumes)

A2004   Subject files of correspondence received, 1849-1888.
         4.5 cu. ft.

A2006   Outgoing correspondence relating to the State Teachers' Library,
         1896-1900.
         .5 cu. ft. (1 volume)

A2016   Incoming correspondence relating to teacher certification, 1897-1904.
         1 cu. ft.

A2003   Telegrams received, 1868-1880.
         .5 cu. ft.

A2002   Registers of telegrams sent, 1869-1879.
         .5 cu. ft.

A2001   Teachers' institute registers of attendance and accounts of expens-
         es, 1859-1884.
         4 cu. ft.

A2032   List of normal school graduates, 1845-1904.
         .5 cu. ft. (1 volume)

A2031   Record of normal school local board members and employees,
         1864-1873.
         .5 cu. ft.

A2039   Lists of State pupils in institutions for the blind and deaf, 1846-1909.
2 cu. ft. (9 volumes)

A2036   Appointments of students to blind and deaf and dumb institutions, 1886-1904.
.5 cu. ft. (2 volumes)

A2038   Notice to local officials of appointments to blind and deaf and dumb institutions, 1890-1899.
.5 cu. ft. (2 volumes)

A2037   Term extension for State pupils in blind and deaf and dumb institutions, 1895-1904.
.5 cu. ft. (1 volume)

A2030   Appointments of employees to salaried positions, 1895-1901.
.5 cu. ft. (1 volume)

A2033   National Education Association Meeting attendance register, 1896.
.5 cu. ft. (2 volumes)

A2009   Draft of code of public instruction, 1897.
.5 cu. ft.

A2005   Affidavits relating to loss of teaching certificates, 1897-1904.
.5 cu. ft.

Bureau of Examinations

A4202   School commissioners' reports of teaching certificates issued, 1890-1901, bulk 1890-1896.
4 cu. ft. (12 volumes)

New York State Teachers' Library

A2008   List of books loaned to teachers, 1896-1900.
1 cu. ft. (2 volumes)

Other Records

A0300   Exhibits of public school student's work, 1888-1893.
ca. 10 cu. ft. (20 volumes, ca. 20 loose pages)

A2011   Richmond County school commissioner's incoming correspondence, 1887-1897.
.5 cu. ft.

A2010   Richmond County school commissioner's teacher certification records, 1893-1897.
.5 cu. ft. (1 volume)

State University of New York

Current Functions. The State University of New York (SUNY) provides a State-supported system of higher education for the citizens of the State. It accomplishes this through geographically dispersed college and university campuses offering degree and nondegree programs. SUNY offers traditional college curricula, specialized curricula in fields such as veterinary medicine and forestry, public service courses for State and local government officials, degree programs for full-time employed students, high school equivalency and college preparatory courses, and counseling and financial aid services for economically disadvantaged students.

Organizational History. State administration of higher education began in 1784 (Chapter 51) with the creation of the Board of Regents of The University of the State of New York to act as the governing body of Columbia College, which had been founded in 1754 as King's College. Three years later the Regents were relieved of direct operating responsibility for Columbia College and were authorized instead to charter and supervise it along with any new colleges and academies.

The growth of New York State's common school system in the early 19th century brought about a demand for trained teachers, resulting in the establishment of a tuition-free normal school in Albany in 1844 (Chapter 311). This was the first State-supported institution of higher learning in New York State.

Following passage of the Federal Morrill Land Grant College Act of 1862, under which each state received a grant of public land to provide an endowment for the establishment of colleges in the fields of agriculture and mechanical arts, the State legislature assigned New York's grant to a private institution called People's College, which had been chartered in 1853. That institution was unable to comply with certain financial requirements, and in 1865 (Chapter 585) the grant was shifted to Cornell University, which was incorporated by the same act. Cornell was required annually to admit and provide instruction free of charge to one student from each assembly district. This was the first instance, other than teacher training, in which the State assumed direct financial responsibility for higher education.

After an 1867 State law that required free common school education, increased demand for teachers resulted in the establishment of additional normal schools for training teachers. These schools were placed under the jurisdiction of the superintendent of public instruction. At the time of the creation of the State Education

Department in 1904 (Chapter 40), there were 12 normal schools and 78 private universities, colleges, and professional schools that came under the supervision of the Board of Regents and the new department. During the next 40 years, New York developed a State-supervised, decentralized network of private institutions augmented by 32 colleges that were largely State-supported. Among these were 11 colleges devoted to teacher education, the core of current colleges of arts and science; five institutes of applied arts and sciences, which later became community colleges; six agricultural and technical institutes (now colleges of agriculture and technology); and five statutory colleges, the administration of which is now shared with private institutions.

A shortage of facilities to meet the increased demand by returning World War II veterans for higher education, economic considerations making college education inaccessible to a large segment of the population. A lack of coordination between the many State-supported schools already operating, led to the establishment of a Temporary Commission on the Need for a State University in 1946 (Chapter 353). It was mandated to study the need for a State university and make appropriate recommendations. Two years later the commission proposed the establishment of a State university with units located throughout the State.

The State University of New York was established as a corporate entity in the State Education Department under the Board of Regents of The University of the State of New York in 1948 (Chapters 695 and 698). (See the entry for State Education Department.) Existing State-supported institutions became part of the State University, which was administered by a 15-member board of trustees appointed by the governor. Although certain policy issues such as curriculum, standards of instruction, the establishment of new SUNY entities, and tuition rates had to be submitted to the Board of Regents for approval, the SUNY trustees were given broad authority and responsibility, including a specific charge to develop a master plan to serve as a long-range planning guide. The master plan, adopted by the trustees in 1950, established the pattern of a centrally managed system of geographically dispersed two-year, four-year, and graduate institutions.

In the 1950s, the Upstate and Downstate medical centers (now the Health Science Centers at Syracuse and Brooklyn) were established; the Research Foundation of the State University of New York was chartered by the Board of Regents in 1951 to receive and administer gifts, grants, and contracts for the State University. Legislation in 1953 (Chapter 525) provided for 9-member (later 10-member) local councils to supervise the State-operated colleges. That same year, the Middle States Association accredited the State University as a single institution. During the 1960s the single-purpose teachers colleges were reshaped into strong liberal arts institutes; four major university centers, offering graduate study, were established; an entirely new health sciences center was founded; and a framework for the present 30 locally sponsored community colleges was set into place. The SUNY board of trustees was increased in number to 16 in 1975 (Chapter 587) with the addition of the president of the State University Student Assembly.

The current State University of New York is a system of sixty-four campuses enrolling more than 378,000 students. The components of the SUNY system, the largest of its kind in the country, are 4 university centers offering a range of under-graduate and graduate programs; 5 colleges and centers for the health sciences (two of which are located at university centers); 12 colleges of arts and sciences offering liberal arts and teacher-training programs at the undergraduate and graduate level; 6 agricultural and technical colleges offering two-year programs; four specialized colleges (College of Environmental Science and Forestry, Maritime College, College of Technology, and Fashion Institute of Technology); 5 statutory colleges operated as "contract colleges" on the campuses of private universities (College of Agriculture and Life Sciences, College of Ceramics, College of Human Ecology, School of Industrial and Labor Relations, College of Veterinary Medicine); and 30 community colleges offering two-year degree programs. In addition, SUNY includes the Empire State College, a nonresidential college of arts and sciences that allows students working at home or on the job to pursue degree programs. SUNY also operates nine educational opportunity centers, which offer vocational, high-school equivalency, and college-preparatory courses.

No records in the State Archives

Department of Environmental Conservation

Current Functions. The Department of Environmental Conservation is responsible for protecting and enhancing the State's natural resources. It carries out this responsibility by planning for and regulating disposal of solid and hazardous wastes, remediating hazardous-waste disposal sites, coordinating responses to hazardous-substance spill emergencies, and encouraging recycling of solid wastes; reducing air contamination and regulating emissions; controlling and managing fish and wildlife populations for recreational and ecological benefits; managing the Adirondack and Catskill forest preserves and other forest lands, and assisting private forest landowners in forest management and fire prevention and control; managing marine and coastal resources; overseeing and protecting wetlands, floodplains, and rivers; promoting wise use of water resources; monitoring environmental conditions, testing for contaminants, and providing for the abatement of pollution; regulating mining, reclamation of mined lands, extraction of oil and gas, and storage of natural gas; regulating use of pesticides; and informing the public on environmental conservation principles and encouraging public participation in environmental affairs.

Organizational History. Creation of the Department of Environmental Conservation in 1970 (Chapter 140) was preceded by over a century of State conservation activity carried out by a number of agencies. The first, a three-member Fisheries Commission was established in 1868 (Chapter 285) to restore and protect the propagation of fish in the State's rivers, lakes, and streams. A three-member Forest Commission was established in 1885 (Chapter 283) to maintain and protect land in the Catskill and Adirondack mountains to be designated as a State forest preserve and to protect public interests in the State relating to forests, tree planting, and forest fires. This board was abolished by a law of 1893 (Chapter 332) establishing a new five-member Forest Commission with the same duties.

In 1895 (Chapter 395), the Fisheries Commission and Forest Commission were combined into a Fisheries, Game, and Forest Commission headed by five gubernatorial appointees. This commission was renamed the Forest, Fish and Game Commission in 1900 (Chapter 20) and after 1903 was headed by one commissioner. In 1906 (Chapter 199) the commission was authorized to employ a counsel to represent them in legal actions brought under provisions of the forest, fish, and game law.

Other laws further regulated State lands, including one in 1897 (Chapter 220) creating the Forest Preserve Board to acquire additional land for the State.

A Water Storage Commission consisting of five gubernatorial appointees, the superintendent of public works, the forest, fish and game commissioner, the State engineer and surveyor, and the attorney general was established in 1902 (Chapter 406) to investigate and report on the State's water supply. This was followed in 1905 (Chapter 723) by a five-member Water Supply Commission established to administer a systematic plan for maintaining water supplies for the State's municipalities. This commission absorbed the River Improvement Commission established the previous year (Laws of 1904, Chapter 734). The functions and powers of the Water Supply Commission, Forest Preserve Board, and Forest, Fish, and Game Commission were combined in 1911 (Chapter 657) to form the Conservation Commission. The commission was headed by three commissioners in charge of divisions of lands and forests, fish and game, and inland waters.

In 1921 (Chapter 579), a Water Power Commission, consisting of the three conservation commissioners, the State engineer and surveyor, the attorney general, the temporary president of the senate, and the speaker of the assembly, was established to issue licenses for the development of State power resources. A Water Control Commission was established in 1922 (Chapter 413) to supervise water flow and supply and to administer the Black River and Hudson River regulating districts.

After the 1925 constitutional reorganization of State government, enabling legislation in 1926 (Chapter 619) established the Conservation Department to assume the functions and duties of the Conservation Commission, Water Control Commission, and Water Power Commission, all of which were abolished. The new department included a Division of Parks, which supervised all State parks, reservations, historic sites, and recreational areas (except the forest preserve).

When the Department of Environmental Conservation was established in 1970, it assumed all functions of the Conservation Department except administration of State parks, which was transferred to the new Office of Parks and Recreation in the Executive Department. In addition, the Department of Environmental Conservation assumed primary responsibility for State policy relating to air and water pollution, waste management, and pesticide use, areas formerly supervised by the Department of Health and the Department of Agriculture and Markets. The Air Pollution Control

Board, Water Resources Board, Pesticide Control Board, and Natural Beauty Commission, all formerly within other State agencies, were abolished and their functions assumed by the Department of Environmental Conservation.

The commissioner of the Department is also an ex officio member and chair of the New York State Environmental Facilities Corporation, established in 1970 as a public-benefit corporation to assist State agencies and local governments in environmental management projects and to provide financing for pollution control facilities. The commissioner is also an ex officio member of numerous other commissions, authorities, boards, and committees.

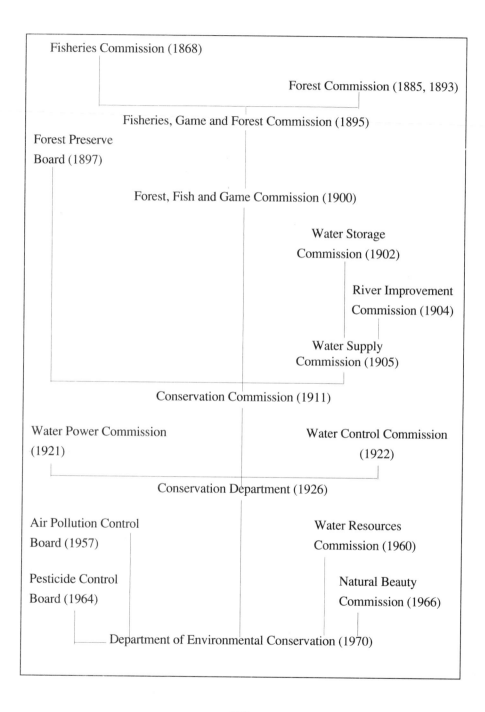

Fisheries Commission (1868)

Forest Commission (1885, 1893)

Fisheries, Game and Forest Commission (1895)

Forest Preserve
Board (1897)

Forest, Fish and Game Commission (1900)

Water Storage
Commission (1902)

River Improvement
Commission (1904)

Water Supply
Commission (1905)

Conservation Commission (1911)

Water Power Commission
(1921)

Water Control Commission
(1922)

Conservation Department (1926)

Air Pollution Control
Board (1957)

Water Resources
Commission (1960)

Pesticide Control
Board (1964)

Natural Beauty
Commission (1966)

Department of Environmental Conservation (1970)

DEPARTMENT OF ENVIRONMENTAL CONSERVATION

General Agency-level Records

15496   Department policies and procedures manual, 1973-1984.
.2 cu. ft.

Executive Office

13063   Commissioners' and deputy commissioners' correspondence, subject files, and orders, 1952-1987.
596 cu. ft.

Office of Counsel

10407   Water pollution control case files, 1929-1973, bulk 1954-1973.
4 cu. ft.

Bureau of Environmental Quality Review

15804   State environmental quality review (SEQRA) repository positive declaration files, 1978-1980.
15 cu. ft.

Office of Program Development, Planning and Research

10770   Hurricane Agnes damage files, 1972-1973.
2 cu. ft.

Division of Law Enforcement

15122   Winter Olympics security files, 1979-1980.
3 cu. ft.

Division of Fish and Wildlife

A0743   Freshwater wetlands inventory maps, 1973-1975.
40 cu. ft. (971 maps)

Division of Water

A1117   Statewide sewage disposal and pollution control files, ca. 1900-1975.
177 cu. ft.

A1121   State and federal institution wastewater disposal files, ca. 1900-1975.
5 cu. ft.

A1123   State park and campsite wastewater disposal files, ca. 1925-1976.
2 cu. ft.

A1122   Pure waters files, ca. 1951-1975.
2 cu. ft.

A1118   Interstate basin commission administration files, ca. 1948-1975, bulk 1957-1975.
18 cu. ft.

A1120   Drainage basin subject files, ca. 1904-1977, bulk 1950-1975.
34 cu. ft.

Division of Air Resources

– Bureau of Abatement Planning

15491   State implementation plan planning files, 1972-1987.
9 cu. ft.

CONSERVATION DEPARTMENT

14297   Photographic prints and negatives, 1904-1949.
46.3 cu. ft.

A3268   Civilian Conservation Corps camp and personnel files, 1935-1942.
2.1 cu. ft. R

Executive Office

B1004   Index to department orders, 1911-1930.
4.5 cu. ft.

Division of Pure Waters

A1119   Interstate water quality standards files, ca. 1965-1968.
1 cu. ft.

CONSERVATION COMMISSION

A0280   Assessment rolls of towns in which the State owns land, 1886-1921.
51 cu. ft.

ADIRONDACK MOUNTAIN AUTHORITY

11263   Legal and administrative files, 1957-1968.
2 cu. ft.

WATER SUPPLY COMMISSION

B0242   Reports to or by the commission regarding the Genesee River Improvement, 1904-1911.
.3 cu. ft.

B0917   Sacandaga Reservoir proposed flow line maps, ca. 1908-1912, bulk 1908.
3 cu. ft. (49 maps)

WATER POWER COMMISSION

A4219   American Super-Power Corporation license application maps and drawings, 1922-1923.
.5 cu. ft. (1 volume)

Department of Health

Current Functions. The Department of Health is responsible for safeguarding the health of New York State's residents. The department has direct authority over all health care institutions in the State covered by the Public Health Law, including hospitals, nursing homes, diagnostic and treatment centers, and many home-care providers. To protect the welfare of patients, the State certifies all health care institutions and sets standards governing nearly every aspect of health-facility operation. The department administers programs to monitor the cost of health care services. In carrying out these mandates, the department develops reimbursement methods and sets the rate each health facility will be paid for services to patients covered by Medicaid. It also audits health care facility costs and fees, and reviews the financial implications of health-facility construction and expansion. Finally, the department is responsible for statewide planning to assure that State health care resources are efficiently allocated.

The department is responsible for preserving the health of New York State's residents through education, research, and prevention of accidents and diseases. Programs administered by the department range from prenatal care and teen counseling to monitoring the purity of drinking water and assessing the health threat of toxic contaminants. Research is another major function of the department. Clinical, laboratory, and epidemiological studies are focused on such public health problems as birth defects, health staffing needs, and cancer. Other research efforts aim to improve laboratory testing methods.

The department monitors skilled health professionals throughout the State and identifies underserved areas for training support programs. It also oversees the medical conduct of physicians and takes disciplinary action against individuals who violate medical professional law.

The Department of Health is responsible for maintaining records of every birth, death, marriage, and divorce that occurs in the State, and for operation of an adoption registry. The department operates three health institutions: Roswell Park Center Institute in Buffalo, a cancer care and research facility; the Veterans Home in Oxford, a residential long-term-care facility; and Helen Hayes Hospital in West Haverstraw, a medical rehabilitation and research facility.

Organizational History. In the colonial and early statehood periods, public health issues were handled by localities, if addressed at all. On a few occasions, the legislature was involved in establishing quarantine regulations, particularly for New York City. In 1832, the legislature required all port cities, villages, and villages along the canal to appoint health officers and establish health boards. A more general public health law was passed in 1850, requiring all towns, villages, and cities (except the cities of New York and Brooklyn) to set up health boards and designate public health officers. These officials were responsible for regulating local sanitary conditions and providing for the control and prevention of contagious diseases.

A State Board of Health was created in 1880 (Chapter 322) to undertake a variety of health-related activities, including researching diseases and their causes; promoting public health; supervising the registration of vital statistics; and investigating the effect of localities, employment, and other conditions on public health. These responsibilities were strengthened and expanded in 1885 (Chapter 270) as the State board was mandated to report on the incidence of certain infectious or epidemic diseases, to investigate complaints of health threats made by citizens, and to issue orders or regulations on health issues and impose penalties for violations.

In 1901 (Chapter 24), the State Board of Health was replaced by a Department of Health, headed by a commissioner appointed by the governor. In addition to assuming the duties of the State Board of Health, the department was responsible for inspecting public structures and works, hearing complaints regarding health problems stemming from Canal water overflow, and exercising the powers of a local board of health in communities where none existed. A Public Health Council, consisting of the commissioner of health and six gubernatorial appointees, was established in 1913 (Chapter 559). It was charged with establishing and maintaining the Sanitary Code, which dealt with any matter affecting the security of life or health, and the preservation and improvement of public health.

The Department of Health was continued following the 1925-26 reorganization of State government, with the addition of jurisdiction over the Institute for the Study of Malignant Diseases (later renamed Roswell Park Memorial Institute), which had been established in 1911 for the study and treatment of cancer and allied diseases. In addition, the department was given responsibility for establishing and maintaining hospitals for specific diseases. As a result, in 1931 the department assumed responsibility from the Department of Social Welfare for the supervision of the Raybrook Hospital for Treatment of Incipient Pulmonary Tuberculosis (established in 1900 and closed in 1970), and the Women's Relief Corps Home, transferred from the Department of Social Services in 1971. The Department of Health also operated the Kidney Disease Institute (established 1965), the Birth Defects Institute (established in 1966), and the Burns Care Institute (established 1970).

In 1960, a State Hospital Review and Planning Council, consisting of thirty-one members appointed by the governor, was established to cooperate with regional hospital councils in reviewing applications for the construction of new hospital facilities and insuring that hospital services are adequate in all areas of the State. This council was directed to make reports and recommendations to the commissioner of health, the Public Health Council, and the Health Planning Committee. The latter was an interdepartmental body created by Executive Order in 1975 to advise the governor on health policy matters, and was dissolved in 1985.

When the Department of Environmental Conservation was created in 1970, it assumed from the Department of Health the primary responsibility for monitoring and regulating water and air pollution and waste management. The Department of Health remains responsible for assessing the health consequences of such contaminants.

In 1977, the Department of Health was reorganized into two major offices: the

Office of Health Systems Management and the Office of Public Health. The Office of Health Systems Management was assigned all regulatory activities including the delivery of health care by institutions and individual providers. The Office of Public Health assumed responsibility for all traditional public health activities including research, disease control, and coordination of local public health activities.

The AIDS Institute was established in 1983 within the department to develop public policy and administer State-funded research, education, and support services related to AIDS. The New York State Task Force on Life and the Law was created in 1984 to evaluate ethical, legal, and public-policy implications stemming from major advances in medical science and technology.

DEPARTMENT OF HEALTH

General Agency-level Records

11460	Sewage treatment works construction planning grants files, ca. 1942-1963. 15 cu. ft.

Commissioner's Office

13307	Subject files, 1952-1989. 164 cu. ft.
B1072	Transcripts of public hearings on medical services regulatory policies, 1969-1971. .5 cu. ft. (4 volumes)

Executive Deputy Commissioner

B1214	Subject files, 1974-1987. 69 cu. ft.

Office of Legal Affairs

B1335	Legislative bill files and correspondence and opinions of the attorney general, 1890-1959. 49 cu. ft.

Office of Counsel

10407	Water pollution control case files, 1929-1973. 4 cu. ft.

Office of Public Health

16570   Subject files, 1969-1987.
         8 cu. ft.

Division of Communicable Diseases

B0290   Reports of contagious diseases from local boards of health, 1907-
         1914.
         .5 cu. ft. (8 volumes)

B0167   Smallpox case report cards, 1922-1947, bulk 1922-1939.
         1 cu. ft. R

Bureau of Acute Communicable Disease Control

B0163   Poliomyelitis case report cards, 1915-1974, bulk 1915-1961.
         6.5 cu. ft. R

Bureau of Communicable Disease Control

13855   Director's subject files, 1908-1982, bulk 1975-1982.
         14 cu. ft.

B0162   Tuberculosis reporting cards, 1939-1975.
         10 cu. ft. R

B0168   Typhoid fever positive lab reports, ca. 1956-1969.
         .5 cu. ft. R

B0165   Deceased and released typhoid carriers case files, 1919-1976.
         3.5 cu. ft. R

10415   Tuberculosis hospital policy and administration files, 1905-1975.
         6 cu. ft.

Bureau of Tuberculosis Control

10416   General hospital admission chest x-ray program administrative
         files, 1934-1973, bulk 1946-1966.
         4 cu. ft.

Bureau of Epidemiology and Communicable Disease Control

B0164   Typhoid fever case report cards, 1914-1954.
         5.5. cu. ft. R

B1068   Typhoid fever carriers case control cards, 1918-1953.
         1 cu. ft. (1,675 index cards) R

Bureau of Epidemiology

> B0166   Typhoid fever case investigation files, 1959-1971.
> 1 cu. ft. R

Bureau of Funeral Directing

> 14333   Registers of embalmers' and undertakers' licenses, 1899-1927.
> .6 cu. ft.

Division of Laboratories and Research

> 14600   Central administrative files for laboratory and research activities,
> 1895-1950.
> 112 cu. ft. R

> B1336   Case reports on use of state-provided antibacterial and antiviral
> sera, 1902-1968.
> 16 cu. ft. R

Division of Maternity, Infancy, and Child Hygiene

> A0774   Record of Sheppard-Towner funds, 1923-1924.
> .3 cu. ft. (1 volume)

Division of Public Health Education

> B1059   Educational motion picture, ca. 1965.
> .2 cu. ft.

> B1070   "Empire county" electrical transcription disks, 1949-1958.
> 9.9 cu. ft.

Bureau of Hospital Certification

> 10579   Director's State hospital code correspondence files, 1966-1971.
> 1 cu. ft.

Bureau of Communications Production

> – Photography Unit

> 14655   Photographic prints and negatives of department officials, facili-
> ties, and activities, ca. 1920-1983.
> 41.4 cu. ft.

Departmental Committee on Rehabilitation

> 10775   Reports, memoranda, and minutes, 1960-1961.
> .2 cu. ft.

Bureau of Nutrition

15483   Supplemental nutrition assistance program homeless/destitute
         files, 1985-1987.
         5 cu. ft.

Other Records

12205   Reports of pollutants discharged into State waterways by shop,
         factory, mill or industrial establishments, 1903.
         2.5 cu. ft.

B1074   Register of licensed midwives, 1914-1962.
         .6 cu. ft.

A0794   Journal of accounts, 1917-1922.
         1.5 cu. ft. (7 volumes)

A0778   Ledger of expenditures of accounts, 1918-1920.
         .3 cu. ft. (1 volume)

A0772   Accounts of expenditures for fighting the influenza epidemic,
         1920-1921.
         .3 cu. ft. (1 volume)

A3273   Subject and correspondence files of Dr. H. Jackson Davis, ca.
         1920-1938.
         25 cu. ft.

A3269   Photographs of Health Department offices and employees, 1924.
         .3 cu. ft.

B1337   Files on milk-borne disease outbreaks, 1939-1942.
         .2 cu. ft.

A3270   Motion picture photograph, release, and script files, ca. 1955-1965.
         2 cu. ft.

A0792   Hospital certification and oversight files, ca. 1965-1975.
         18 cu. ft.

A0783   Correspondence relating to State hospital code, 1965-1977.
         2.5 cu. ft.

BOARD OF HEALTH

A0769   Minutes, 1880-1899.
         1 cu. ft.

A0770   Secretary's log of transactions, 1880-1882.
.3 cu. ft. (1 volume)

A0779   Account books, 1880-1901.
1 cu. ft. (6 volumes)

A3310   Index to letters, 1892-1893.
.3 cu. ft.

PUBLIC HEALTH COUNCIL

10740   Public Health Council and Establishment Committee meeting agendas and minutes, 1913-1985.
75 cu. ft.

HEALTH PLANNING COMMISSION

12983   Chairperson's and executive director's subject files, 1973-1986.
14 cu. ft. R

A0738   Subject files, 1975-1977.
5.5 cu. ft.

STATE HOSPITAL REVIEW AND PLANNING COUNCIL

13055   Meeting agendas and minutes, 1960-1986.
57 cu. ft.

STATEWIDE HEALTH COORDINATING COUNCIL

14639   Subject files, 1977-1986.
4 cu. ft.

INTERDEPARTMENTAL HEALTH AND HOSPITAL COUNCIL

B1113   Minutes and reports, 1959-1969.
4 cu. ft.

INTERDEPARTMENTAL HEALTH RESOURCES BOARD
Committee on Rehabilitation

    B1112   Minutes and reports, 1956-1959.
                1 cu. ft.

NUTRITION WATCH COMMITTEE

    B1073   Meeting agendas, minutes, and briefing books, 1982.
                1 cu. ft.

NEW YORK CITY REGIONAL INTERDEPARTMENTAL REHABILITATION COMMITTEE

    B1114   Minutes and correspondence, 1964-1970.
                2 cu. ft.

NEW YORK STATE HOSPITAL FOR THE TREATMENT OF INCIPIENT PULMONARY TUBERCULOSIS (RAYBROOK, N.Y.)

    A0703   Patient admission application books, 1932-1942.
                .5 cu. ft. (2 volumes)

NEW YORK STATE VETERANS' HOME AT OXFORD

    A0710   Admission case files, 1897-1963.
                57 cu. ft. R

BLUE RIBBON PANEL ON MUNICIPAL HOSPITALS OF NEW YORK CITY

    B1202   Transcripts of proceedings, 1966-1967.
                .5 cu. ft. (5 volumes)

Insurance Department

Current Functions. The Insurance Department is responsible for supervising and regulating all insurance business in New York State. It carries out its supervisory function by issuing licenses to agents, brokers, consultants, reinsurance intermediaries, adjusters, and bail bondsmen; conducting examinations of insurers to determine their financial condition, treatment of policyholders and claimants, and underwriting practices; and auditing each company's annual reports.

The department carries out its regulatory function by determining qualifications of insurers; regulating rates, certain retirement systems and pension funds; reviewing of policyholders' complaints; supervising the liquidation, rehabilitation, and conservation of insolvent insurers; and approving corporate formations, mergers, and consolidations.

Organizational History. Until 1849, insurance companies doing business in New York State were chartered by special acts of the legislature. A law passed that year (Chapter 308) required prospective insurance companies to file incorporation papers with the secretary of state. The law also vested regulatory power over insurance companies with the comptroller, who was authorized to require the companies to submit annual financial statements and to deny a company the right to operate if capital securities and investments did not remain secure.

The Insurance Department was created in 1859 (Chapter 366) and assumed the functions of the comptroller and secretary of state relating to insurance. The department was headed by a superintendent appointed by the governor. The agency continued unchanged after the 1925 constitutional reorganization of State government (Laws of 1926, Chapter 353).

INSURANCE DEPARTMENT

General Agency-level Records

14394	Superintendent's subject files, 1935-1970. 92 cu. ft.
13877	First deputy superintendent's subject files, 1959-1966. 15 cu. ft.
B0124	Deputy superintendent's subject files, 1959-1965. 15 cu. ft.
A0617	Rulings, opinions, decisions, and reports, 1867-1951, bulk 1900-1925. 1.3 cu. ft.

14361   Annual financial statements of insurance companies, 1866-1984.
             1,154.5 cu. ft.

B1301   Annual financial statements of cooperative fire insurance compa-
             nies, 1909-1984.
             77.6 cu. ft.

B0161   Annual financial statements of employee welfare funds, 1966.
             11 cu. ft.

Corporate Affairs Bureau

14591   Charters and bylaws of active foreign and alien insurance compa-
             nies, ca. 1860-1986.
             22 cu. ft.

Department of Labor

Current Functions. The Department of Labor is responsible for enforcing the
State Labor Law and the rules and regulations issued to protect, assist, and educate
the work force. The department executes the State's labor statutes which were
designed to improve working conditions; broaden employment opportunities through
a statewide employment service; ensure payment of wages and fringe benefits to construction workers and certain service employees on State or municipal work; provide
unemployment, workers' compensation, and disability benefits; foster peaceful labor-
management relations; protect the health and safety of public and certain other
employees; and encourage development of sound apprenticeship training programs.

The department conducts research into labor problems; compiles, analyzes, and
disseminates statistics and other information regarding its activities; and appoints
boards or committees needed to help execute State labor policy.

Organizational History. New York State's official involvement in labor issues
began in 1883 when the Bureau of Labor Statistics was created (Chapter 356) to
gather information and prepare an annual statistical report on the State's labor force.
The State began regulatory activity in labor and industrial affairs in 1886 (Chapter
409) with the establishment of the Office of Factory Inspector (expanded to the
Department of Factory Inspection in 1887) to enforce laws regulating employment of
children in factories, and the Board of Mediation and Arbitration, to assist in the settlement of labor disputes.

These three units were combined in 1901 (Chapter 9) to form the Department of Labor, headed by a commissioner. Two new divisions, the Bureau of Mercantile Inspection and the Bureau of Industries and Immigration, were added to the department in 1909.

The independent office of State fire marshal was established in 1911 (Chapter 451) to enforce laws relating to prevention of fires, use of combustibles and explosives, and availability of fire alarms and fire extinguishers. This office also conducted inspections of steam boilers, regulated fire escapes, and investigated causes of fires.

In 1913 (Chapter 145), the Industrial Board, consisting of the commissioner of labor as chair and four gubernatorial appointees, was created within the Department of Labor to issue and interpret rules and regulations known as Industrial Code Rules. These rules established standards for the health and safety of employees. Another 1913 law created an independent Workmen's Compensation Commission to ensure payment of compensation to disabled employees and set up the State Insurance Fund, administered by the commission, to insure employers against liability.

A law of 1915 (Chapter 674) reorganized the Department of Labor, replacing the commissioner of labor with a five-member Industrial Commission appointed by the governor. The commission headed the Department of Labor and assumed responsibilities formerly exercised by the Industrial Board, the Workmen's Compensation Commission, and the State fire marshal, which were abolished. In addition, an Industrial Council composed of ten gubernatorial appointees was created to provide advice to the Industrial Commission.

Another reorganization in 1921 (Chapter 50) replaced the Industrial Commission with a single industrial commissioner and established a three-member Industrial Board to issue, amend, and interpret the Industrial Code Rules and to review and determine claims in workers' compensation cases. This departmental structure was reestablished by law in the 1925-26 reorganization of State government.

Labor legislation of 1935 and 1936, including the Unemployment Insurance Law of 1935 (Chapter 468), providing for payment of benefits to eligible unemployed workers, resulted in additional restructuring. A Division of Unemployment Insurance was established within the department to administer the Unemployment Insurance Law. The department's jurisdiction in workers' compensation matters was extended to cover occupational diseases. Its regulatory powers over industrial homework were expanded to the entire State (formerly its jurisdiction was confined to cities of over 200,000 people).

Several laws of 1937 changed the administrative structure of the department. A newly established Board of Standards and Appeals assumed the functions of the Industrial Board in regard to industrial code matters, and the Industrial Board became concerned exclusively with workers' compensation matters. A Labor Relations Board was established to supervise labor-management relations, and a State Board of Mediation was set up to mediate settlements in labor disputes.

In 1938, the State Insurance Fund was removed from the direct administrative jurisdiction of the industrial commissioner, who continued to serve as an ex officio member of the newly created Board of Commissioners of the State Insurance Fund. An Unemployment Insurance Appeal Board was established in 1944 to hear appeals from claimants or employers dissatisfied with departmental administrative determinations under the unemployment insurance programs mandated by 1935 and subsequent legislation.

In 1945, the Industrial Board was replaced by a 10-member Workmen's Compensation Board, which was renamed the Workers' Compensation Board in 1971. The Board of Standards and Appeals was renamed the Industrial Board of Appeals in 1971.

The department administers certain programs under federal legislation, such as the Job Training Partnership Act of 1983, which provides localities with federal funds for employment training.

DEPARTMENT OF LABOR

Executive Office

     15381   Commissioner's subject files, ca. 1917-1988.
               507 cu. ft. R

Industrial Commissioner

     B0324   Speech files, 1959-1970.
               7 cu. ft.

     B0322   Bureau of Public Work wage claim case files, 1960-1968.
               1 cu. ft.

     B0308   Boards of Inquiry files dealing with strikes, 1963-1969, bulk 1964-1966.
               1 cu. ft.

Division of Employment

> 15382   Executive Director's subject files, 1938-1972.
> 87 cu. ft.

> B1343   Administrative Assistant's subject files, 1939-1972.
> 19 cu. ft.

Division of Industrial Hygiene

> B1347   Subject and correspondence files, 1933-1976.
> 5 cu. ft. R

> 16089   Occupational health investigation files, 1942-1975.
> 149 cu. ft. R

> B1348   Special occupational health studies research files, 1942-1973.
> 16 cu. ft. R

> B1346   Medical reference file, 1929-1973.
> 7 cu. ft. R

STATE MEDIATION BOARD

> B0307   Strike case files, 1965-1975.
> 5.5 cu. ft.

STATE INSURANCE FUND

Actuarial Division

> A0030   Aggregate Trust Fund deposit lists, 1948-1965.
> .3 cu. ft. (5 volumes)

FIRE MARSHAL

> B0820   Incoming correspondence from inspectors, 1912.
> .2 cu. ft.

> B0821   Incoming correspondence identifying persons convicted and suspected of arson, 1913.
> .2 cu. ft.

> A4257   Register of correspondence received, 1913-1914.
> .1 cu. ft. (3 volumes)

A4258   Register of correspondence sent, 1911-1912.
.1 cu. ft. (1 volume)

A4255   Current accounts ledger, 1912-1914.
.1 cu. ft. (2 volumes)

A4248   Appropriations ledger, 1912-1915.
.1 cu. ft. (1 volume)

A4247   Expenditure analysis ledger, 1913-1914.
.5 cu. ft. (1 volume)

A4260   Cashbooks for official salaries and graded employees, 1911-1913.
.1 cu. ft. (2 volumes)

A4259   Travel expense accounts ledger, 1911-1912.
.1 cu. ft. (1 volume)

A4261   Accounts ledger for fires reported, 1912-1914.
.1 cu. ft. (1 volume)

B0842   Bills for expenditures, 1912-1913.
.3 cu. ft.

A4264   Statements of expenditures filed by local investigators, 1912-1915.
2 cu. ft.

B0835   Bank account book for State fire marshal magazine, 1912-1914.
.1 cu. ft.

B0838   Check book for magazine account, 1912-1913.
.1 cu. ft. (1 volume)

B0836   Bank account book for State fire marshal boiler fund, 1912.
.1 cu. ft.

B0839   Check book for boiler account, 1913-1915.
.1 cu. ft. (1 volume)

B0818   Inspector's weekly summaries, 1914.
.2 cu. ft.

A4262   Register of fires investigated, 1911-1912.
.1 cu. ft. (1 volume)

A4252   Register of investigations for fires of suspicious origin, 1912-1914.
.1 cu. ft. (1 volume)

A4249   Index to register of fires of suspicious origin, 1912-1914.
.1 cu. ft. (1 volume)

A4254   Register of inspections, 1912-1915.
.1 cu. ft. (1 volume)

A4253   Register of non-violation inspections, 1912-1913.
.1 cu. ft. (1 volume)

A4250   Violations register, 1911-1913.
2 cu. ft. (2 volumes)

B0817   Inspector's reports on investigations, 1911-1914.
1 cu. ft.

A4251   Complaint register, 1912-1913.
.1 cu. ft. (1 volume)

A4246   Register of approved plans and specifications, 1912-1913.
.1 cu. ft. (1 volume)

B0832   List of members of various fire companies, 1912-1915.
.3 cu. ft.

Workers' Compensation Board/State Insurance Fund

Current Functions. Workers' compensation insurance provides weekly cash payments and the cost of full medical treatment, including rehabilitation, for covered employees who become disabled as a result of a disease or injury connected with their employment. It also provides payments for qualified dependents of a worker who dies from a compensable injury or illness.

In administering this program, the Workers' Compensation Board receives and processes workers' claims for benefits, employers' reports of injury, and medical reports from physicians and other health care providers. The board adjudicates and resolves all issues and makes awards and findings as rapidly as possible to ensure that an entitled claimant receives benefits and medical treatment promptly. Hearings are conducted before law judges, or, on review or appeal, before panels of three board members.

The supplementary responsibilities of the Workers' Compensation Program include the authorization and rating of physicians to treat compensation cases, licensing of medical bureaus, and the arbitration of disputed medical and hospital bills. The board also processes applications for self-insurance of corporate entities and political subdivisions and supervises and controls their performance.

Organizational History. The Workmen's Compensation Commission was established under the Workmen's Compensation Act of 1913 (Chapter 816), requiring employers to compensate employees disabled by industrial accidents or occupational diseases. Employers subject to the provisions of the Workmen's Compensation Act were required to establish a self-insurance program, to provide disability insurance through a commercial carrier, or to contribute to the State Insurance Fund, which was also established in 1913. The commission, comprised of five gubernatorial appointees and the commissioner of labor, administered the law, including arbitration of claims settlements between employers and employees, and collection, maintenance, and distribution of the State Insurance Fund.

The Workmen's Compensation Commission was abolished in 1915 and the five-member Industrial Commission, which began heading the newly reorganized Department of Labor, assumed its responsibilities. When the department was again reorganized in 1921, the Industrial Commission was replaced by an industrial commissioner, who became responsible for administration of the State Insurance Fund, and a three-member Industrial Board reviewed all compensation cases.

In 1945 (Chapter 74), responsibility for review of workers' compensation cases was transferred from the Industrial Board to a Workmen's Compensation Board located within the Department of Labor. This board, renamed the Workers' Compensation Board in 1971, is comprised of 13 gubernatorial appointees, 1 of whom is named by the governor as chair. Since 1945 the board has administered and adjudicated claims for the steadily expanding coverage required by law to be provided to workers. The 1949 Disability Benefits Law (Chapter 600) provided for benefits for workers suffering disabilities resulting from nonoccupational injuries or illnesses. The 1951 Workmen's Compensation Act for Civil Defense Volunteers (Chapter 788) and the 1956 Volunteer Firefighters' Benefit Law (Chapter 696) provided for coverage for these volunteer workers. Effective January 1, 1989, the Volunteer Ambulance Workers' Benefit Law provided cash payments for all volunteer ambulance workers injured in the line of duty and for all necessary medical care. The board began its vocational rehabilitation program for injured workers in 1959. By 1962, all employers, including single-employee firms, were required to provide worker's compensation and disability benefits protection.

No records in the State Archives

Department of Law

Current Functions. The Department of Law protects the legal rights of New York State citizens by representing the State in all of its litigation and other legal affairs. It carries out this responsibility by prosecuting or defending all actions and proceedings for or against the State and its departments; prosecuting certain criminal violations of the Labor Law, Workers' Compensation Law, and Unemployment Insurance Law; investigating and prosecuting other criminal cases at the request of the governor or the commissioner of a State department; bringing civil/criminal actions against polluters of the environment, violators of the antitrust laws, and those who defraud consumers or investors; mediating consumers' complaints; and defending the legal and civil rights of New Yorkers.

Organizational History. The earliest predecessor to this department was the Dutch colonial office of schout-fiscal, which combined the functions of auditor, sheriff, and attorney general. Later, British colonial authorities appointed an attorney general as chief law enforcement officer of New York.

The first State constitution in 1777 created the office of attorney general, to be selected by the Council of Appointment. The constitution of 1821 transferred this appointment function to the legislature, and the constitution of 1846 made the office elective on a biennial basis. A 1937 constitutional amendment extended the term of elective office to four years.

The constitutional reorganization of State government in 1925 authorized creation of a Department of Law. Enabling legislation in 1926 (Chapter 347) established the department, transferred to it all powers previously exercised by the attorney general, and made the attorney general chief administrative officer of the department.

DEPARTMENT OF LAW

General Agency-level Records

A0536 Construction photographs of the Alfred E. Smith State Office Building, 1927-1928.
.3 cu. ft. (1 volume)

Legislative Bureau

15433 Legislative program bill files, 1985-1986.
12 cu. ft.

Office of Special Prosecutor

16104 Executive files, 1967-1990.
106 cu. ft. R

16012 Background and investigation files of the New York City Commission to Investigate Allegations of Police Corruption and the City's Anti-Corruption Procedures, 1960-1975.
63 cu. ft. R

ATTORNEY GENERAL'S OFFICE

B0609 Letter books, 1842-1844, 1872-1873.
.5 cu. ft. (4 volumes)

B0900 Correspondence and legal documentation relating to land sales, 1770-1906.
37.5 cu. ft.

B0908 Daily journals from the office of the attorney general, 1883-1891.
.6 cu. ft. (7 volumes)

B0611 Index to attorney general's cases, 1876-ca. 1900.
.5 cu. ft. (3 volumes)

B0909 Index to office registers, 1884.
.2 cu. ft. (1 volume)

B0907 Case status registers, 1882-1890.
1.5 cu. ft. (11 volumes)

B0606 Case and action registers, 1813-1831, 1841-1883.
3 cu. ft. (15 volumes)

B0910 Register containing abstracts of legal matters, ca. 1885.
.2 cu. ft. (1 volume)

B0610   Register of railroad cases, 1853.
.2 cu. ft. (1 volume)

B0614   Register of corporation cases, 1899-1908.
.2 cu. ft. (1 volume)

B0617   Blotter of legal papers sent and received, 1900.
.2 cu. ft. (1 volume)

B0901   Account book from the attorney general's office, 1824-1861.
.2 cu. ft. (1 volume)

B0902   Account book of costs in cases concerning the people of the State of New York, 1828-1840.
.2 cu. ft. (1 volume)

B0616   Cash book, 1903-1904.
.3 cu. ft. (1 volume)

B0903   Statement of interest due on mortgages, 1848.
.2 cu. ft. (1 volume)

B0904   Canal fund daybook, 1854-1855.
.2 cu. ft. (1 volume)

B0608   Ledger of accounts with attorneys, 1834-1837.
.2 cu. ft. (1 volume)

B0914   Legal documentation relating to the attorney general's office, ca. 1910-1920.
1 cu. ft.

A0634   Contracts, ca. 1910-1925.
1 cu. ft.

B0615   Register of bonds received, 1899-1905.
.3 cu. ft. (1 volume)

B0998   Register of hearings and receivership cases, 1884-1902.
.3 cu. ft. (1 volume)

B0612   Scrapbook of legal notices of mortgage foreclosure sales, 1838-1870.
.2 cu. ft. (1 volume)

B0905   Transcripts of hearings and stenographer's notes relating to the investigation of James Eaton, superintendent of the new Capitol, ca. 1876.
1 cu. ft.

B0906   Transcripts of hearings and stenographer's notes for the case of the People of New York vs. Henry D. Denison, et al. relating to work done on the Erie Canal, ca. 1880.
3 cu. ft.

B0911   Report by the special deputy attorney appointed to investigate the murders of Charles Phelps and Margaret Wolcott, 1917.
.5 cu. ft. (1 volume)

B0912   Photographs of the Alfred E. Smith State Office Building submitted to the Appellate Division, Third Department as evidence in the case of Seglin Construction Co., et al. vs. New York, 1927-1928.
.5 cu. ft. (1 volume)

New York City Office

B0613   Register of papers served and other business conducted, 1894-1899.
.5 cu. ft. (6 volumes)

Department of Mental Hygiene

Current Functions. The function of the Department of Mental Hygiene is to protect the mental health of the people of New York State. To meet the specific needs of diverse client groups, the department operates through three autonomous offices: the Office of Mental Health, the Office of Mental Retardation and Developmental Disabilities, and the Office of Alcoholism and Substance Abuse. The Office of Alcoholism and Substance Abuse is comprised of two autonomous agencies: the Division of Alcoholism and Alcohol Abuse and the Division of Substance Abuse Services.

Organizational History. For the first 50 years of the State's history, local governments and private agencies were responsible for the care of New York State's mentally ill. In 1836 (Chapter 82), the legislature authorized the construction of the State's first mental health institution, the State Lunatic Asylum at Utica, which opened in 1843. By 1890, the State had opened nine additional asylums for the mentally ill. Local governments were responsible for expenses of inmates at these asylums and many local governments also continued to confine the mentally ill in jails and poorhouses. In 1867 (Chapter 951), the legislature established the Board of State Commissioners of Public Charities to inspect and report to the legislature on all publicly funded charitable and custodial institutions. Legislation in 1873 (Chapter 571) replaced this board with a new State Board of Charities, mandated licensing of public and private institutions for the mentally ill, and created the office of state commissioner in lunacy. This commissioner's office was abolished in 1889 (Chapter 283) and replaced by an independent State Commission in Lunacy consisting of three gubernatorial appointees. The 1894 State constitution subsequently transferred the responsibility for inspecting mental institutions from the State Board of Charities to this commission.

In 1890 (Chapter 126), the State took on the entire responsibility for the care of New York State's mentally ill. The State thereby began providing for the care of all indigent mentally ill at State expense in State institutions and prohibited their confinement in jails and poorhouses. In 1912 (Chapter 121), the commission was renamed the State Hospital Commission and was given responsibility for the administration of the State's mental hospitals. In 1918 (Chapter 197), State supervision of care for the mentally handicapped was further centralized with the creation of the State Commission on the Feeble-Minded. Renamed the State Commission for Mental Defectives in 1919 (Chapter 633), it supervised the care of "mentally defective" persons at five State special-care institutions.

A Department of Mental Hygiene was established in 1926 (Chapter 584) as part of the constitutional reorganization of State government. The new department took over all the functions of the State Hospital Commission and the State Commission for Mental Defectives, which were abolished. A Division of Mental Disease was assigned the oversight of State hospitals for the mentally ill.

Although the organization of the department remained essentially the same until 1966, changes in the 1950s began a shift to a decentralized approach to care for the mentally ill. In 1954 (Chapter 10), the legislature established community mental health boards and provided for partial State funding of local mental health services. The federal Community Mental Health Act of 1963 provided additional funding for community mental health centers, and further State legislation strengthened the role of local governments and community-based services in New York State throughout the 1970s. As a result of decentralization, patient population in large State mental institutions declined over 60 percent from 1955 to 1975.

During this same period, State programs began reflecting the growing societal awareness of the problems caused by alcoholism and drug abuse. In 1966 (Chapter 192), the Narcotic Addiction Control Commission was created within the department to supervise the operation of alcohol and narcotics-addiction treatment centers and to coordinate community rehabilitation and prevention programs. In 1973 (Chapter 676), this commission was renamed the Drug Abuse Control Commission and two years later (Laws of 1975, Chapter 667) the commission was replaced by the Office of Drug Abuse Services.

In 1977 (Chapter 978), the Department of Mental Hygiene was divided into its current organization comprising three autonomous agencies: the Office of Mental Health, the Office of Mental Retardation and Developmental Disabilities, and the Office of Alcoholism and Substance Abuse (comprised of two autonomous divisions: the Division of Alcoholism and Alcohol Abuse and the Division of Substance Abuse Services). The previous administrative structure of the department was heavily weighted in favor of mental health programs, and it was difficult for programs in mental retardation and alcoholism/substance abuse to receive proper attention. In addition, the previous department structure continued to emphasize institutional care of the mentally ill and was unable to effectively support the growth of needed community care. This significant new legislation created the new units to function independently with complete responsibility for planning and administrating their respective programs. Each office or division is headed by a commissioner or a director appointed by the governor.

Although there is no central authority within the department, several mechanisms coordinate the work of the autonomous offices and divisions. An Inter-Office Coordinating Council coordinates the care of the multiply disabled and department research efforts and assists in administering local assistance programs. The Council for Mental Hygiene Planning formulates statewide goals and objectives for the care and treatment of the mentally disabled. In addition, advisory councils established by each office or division review any matters relating to their specific programs.

DEPARTMENT OF MENTAL HYGIENE

General Agency-level Records

  A1110 Departmental reorganization records, ca. 1978.
       4 cu. ft.

A0764   Research files for a department history, 1941-1948.
7 cu. ft.

Office of Mental Health

Current Functions. The function of the Office of Mental Health is to ensure the availability of appropriate and cost-effective mental health services to the people of New York State. It establishes and monitors the immense system of decentralized care, treatment, and rehabilitation of the State's mentally ill. The office performs several major activities to meet its mandate. The office operates 31 State psychiatric facilities caring for an average of 17,000 patients each day. Twenty-two of these facilities are for adults, six care for children and adolescents, and three serve forensic patients. In addition, the office directly operates small residential-care facilities in the State. The office regulates and licenses over 1,000 mental health programs operated by local governments and private agencies that serve over half a million people each year. The office plans and directs this decentralized system, monitors program quality, and provides financial oversight. The office conducts research on the cause and treatment of mental illness through two major research institutes. The office also administers federal funds for mental health programs in New York.

Organizational History. The Office of Mental Health was created in 1977 (Chapter 978) as one of three autonomous offices established within the restructured Department of Mental Hygiene. The office has continued the department's previous functions of caring for the State's mentally ill while further expanding services to clients in community-based programs.

OFFICE OF MENTAL HEALTH

Office of Counsel

    12045   Legal files, 1972-1978.
             20 cu. ft. R

    12046   Legislative files, 1962-1979, bulk ca. 1964-1975.
             5 cu. ft.

Bureau of Planning and Evaluation Research

14230　　　Survey of patient characteristics data files, 1981-1985.
　　　　　　1 cu. ft. (71 microfilm reels)

Office of Mental Retardation and Developmental Disabilities

Current Functions. The Office of Mental Retardation and Developmental Disabilities is charged with developing a comprehensive and integrated system of services for New York State citizens with mental retardation and developmental disabilities. The office operates 16 developmental centers that provide intensive care for approximately 6,800 clients. The office also funds and regulates a network of State and voluntary community-based services consisting of approximately 22,000 residential beds and outpatient services supporting another 43,000 clients. In addition, the office provides respite, crisis intervention, and other support services for the 16,000 families who presently care for disabled family members at home. The office also operates the Institute for Basic Research in Developmental Disabilities, which performs basic research into the causes of developmental disabilities, provides laboratory and clinical services, and prepares materials for public and professional education.

Organizational History. The Office of Mental Retardation and Developmental Disabilities was created in 1977 (Chapter 978) as one of three autonomous offices established within the restructured Department of Mental Hygiene. While continuing the Department of Mental Hygiene's previous functions in mental retardation services, the office's autonomy allows it to develop programs and funding specifically designed to meet the needs of New York State's mentally retarded and developmentally disabled population. The State's mental health system is becoming increasingly community-based, with two institutions scheduled to close during 1991 and to be replaced by local service centers.

OFFICE OF MENTAL RETARDATION AND DEVELOPMENTAL DISABILITIES

CRAIG DEVELOPMENTAL CENTER

14197　　　Patient case files, ca. 1905-1948.
　　　　　　131.5 cu. ft. R

ROME STATE CUSTODIAL ASYLUM

Superintendent's Office

A0423   Cover letter and memo concerning "colonization," 1917.
.1 cu. ft.

Division of Alcoholism and Alcohol Abuse

Current Functions. The Division of Alcoholism and Alcohol Abuse is responsible for all State services to alcoholics, alcohol abusers, and their families. The division plans, promotes, establishes, coordinates, and conducts training programs in prevention, education, early intervention, diagnosis, treatment, rehabilitation, and aftercare. The division assists local governments and volunteer organizations in developing alcoholism services. The division certifies and inspects alcoholism-treatment facilities in relation to treatment standards established by the division. The division is responsible for accrediting alcoholism counselors. The division itself is a major service provider, operating 13 residential alcoholism-treatment centers that provide intensive alcoholism rehabilitation services. It also conducts basic research into the causes of the disease of alcoholism.

Organizational History. With the laws of 1977 (Chapter 978), the Division of Alcoholism and Alcohol Abuse was created as an autonomous agency within the Department of Mental Hygiene's Office of Alcoholism and Substance Abuse. Although the Department of Mental Hygiene had provided residential alcoholism services since 1961, the creation of this new division broadened the State's response to the growing awareness of alcoholism among New Yorkers. The division is assisted by an Advisory Council on Alcoholism Services consisting of the director of the division, the chairperson of the Conference of Local Mental Hygiene Directors, and 24 other members appointed by the governor.

No records in the State Archives

Division of Substance Abuse Services

Current Functions. The Division of Substance Abuse Services plans, develops, administers, funds, and regulates a statewide network of agencies providing prevention, treatment, and rehabilitation services to chemically dependent individuals throughout New York State. To ensure effectiveness, accountability, and quality of care, the division funds, monitors, evaluates, and assists those local programs. These efforts are supported by specialized outreach, intake, and referral programs; training; and research in social sciences providing the basic data for planning and funding determinations.

Organizational History. The Narcotic Addiction Control Commission was created in 1966 (Chapter 192) within the Department of Mental Hygiene to supervise the operation of alcohol- and narcotics-addiction treatment centers and coordinated community rehabilitation and prevention programs. In 1973 (Chapter 676), this commission was renamed the Drug Abuse Control Commission, and in 1975 (Chapter 667) it was replaced by the Office of Drug Abuse Services. The present Division of Substance Abuse Services was created in 1977 (Chapter 978). This law divided the Department of Mental Hygiene into three autonomous offices, including the Office of Alcoholism and Substance Abuse. This new office is comprised of two independent divisions: the Division of Alcoholism and Alcohol Abuse and the Division of Substance Abuse Services.

DIVISION OF SUBSTANCE ABUSE SERVICES

Office of the Director

16082   Executive director's subject files, 1982-1989.
         58 cu. ft.

16084   First deputy director's subject files, 1980-1987.
         6 cu. ft.

16085   Substance abuse service providers program files, 1978-1986.
         3 cu. ft.

16088   AIDS information file, 1985-1989.
         4 cu. ft.

Department of Motor Vehicles

Current Functions. The Department of Motor Vehicles is responsible for protecting the public by establishing and regulating safety standards for vehicles and operators and by conducting research on and developing programs to promote public safety. It regulates safety standards by administering the Vehicle and Traffic Law, which is enforced by State and local police, and by monitoring traffic violations. The department registers motor vehicles, boats, snowmobiles, and all-terrain vehicles; licenses automobile drivers, dealers, repair shops, inspection stations and driving schools; and collects sales taxes on private motor vehicle sales. The department conducts research on and actively promotes programs to reduce drinking driver problems and to encourage general highway safety practices, including the use of seat belts.

Organizational History. The origins of the Department of Motor Vehicles (DMV) can be traced back to 1901 (Chapter 531), when the legislature required all owners of automobiles or motor vehicles to register with the office of the secretary of state, identifying themselves and their vehicles. Two years later certain motor vehicle operators were required to obtain licenses from the secretary of state's office (Chapter 625). Examinations were instituted for chauffeurs in 1910 (Chapter 374), for New York City drivers in 1919 (Chapter 472), and for all drivers in 1924 (Chapter 360).

The secretary of state registered and licensed motor vehicles and operators until 1921, when these functions were transferred to the State Tax Department (Chapter 90). From July 1921 through July 1924, motor vehicle and motor cycle laws were administered through the State Tax Department's Automobile Bureau. In July 1924, the bureau's name was changed to the Bureau of Motor Vehicles, and the Office of Commissioner of Motor Vehicles established.

With the constitutional reorganization of State government in 1926, the Bureau of Motor Vehicles became a part of the newly created Department of Taxation and Finance (Chapter 553). The bureau's duties remained substantially the same except that all policing and enforcement procedures relating to the Highway Law were transferred to the State Police.

In 1936 (Chapters 910 and 919), the State Traffic Commission was created and attached to the Department of Taxation and Finance. Consisting of the commissioner of motor vehicles, the chief engineer of the Department of Public Works' Highway Division, and the superintendent of state police, the commission was mandated to survey traffic conditions, plan and coordinate safety programs, advise local govern-ments on traffic matters, and promulgate rules and regulations for traffic control.

With the proliferation of automobiles the functions and duties of the bureau were increased through legislation. Statutes dealing with uninsured drivers were enacted in 1921, 1941, and 1956. Chemical tests for alcoholic content in the blood of drivers were implemented in 1954. Vehicle inspection began the following year and legisla-tion on driving while intoxicated was enacted in 1960.

In 1959, a constitutional amendment provided for the creation of a Department of Motor Vehicles. Chapter 464 of the Laws of 1960 abolished the Bureau of Motor Vehicles in the Department of Taxation and Finance and transferred its duties to the new department. The law also transferred to the department the State Traffic Commission, which functioned until 1967 when it was abolished and its duties transferred to the newly established Department of Transportation (Laws of 1967, Chapter 717).

No records in the State Archives

Department of Public Service/Public Service Commission

Current Functions. The Department of Public Service is the staff arm for the Public Service Commission. The commission is responsible for regulating the rates and services of public utility companies in order to ensure safe, adequate service for the public at reasonable rates and with the least adverse effect upon the environment. These regulatory responsibilities apply to electric, steam, telephone, gas, and water companies. Although its most publicized activity is determining utility rates, the commission has a number of other specific responsibilities such as establishing ser-vice standards and monitoring the operation of utilities; reviewing and resolving cus-tomer complaints; supervising utilities' accounting and financial practices; exercising jurisdiction over the siting of major utility facilities and electrical and gas transmis-sion lines; and ensuring the safety of natural gas facilities and petroleum pipelines.

Organizational History. State regulation of public utilities dates from the early nineteenth century, when the legislature began including financial and service requirements in incorporation statutes. More systematic oversight began with an 1843 assembly resolution requiring railroads to submit reports to the secretary of state. Five years later (Laws of 1848, Chapter 140), the railroads were required to report instead to the state engineer and surveyor on financial affairs, equipment, and passengers and freight carried. A Railroad Commission was established in 1855 (Chapter 526) to receive reports and investigate railroad operation, but this commission was abolished two years later, and the railroads resumed reporting to the engineer and surveyor. In 1882 (Chapter 353), a Board of Railroad Commissioners was created with power to require reports, investigate complaints, and recommend service improvements and rate adjustments, but without any enforcement power. Nine years later (Laws of 1891, Chapter 4), the State recognized New York City's special transportation needs by establishing a Board of Rapid Transit Commissioners to oversee the expansion of surface rapid transit facilities and plan the construction of subways. Turning to other utilities, the legislature established the office of inspector of gas meters to inspect and seal meters (Laws of 1859, Chapter 311) and, later, a Commission of Gas and Electricity to regulate rates (Laws of 1905, Chapter 737).

In 1907 (Chapter 424), Governor Charles Evans Hughes proposed systematic, comprehensive, statewide public utility regulation and convinced the legislature to pass the Public Service Commissions Law. This statute replaced existing State regulatory authorities with two district public service commissions (one for New York City and the other for the remainder of the State) with sweeping powers to investigate complaints, order improved service, establish rates, and supervise the issue of securities. The first district (New York City) commission also inherited the powers of the Rapid Transit Commission to plan and construct subways.

During the following decade, PSC supervisory responsibilities were expanded to include telephone and telegraph lines, steam companies, water carriers, and bus lines. A series of 1930 statutes increased the commissions' regulatory powers over utility holding companies and financial transactions. Organizational changes were also made over the years. In 1919 (Chapter 263 and Chapter 520), the first district commission was replaced by a single public service commissioner to carry out regulatory functions and a transit construction commissioner to carry out subway construction. Two years later (Laws of 1921, Chapter 134), the two public service districts were abolished and replaced by a single Public Service Commission with statewide authority over all public utilities except rapid transit in New York City, which was placed under a new Transit Commission. In 1924 (Chapter 573), a Board of

Transportation was established to continue subway construction and to operate existing city subways and surface rapid transit lines, leaving the Transit Commission with supervisory authority over only private transit facilities.

When the constitutional reorganization of state government was implemented in 1926 (Chapter 350), the Department of Public Service was created. It took over the Transit Commission and the Public Service Commission. Later (Laws of 1943, Chapter 170), the Transit Commission was abolished and the Public Service Commission assumed its duties. All Department of Public Service transportation-related regulatory functions were transferred to the Department of Transportation in 1970 (Chapter 267). As part of the 1970 reorganization (Chapter 272), the Department of Public Service assumed responsibility for considering environmental impacts of utility facilities. In 1977, the legislature expanded the role of the Department of Public Service concerning demand- side aspects of utility regulation with enactment of the Home Insulation and Energy Conservation Act (Laws of 1977, Chapter 858).

In 1981, the department expanded its consumer-related activities through creation of a Consumer Services Division. The division provides information and advice to utility customers, monitors utility compliance with commission directives, and settles disputes between utilities and their customers.

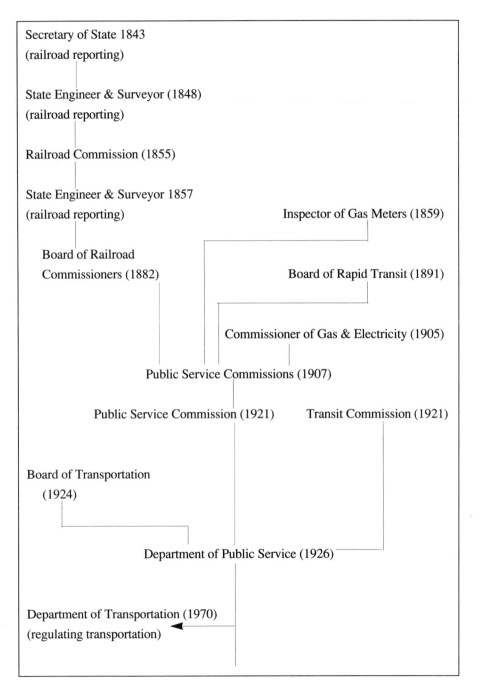

Secretary of State 1843
(railroad reporting)

State Engineer & Surveyor (1848)
(railroad reporting)

Railroad Commission (1855)

State Engineer & Surveyor 1857
(railroad reporting)

Inspector of Gas Meters (1859)

Board of Railroad
Commissioners (1882)

Board of Rapid Transit (1891)

Commissioner of Gas & Electricity (1905)

Public Service Commissions (1907)

Public Service Commission (1921)

Transit Commission (1921)

Board of Transportation
(1924)

Department of Public Service (1926)

Department of Transportation (1970)
(regulating transportation)

PUBLIC SERVICE COMMISSION

B1331 Minutes of commission proceedings, 1907-1977.
31.8 cu. ft.

B1332 Commission docket books, 1907-1982.
46.6 cu. ft.

B0299 Annual reports, 1907-1920.
8 cu. ft. (68 volumes)

B0300 Reports of decisions of the Public Service Commission, 1907-1920.
2 cu. ft. (18 volumes)

A0414 New York City subway drawings and plans, ca. 1900.
3 cu. ft.

A0446 Projected railroad centerline maps, ca. 1850-1950.
160 cu. ft. (614 maps)

A0773 Conference minutes, 1930-1942.
3 cu. ft. (11 volumes)

A0776 Calendars and notes of conferences, 1948-1960.
8 cu. ft.

B0298 Correspondence files pertaining to steam railroad and electric railway companies' annual reports, ca. 1907-1933.
8 cu. ft.

B0302 Correspondence files pertaining to stage coach and omnibus companies' annual reports, ca. 1910-1962, bulk 1926-1957.
11 cu. ft.

10093 Annual reports of steam railroad and electric railway companies, 1883-1975.
224 cu. ft.

13345 Annual reports of public utility companies, 1905-1980.
301 cu. ft.

B1330 Annual reports of municipal water districts and departments, 1932-1957.
7 cu. ft.

Office of the Secretary

B0321   Rebuttal testimony and exhibits concerning the investigation into the cost of the Shoreham Nuclear Generating Facility, 1984.
4.5 cu. ft.

First District

15904   Gas and electric company corporate and franchise document files, ca. 1859-1935.
5 cu. ft.

TRANSIT COMMISSION

B0297   Meeting proceedings, 1916-1943.
3 cu. ft.

BOARD OF RAILROAD COMMISSIONERS

B0296   Minutes of meetings, 1855-1907, bulk 1883-1907.
6 cu. ft. (9 volumes)

B0301   Annual reports on railroads by the State engineer and surveyor and the board of railroad commissioners, 1850-1906.
23.5 cu. ft. (80 volumes)

B0295   Docket books, 1883-1907.
6 cu. ft. (6 volumes)

COMMISSION OF GAS AND ELECTRICITY

B1333   Docket book, 1914-1921.
6 cu. ft.

Department of Social Services

Current Functions. The Department of Social Services supports the health and welfare of citizens by conducting the State's income maintenance, medical assistance, and social supportive-services programs. The department supervises the administration of the functions carried on by the local social services districts in New York State. The department carries out its income-maintenance responsibilities by providing funds to needy persons to sustain them while encouraging their self-sufficiency through education, employment services, and training. This is accomplished through such programs as Aid to Families with Dependent Children and Food Stamps.

The department carries out its medical-assistance responsibilities by providing Medicaid to pay hospitals, physicians, nursing homes, and other providers for medical care and services for which recipients cannot afford to pay. The department carries out its social services responsibilities by providing support for services such as: day-care; foster care; preventive services (e.g., a homelessness prevention program); domestic violence services; housing improvement services; family planning; protective services for adults and children; services for the visually handicapped; and services for Native Americans.

Organizational History. The Department of Charities was established by the Laws of 1926 (Chapter 651), following the 1925-26 constitutional reorganization of State government. The administrative head of the department was the Board of Charities, originally established in 1867. The department implemented the public-assistance policies and programs of the Board of Charities and assumed administrative control of institutions for dependents from the local boards of managers. Duties of the commissioner of education relating to Native American affairs (except the education of children on reservations) were transferred to the Department of Charities. The State Commission for the Blind, originally established in 1913, became a bureau in the new department.

In 1929 (Chapter 654), the department was renamed the Department of Social Welfare, while its administrative head was renamed the Board of Social Welfare. This law and a series of public welfare laws that year reflected the importance of a new State emphasis on home relief rather than institutionalization as the fundamental basis of public welfare administration.

The Public Welfare Law was amended in 1936 (Chapter 873) to provide for a permanent system of State aid for public relief. The Board of Social Welfare was reorganized and given authority to appoint a commissioner of public welfare. In 1967 (Chapter 728), the department was renamed the Department of Social Services.

In 1971 (Chapter 110), the Board of Social Welfare was transferred from the Department of Social Services to the Executive Department. The Bureau of Proprietary Organizations, which had the power to approve certificates of incorporation for public welfare agencies and institutions, was removed from the department and placed under the Board of Social Welfare. The board's authority to appoint the commissioner of social services was transferred to the governor. The commissioner assumed the board's authority relating to administration of public assistance. Under the 1971 law, responsibility for all training schools and facilities for juvenile delinquents was transferred to the Division for Youth, and responsibility for the Women's Relief Corps Home was transferred to the Department of Health.

State Commission for the Blind (1926)

Department of Charities (1926)

Department of Social Welfare (1929)

Department of Social Services (1967)

DEPARTMENT OF SOCIAL SERVICES

Commissioner's Office

16034   Commissioner's subject files, 1947-1984.
50 cu. ft. R

– Local District Liaison Unit

11909   Official policy and procedures releases to local social services agencies, ca. 1940-1985.
103 cu. ft.

Division of Operations Analysis

16002   Research documentation and findings files, 1982-1984.
2 cu. ft.

Office of Audit and Quality Control

A0420   Income maintenance separation system planning files, 1967-1972.
7 cu. ft.

DEPARTMENT OF SOCIAL WELFARE

A0742   Indian census rolls, 1881-1950.
         4 cu. ft.

A3274   Files relating to public health, ca. 1937-1943.
         9 cu. ft.

A3275   Working and reports files relating to Temporary State Commission
         to Formulate a Long Range State Health Program, ca. 1938-1943.
         10.8 cu. ft.

Division of State Institutions

B0645   Minutes of meetings of boards of visitors and monthly reports of
         institutions, 1936-1961.
         13 cu. ft. R

B0816   Monthly reports of activities at institutions, 1927-1961.
         .4 cu. ft.

B0646   Population reports of institutions, 1940-1961.
         3 cu. ft.

B0647   Monthly reports of runaways from institutions, 1943-1960.
         .4 cu. ft. R

B0649   Weekly reports of commitments to training schools from New
         York City, 1945-1959.
         .4 cu. ft. R

B0648   Orders transferring inmates to the Annex of State Training
         Schools for Boys, 1947-1960.
         .5 cu. ft. R

COMMISSION FOR THE BLIND

A0185   Minutes, 1913-1914.
         .5 cu. ft.

A3309   Photographs of occupations, programs, and activities for the blind,
         1923-1963.
         .4 cu. ft.

TEMPORARY EMERGENCY RELIEF ADMINISTRATION

A3263   Manual of procedure for local relief administrations, 1935.
.4 cu. ft.

Joint Committee for Study of Organization and Functioning of Emergency Relief Bureau, New York City

B0997   Report, 1936.
.3 cu. ft. (1 volume)

THOMAS INDIAN SCHOOL (THOMAS ASYLUM FOR ORPHAN AND DESTITUTE INDIAN CHILDREN)

B0640   Correspondence and subject files, 1855-1958.
2.5 cu. ft. R

B0599   Superintendent's daily diaries, 1908-1944.
1 cu. ft. (35 volumes)

B0595   Children's case files, ca. 1892-1957.
28 cu. ft. R

A1910   Child commitment contracts, 1881-1896.
.1 cu. ft. (1 volume)

B0644   Statistical and financial reports, 1881-1893.
.2 cu. ft. (1 volume)

B0596   Treasurer's monthly reports, 1901-1944.
6 cu. ft.

B0642   Journal accounts, 1879-1914.
3.5 cu. ft. (14 volumes)

B0643   Ledger accounts, 1881-1944.
3 cu. ft. (9 volumes)

B0597   Monthly farm production reports, 1918-1949.
1 cu. ft.

B0641   Farm expenditure and production journals, 1918-1947.
2 cu. ft. (4 volumes)

B0598   Children's daily diet logs, 1889-1944.
1 cu. ft. (4 volumes, 1 unbound report)

A1913   Photographs of activities and facilities, ca. 1895-1950.
1 cu. ft. (174 photographs)

A1909   Register of trustees, Indian children, and visitors, 1855-1881.
.1 cu. ft. (1 volume)

A1911   Register of visitors, 1881-1906.
.1 cu. ft. (1 volume)

Department of State

Current Functions. The Department of State is responsible for a wide variety of licensing, regulatory, record-keeping, municipal assistance, and planning functions. The department licenses and regulates real estate brokers and salespersons; barbers; cosmetologists and hair dressers; private investigators; watch guard and patrol agencies; the manufacture, renovation and sale of articles of bedding and upholstered furniture; apartment information vendors; and hearing aid dealers. It registers charitable organizations, trademarks, trading stamp companies, hotel and motel names, and games of chance utilized in promoting retail sales. It also supervises the administration of cemetery corporations. Notaries and commissioners of deeds in other states and territories are appointed by the Department of State.

The department is the official office of record for filing many documents, including executive proclamations, commissions, pardons and commutations; land patents; laws signed by the governor; financing statements under the Uniform Commercial Code; and certificates of incorporation except for banking, insurance, or educational corporations. As an extension of its record-keeping function, the department certifies copies of State laws and publishes the *Legislative Manual*; the *Official Compilation of Codes, Rules and Regulations of the State of New York*; and the *New York State Register*, the official State publication announcing proposed administrative regulations.

It coordinates fire safety activities of State and local agencies and advises and assists local governments with planning and development activities. The department administers the State's coastal-management program and ensures that efforts concerning the coastal zone are useful to the planning, development, and regulatory activities of State, regional and local agencies. It also provides oversight, technical assistance, guidance, and training programs for local governments and local code-enforcement officials in support of the Uniform Fire Prevention and Building Code. The department is the administrative location for the State Athletic Commission and the State Ethics Commission and serves as secretariat to the Committee on Open Government. The secretary of state serves as a member of several state boards and commissions.

Organizational History. The office of secretary of state was inherited from the colonial period during which the secretary of the Province of New Netherland and the secretary of the Colony of New York acted as clerks to the governor's council and maintained the records of the colonial governments. Although neither the first State constitution of 1777 nor any statute specifically created the office within State government, the Council of Appointment appointed a secretary of state in 1778. Records of the colonial governments were immediately transferred to the secretary, thus establishing the office's role as records custodian. Beginning with oaths of office in 1778 (Chapter 7), several statutes in subsequent years required the official filing of specific documents or records with the secretary.

The means of selecting the secretary of state changed several times. The constitution of 1821, which abolished the Council of Appointment, provided that the secretary be selected by the legislature. The State's third constitution of 1846 made the office elective. It remained that way until 1926 (Chapter 437), when the act creating the modern Department of State allowed the governor to appoint the secretary as head of the new department.

From the year the first secretary was appointed, the office was assigned certain duties by statute. In 1778 the secretary was made ex officio clerk of the Council of Appointment. Several years later (Laws of 1784, Chapter 60), the secretary was designated a commissioner of the land office. When the commissioners of the canal fund were established in 1817 (Chapter 262), the secretary was a member. In 1821 (Chapter 240) the office of superintendent of common schools was abolished and its duties transferred to the secretary of state, where they remained until they were transferred to the newly created Department of Public Instruction in 1854. The secretary also was a member of the Board of Regents of the University of the State of New York by virtue of his office from 1842 (Chapter 142) to 1904 (Chapter 40), when ex officio membership on the board was ended.

The 1925-26 reorganization of State government resulted in the creation of the Department of State in 1926 (Chapter 437), with the secretary of state as department head. As constituted by law, the department included the Board of Commissioners of the Land Office, of which the secretary was chairperson (transferred to the Office of General Services by the Laws of 1960, Chapter 462); the State Athletic Commission, which regulated boxing and the members of which were appointed by the secretary; the State Racing Commission, which regulated horse racing and whose members were appointed by the secretary (duties transferred to the New York State Racing and Wagering Board in the Executive Department by the Laws of 1973, Chapter 346); the State Board of Canvassers, which certified election results and whose administrative staff was provided by the department; the port wardens of the Port of New York, whose members were appointed by the secretary (abolished by the Laws of 1928, Chapter 377); the Hell Gate Pilots, who were appointed by the secretary (transferred to the Board of Commissioners of Pilots by the Laws of 1939, Chapter 661); and a Division of Licenses responsible for the regulation and licensing of various business activities.

In 1975 (Chapter 464), the Office for Local Government (established by the Laws of 1959, Chapter 335) and the Office of Planning Services (previously the Office of Planning Coordination, established by the Laws of 1966, Chapter 528, and changed to the Office of Planning Services by the Laws of 1971, Chapter 75) were abolished and their functions transferred to the Department of State. These functions included coordinating fire services in the State and advising and assisting local governments in their planning and resource development activities.

When the State's Freedom of Information Law was revised in 1977 (Chapter 933), the secretary of state was made a member and secretariat of the Committee on Public Access to Records created in 1974 (Chapter 579) to administer the law.

In 1983, Executive Order No. 23 established the Office of New York State Ombudsman under the jurisdiction of the secretary of state. Among other things, the office serves as a clearinghouse for information relating to services to which persons are entitled; provides referral services for individuals seeking Federal, State, or local assistance; and investigates complaints concerning the delivery of services by State agencies.

The Ethics in Government Act (Laws of 1987, Chapter 73) created the State Ethics Commission to interpret, administer, and enforce the provisions of the law. The commission receives, files, and reviews annual financial disclosure statements of policy-making officials of the State's departments, divisions, and agencies and issues advisory opinions concerning possible conflicts of interest resulting from financial holdings or outside employment.

The office of the secretary of state has served as the general recording office for State government since its creation in 1778. Cognizant of the historical value of many of the records in the secretary's custody, the legislature authorized by concurrent resolution in 1847 the transfer of the most valuable of these records to the New York State Library. The first transfer occurred shortly thereafter, and the library continued to accept and preserve records from the department until 1978, when custody of these records was transferred to the newly created New York State Archives.

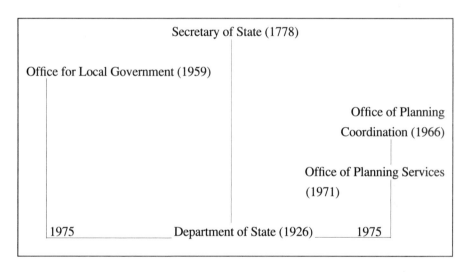

NEW YORK (COLONY)
SECRETARY

A3077	Laws promulgated at Hempstead, 1665. .3 cu. ft. (1 volume)
A3078	Laws passed by the first Assembly, 1683-1684. .3 cu. ft. (1 volume)
A1888	Copy of the charter of the city of New York, 1730. .1 cu. ft.
A1892	Minutes of the proceedings of the Commissioners for Settling the Boundaries between Rhode Island and Massachusetts, 1741-1742. .3 cu. ft. (1 microfilm reel)

A1889   Minutes of Court of Commissioners appointed to examine the controversy between Connecticut and the Mohegan Indians, 1743.
.5 cu. ft. (1 microfilm reel)

A1893   Marriage bonds executed by persons obtaining marriage licenses, 1753-1783.
3 cu. ft.

SECRETARY OF THE PROVINCE

A0270   Register of the provincial secretary, 1642-1660.
1.5 cu. ft.

NEW YORK (STATE)

SECRETARY OF STATE/DEPARTMENT OF STATE

A0325   Secretary of state's letterbooks, 1831-1905.
1 cu. ft.

A0323   Deputy secretary of state's letterbooks, 1880-1883.
2 cu. ft. (3 volumes)

A0326   Registers of letters received and instruments recorded, 1858-1880.
.5 cu. ft. (3 volumes)

Division of Legal Affairs

A0726   Moss Lake Indian lands negotiation files, ca. 1974-1979.
3 cu. ft.

Bureau of Legal Services

13029   1980 Olympics legal issues files, 1976-1980.
2 cu. ft.

Office of Charities Registration

13011   Registration statements and annual financial reports of charitable organizations, 1950-1987.
433 cu. ft.

Division of the Land Office

B0635   Terminations of easements, ca. 1948-1960.
4 cu. ft.

Board of Port Wardens

A0387   Records, minutes accounts, cargo surveys, and Hell's Gate pilots and apprentices register, ca. 1903-1928.
2 cu. ft.

Constitutions, Laws, and Treaties

A1800   Engrossed copy of the United States Constitution ratified by the Convention of New York State, 1788.
.5 cu. ft. (1 volume)

A1801   Journal of the proceedings of the State Convention to Consider Ratification of the United States Constitution, 1788.
.3 cu. ft. (1 volume)

A1802   First constitution of the State of New York, 1777.
.3 cu. ft. (1 volume)

A1803   Amendments to the first State constitution, 1801.
.2 cu. ft.

A1804   Second constitution of the State of New York, 1821.
.3 cu. ft. (1 volume)

A3304   Roll of delegates to the 1821 Constitutional Convention, 1821.
.5 cu. ft.

A1805   Third constitution of the State of New York, 1846.
.3 cu. ft.

A3305   Roll of delegates to the 1846 Constitutional Convention, 1846.
.1 cu. ft.

A1806   Proposed constitution of the State of New York, 1867-1868.
.3 cu. ft. (1 volume)

B0005   Oaths of delegates to constitutional conventions, 1867-1938.
1.5 cu. ft. (3 volumes)

A1807   Fourth constitution of the State of New York, 1894.
.3 cu. ft. (1 volume)

A3301   Proposed New York State Constitution, 1915.
.2 cu. ft. (1 volume)

A0211   Proposed constitutional amendments passed by the 1938 Constitutional Convention, 1938.
.3 cu. ft. (1 volume)

13036 Enrolled acts of the State legislature, 1778-1990.
576.5 cu. ft. (1,202 volumes) R

13241 Local laws of cities, counties, towns, and villages, 1924-1983.
137 cu. ft. (240 volumes)

A3303 Record of laws, 1777-1799, 1801-1802.
3.8 cu. ft. (19 volumes)

A0417 Transcriptions of laws, 1777-1802.
2 cu. ft. (19 volumes)

A0158 Laws, 1801-1817.
.5 cu. ft.

13240 Concurrent resolutions of the State legislature, 1985-1990.
1 cu. ft.

13082 Executive orders, 1955-1988.
6.8 cu. ft.

13035 Proclamations by the governor, 1893-1990.
20.6 cu. ft.

A0027 Minutes of the Council of Revision, 1778-1824.
1 cu. ft. (5 volumes)

A0621 Memoranda of bills delivered to secretary of state, 1877, 1878, 1901.
1 cu. ft.

A0074 Register of bills sent to the secretary of state by the legislature, 1873-1876.
.5 cu. ft.

A0209 Copies of bills sent to mayors for approval, 1901-1904.
1 cu. ft. (6 volumes)

14266 New York codes, rules, and regulations amendment files, 1938-1987.
169.5 cu. ft.

A0448 Indian treaties and deeds, 1748-1847.
.6 cu. ft. (3 volumes)

A0232 Indian treaties, 1766-1811.
.5 cu. ft.

B0001   Descriptions and impressions of official seals filed with the secretary of state, 1798-1977.
1 cu. ft. (2 volumes)

Elections

B0016   Certificates of election, 1799-1827.
1 cu. ft. (3 volumes)

A0277   Census of electors, 1801.
.5 cu. ft.

A1836   Census of electors, 1814.
.5 cu. ft.

A1837   Census of electors, 1821.
.5 cu. ft.

B0017   Record of election returns, 1822-1839.
1 cu. ft. (3 volumes)

B0021   List of civil officers elected, 1827-1853.
.5 cu. ft. (1 volume)

B0019   Statements of election returns by boards of county canvassers, 1828-1913.
6 cu. ft. (8 volumes)

B0023   Journal of New York State Electoral College, 1856-1972.
1 cu. ft. (2 volumes)

B0084   Index to statements of election returns by boards of county canvassers, 1859-1864.
.3 cu. ft. (1 volume)

B0039   Certified copies of election returns from boards of county canvassers, 1881-1905.
7 cu. ft.

13245   Certificates of election of members of the Board of Regents, 1889-1984, 1988.
1.2 cu. ft.

B0022   Record of nominations, 1890-1910.
.5 cu. ft.

B0020   Register of electors absent in the military and naval service, 1898.
.3 cu. ft. (1 volume)

A0216 Kings County election returns, 1898-1899.
     5 cu. ft.

A1856 Poll books of electors serving in the military or naval services, 1898.
     1 cu. ft.

A1857 Lists of names and residencies of electors of the State of New
     York absent in the military service of the U.S., 1898.
     1 cu. ft.

B0024 General election committee statements, 1908-1913.
     15.5 cu. ft.

B0036 Detailed statement of expenditures of Republican National
     Committee, 1908.
     .3 cu. ft.

B0041 Local committee statements, 1909-1911.
     8 cu. ft.

B0038 Certificates of election for treasurers of political committees,
     1909-1911.
     1 cu. ft.

B0027 Primary election committee statements, 1910-1913.
     1 cu. ft.

B0032 Statewide Republican statements of campaign receipts and pay-
     ments, 1910.
     .3 cu. ft.

B0033 Special election candidate statements, 1910.
     .3 cu. ft.

B0034 Special election committee statements regarding Monroe County
     congressional seat, 1910.
     .3 cu. ft.

B0035 General election statements of miscellaneous clubs and associa-
     tions, 1910-1911.
     .3 cu. ft.

B0037 Statements of individuals assisting in the election of candidates,
     1910.
     .3 cu. ft.

B0040 List of filing dates of candidates and committees, 1912.
     .3 cu. ft.

B0025   General election candidate statements, 1912-1913.
10.5 cu. ft.

B0026   Primary election candidate statements, 1912-1913.
5 cu. ft.

13251   Oaths of office of members of the Electoral College, 1929-1984, 1988.
1.2 cu. ft.

13247   Certificates of election to the Board of State Canvassers, 1935-1979.
.5 cu. ft.

13246   Reapportionment orders, 1944-1974.
.5 cu. ft.

Judicial Administration

B0061   Assignments of judges and court terms for the State Supreme Court, 1848-1924, 1960-1979.
10 cu. ft.

A1864   Certificates of designation of judges, 1848-1905.
1 cu. ft.

12944   Appointments of judges and assignments of court terms, 1987.
.4 cu. ft.

A1866   Supreme Court summonses and subpoenas, 1854-1882.
.1 cu. ft.

A1863   Records of Supreme Court judgments against defendants in actions to vacate letters patent or articles of incorporation, 1857-1883.
.5 cu. ft.

B0081   Letters of administration and copies of wills of out-of-state residents, 1823-1966.
47 cu. ft.

A1865   Transcript of testimony in case of New York vs. Lockwood, 1856-1857.
1 cu. ft.

A1867   Register of judgments for violation of Highway Law, Article II, 1910-1911.
2 cu. ft. (1 volume)

A1868   Docket book of selected cases heard in Albany courts, 1877-1882.
.3 cu. ft. (1 volume)

Appointments and Commissions

A1845   Minutes of the Council of Appointment, 1786-1822.
2.5 cu. ft.

A1846   Index to Council of Appointment minutes, 1777-1786.
.3 cu. ft. (1 volume)

A1847   Administrative files of the Council of Appointment, 1777-1821.
7 cu. ft.

B0018   Oaths of office of State officials, 1778-1983.
35 cu. ft. (69 volumes)

13252   Commissions by the governor, 1823-1986.
16.5 cu. ft.

13254   Letters of appointment by the governor, 1866-1971, 1984-1987.
6.6 cu. ft.

A1851   Executive orders for commissions to public offices, 1839-1926.
8 cu. ft.

B0002   Senate resolutions confirming·commissions by the governor, 1834-1870.
3 cu. ft. (38 volumes)

A1852   Record of commissions by the governor and the senate, 1823-1927.
55 cu. ft. (53 volumes)

A1854   Record of commissions, 1770-1827.
14.5 cu. ft. (33 volumes)

A0472   Register of officers elected or appointed to State offices and boards, 1778-1939.
2.5 cu. ft. (5 volumes)

B0003   Notices of appointment of State officials, 1855-1893.
.5 cu. ft.

A1951   Register of nominations for State offices, 1890-1910.
.5 cu. ft.

A1850   Index to commissions for public offices, n.d.
.3 cu. ft. (1 volume)

A1848   Abstract of civil appointments, 1804-1939.
6 cu. ft. (9 volumes)

A1855   County officers appointment and election card file, 1913-1926.
.5 cu. ft.

A1853   Register of commissions sent to county clerks, 1816-1850.
.3 cu. ft. (2 volumes)

B0011   Commissions for notaries public, 1923-1926.
2 cu. ft. (4 volumes)

B0012   Senate resolutions confirming governor's appointments for notaries public, 1923-1927.
2 cu. ft. (5 volumes)

B0013   Commissions by the governor for notaries public, recess appointments, 1895-1927.
12 cu. ft. (20 volumes)

B0014   Commissions by the governor for bank notaries, 1890-1894.
1 cu. ft. (1 volume)

B0009   Registers of commissions of notaries public, 1850-1913.
12 cu. ft. (23 volumes)

B0304   Out-of-state commissioners of deeds appointment files, ca. 1900-1977.
8 cu. ft.

B0006   Registers of appointment of commissioners of deeds for other states, territories, and foreign countries, 1850-1962.
3.5 cu. ft. (7 volumes)

B0007   Abstracts of appointments of commissioners of deeds for other states, territories, and foreign countries, 1850-1908.
1 cu. ft. (3 volumes)

B0008   Oaths of commissioners of deeds for other states, territories, and foreign countries, 1850-1930.
9 cu. ft.

13250   Miscellaneous appointments, ca. 1950-1986.
6 cu. ft.

B0004   Resignations and removals, 1867-1969.
9 cu. ft.

13248	Removals and resignations from office, 1945-1986. 1 cu. ft.
13249	Notices of resignations, deaths and removals from office, 1984-1990. .5 cu. ft.
B1329	Notices of Senate confirmation of gubernatorial appointments, 1971-1986. 2.8 cu. ft.

Executive Clemency

B0042	Executive pardons, 1799-1931. 4 cu. ft. (10 volumes)
B1201	Name index to executive pardons, respites, commutations, restorations of citizenship and certificates of good conduct, 1799-1982. 3.9 cu. ft.
B0047	Records of supersedeas, 1813-1881. 2 cu. ft. (3 volumes)
B0049	Executive orders for commutations, pardons, restorations, and respites, 1840-1929. 12 cu. ft. (28 volumes)
B0043	Lists of convicts discharged by expiration of sentence or pardon, 1848-1888. 3 cu. ft. (7 volumes)
B0048	Respites and commutation, 1854-1931. .1 cu. ft.
B0045	Reports of admissions to and discharges from county jails, 1866. 1 cu. ft. (2 volumes)
B0046	Executive restoration of citizenship rights, 1869-1931. 6 cu. ft. (8 volumes)
B0044	Abstracts of convictions and sentences returned by county clerks, 1901-1912. 1 cu. ft. (1 volume)
A1858	Petition to governor for pardon, 1914. .5 cu. ft.

13253   Executive pardons, respites, commutations, restorations of citizenship, and certificates, 1931-1990.
4.5 cu. ft.

Land Records

A0480   Indexes and translations of Dutch patents, 1630-1674.
.6 cu. ft. (4 volumes)

A0479   Index to deeds and mortgages, 1641-1842.
.7 cu. ft. (1 volume)

A0272   Applications for land grants, 1642-1803.
22 cu. ft. (63 volumes) (39 microfilm reels)

A0453   Record of deeds, 1652-1884.
22.2 cu. ft. (43 volumes)

A3074   Abstracts and indexes of deeds, 1640-1855.
4.2 cu. ft. (7 volumes)

12943   Letters patent, 1664-1990.
39 cu. ft.

A0487   Transcribed letters patent, 1664-1786.
1.5 cu. ft. (12 volumes)

A3121   Geographical index to patents, ca. 1786-1899.
.6 cu. ft.

A1891   Evidence upholding territorial rights and jurisdiction of New York
against Massachusetts, New Hampshire, and Vermonters, 1664-
1773.
.5 cu. ft. (1 microfilm reel)

A3302   Indian deed for lands in Schaghticoke, 1707.
.1 cu. ft. (1 item)

A0452   Field books, 1762-1845.
11 cu. ft. (55 volumes)

A0447   Military patents, 1764-1797.
4 cu. ft. (8 volumes)

B1065   Map of part of the River Delaware, showing the beginning of the
43rd degree of north latitude, 1774.
.1 cu. ft.

A0451   Original releases to the State, 1782-1929.
9 cu. ft. (13 volumes)

A0025   Holland Land Company maps and field notes, 1788-1899, bulk
         1788-1839.
         8 cu. ft.

A0478   Copies of releases to the State, 1788-1887.
         1 cu. ft. (3 volumes)

A3124   Abstracts of patents for lands in the military tract, including a copy
         of the "Balloting Book", 1790-1869.
         .3 cu. ft. (1 volume)

A0470   Abstract of title to land purchased from William Seward Webb
         and the Ne-Ha-Sa-Ne Park Association, 1792-1896.
         .3 cu. ft. (1 volume)

A0558   Records of original land grants and land under water, ca. 1799-
         1849.
         26 cu. ft.

A0477   Registers of mortgages to the State, 1807-1883.
         2.1 cu. ft. (4 volumes)

A0454   U.S. Loan mortgages, 1814-1903.
         1 cu. ft. (3 volumes)

A0481   Patents of land sold for arrears of quit rents, 1815, 1822.
         .3 cu. ft. (1 volume)

A3123   Index and abstracts of patents for lands in the military tract, ca.
         1820.
         .3 cu. ft.

A0476   Register of military bounty land grants, 1825.
         .5 cu. ft. (1 volume)

A0482   U.S. Loan mortgage foreclosure records, ca. 1841-1939.
         .3 cu. ft. (1 volume)

12945   Miscellaneous deeds and title papers, 1847-1990.
         11.7 cu. ft.

A0461   Town boundary establishment and alteration reports, 1849-1960.
         4 cu. ft. (3 volumes) (3 microfilm reels)

A0464   Original deeds and title papers, 1855-1975.
         16 cu. ft. (40 volumes)

A0324   Land Office records, 1877-1912.
         3 cu. ft.

A0468   Gettysburg Battlefield title papers, 1887-1889.
.5 cu. ft. (1 volume)

A0463   Miscellaneous deeds, leases, and releases, 1897-1901.
.5 cu. ft. (1 volume)

A0473   New York-Connecticut boundary line maps, 1908-1912.
2 cu. ft. (2 volumes)

A0459   Deeds of the superintendent of public works, 1910-1945.
1 cu. ft. (6 volumes)

B0252   Whiteprint copies of maps of lands permanently appropriated by the State for canal purposes, 1917-1948.
62 cu. ft. (69 portfolios containing 805 maps)

A0460   Land appropriation correspondence and maps, 1924-1974.
18 cu. ft. (50 volumes)

13010   Land appropriation maps for easements, ca. 1978-1983.
17 cu. ft.

Corporations

A1859   Incorporation certificates, 1811-1826.
.3 cu. ft. (1 volume)

A1860   Register of bonds for the New York and Erie Railroad Company, 1847.
.3 cu. ft. (1 volume)

A1862   Register of bonds for the Hudson and Berkshire Railroad Company, 1848-1849.
.3 cu. ft. (1 volume)

A1861   List of corporations filing annual reports, 1876.
.3 cu. ft.

B0070   Annual reports of name changes of corporations and individuals, 1900-1940.
1.5 cu. ft.

A0474   Records of conditional sales contracts for transportation company rolling stock, 1922-1969.
2.3 cu. ft. (7 volumes)

12958   List of corporations dissolved and annulments of dissolutions of corporations, 1924-1982.
41 cu. ft.

Census

A0028	Statistical summary of State census, 1825. .3 cu. ft. (1 volume)
A1829	Statistical summary of State census, 1835. .3 cu. ft. (1 volume)
A1830	Statistical summary of 1845 census, 1845. .6 cu. ft. (2 volumes)
A1832	Statistical summaries of State Indian census, 1845. .3 cu. ft. (1 volume)
A0275	State population census schedules, 1915. 175 cu. ft. (491 volumes)
A0035	Statistical summary of State census, 1915. 1.5 cu. ft.
A0276	State population census schedules, 1925. 175 cu. ft. (480 volumes)
A0415	Report of the enumeration of inhabitants, 1925. 2 cu. ft. (20 volumes)
A0430	Indian reservations population survey from 1925 census, 1925. .1 cu. ft. (1 microfilm reel)
A0375	Census of 1925, New York City Sanitary District tabulation, 1925. 1 cu. ft.

Alien Registration and Naturalization

A1869	Alien depositions of intent to become U.S. citizens, 1825-1913. 24.5 cu. ft. (95 volumes)
A1870	Abstracts of alien depositions, 1825-1913. 12 cu. ft. (33 volumes)
A1898	Index to alien depositions of intent to become U.S. citizens, 1825-1913. 2.5 cu. ft. (3 volumes)
A1872	Index to alien depositions, 1880-1890. .4 cu. ft. (1 volume)
A1871	Alien deposition fee registers, 1836-1854. .3 cu. ft. (2 volumes)

B0078   Supreme Court (First Judicial District) record of naturalizations, 1896-1906.
1 cu. ft. (11 volumes)

B0079   Registers of Kings County clerk of naturalizations, 1897-1900.
1 cu. ft. (3 volumes)

B0080   Report of the Erie County clerk of naturalizations, 1896.
1 cu. ft. (1 volume)

Other Records

A0108   Translations of Dutch volumes of colonial manuscripts, ca. 1870.
2 cu. ft.

A3300   Copies of official British colonial records, ca. 1611-1782.
.3 cu. ft. (2 folders)

A0116   Transcriptions of the minutes of the Provincial Congress, Provincial Convention, Committee of Safety, and Council of Safety, 1775-1777.
2 cu. ft.

B0015   Register of legislative agents: counsels, 1906-1920.
1 cu. ft. (2 volumes)

A0377   Expense statements of lobbyists, 1907-1915.
2 cu. ft.

13243   Village incorporation files and maps, 1886-1988, bulk 1908-1987.
52.5 cu. ft.

13242   Interlocal agreements, 1961-1990.
.9 cu. ft.

13244   Interstate compacts and agreements, 1921-1978, 1988, 1990.
2.6 cu. ft.

A0739   Correspondence from the commissioner of the Conservation Commission, 1917-1930.
1 cu. ft.

12979   Union label registration application files, 1901-1942.
.5 cu. ft.

A0356   Applications and registrations for trademarks on bottles and casks, 1847-1908.
2 cu. ft.

A0352   Peddlers licenses, 1840-1896.
1 cu. ft. (4 volumes)

A0449   Register of gold and silver mines, 1791-1914.
4.3 cu. ft. (23 volumes)

A0376   Public notices of discovery of gold and silver in New York State, 1899.
.3 cu. ft.

A0386   Records from the comptroller's New York City office, 1914-1928.
.5 cu. ft.

A0210   Revised Charter of Greater New York sent to the mayor, 1901.
.5 cu. ft.

A0355   Hearing files relating to proposed garbage reduction plant to be erected on Staten Island, 1916.
.5 cu. ft.

A0228   County clerk's reports on common schools, 1821-1822.
1 cu. ft.

A0184   Incoming correspondence relating to common schools, 1843-1847.
.2 cu. ft.

A3306   School and library charters, n.d.
.5 cu. ft.

A1873   Minutes of the meetings of the trustees of the Capitol and State Hall, 1834-1861.
.5 cu. ft. (2 volumes)

A3280   Photocopy of list of records and original wills delivered by Samuel Bayard, secretary of the colony, to John Morin Scott, secretary of state, 1783.
.1 cu. ft.

A0354   Transcript of hearing before the governor relating to charges against the chairman of the Public Service Commission, 1915.
.3 cu. ft.

COMMISSIONERS OF THE LAND OFFICE

A0177   Original minutes, 1785-1798.
.5 cu. ft.

A3249 Register of land grant applications, petitions, and correspondence, 1829.
.1 cu. ft.

A0179 Land patents, 1680-1751.
.5 cu. ft.

B0243 Legal records regarding grants of land under water and sale of State lands, 1899-1913.
.3 cu. ft.

BOARD OF COMMISSIONERS OF THE LAND OFFICE

A3236 Forest Preserve land purchase proposal files, 1920-1948.
2 cu. ft.

OFFICE FOR LOCAL GOVERNMENT

A0719 Research files, ca. 1938-1973.
13 cu. ft.

14261 Subject files, ca. 1957-1975.
14 cu. ft.

NEW YORK HARBOR COMMISSION

B0634 Description of the bulkhead and pier lines of the Port of New York, 1857.
.5 cu. ft.

STATE ATHLETIC COMMISSION

A0385 Financial records and reports, ca. 1920-1937.
3 cu. ft. (36 volumes)

Department of Taxation and Finance

Current Functions. The Department of Taxation and Finance administers the State tax laws, the State treasury, and the lottery. The department collects the following State and local taxes: personal income, business franchise, sales and use, alcoholic beverage, cigarette, motor fuel, highway use, oil, pari-mutuel and off-track betting, estate and gift, gain on real property, transfer of real estate and stocks, mortgage, and land. In administering the treasury the department receives and disperses State funds, reconciles accounts, invests the funds of certain agencies and authorities, and serves as joint custodian with the comptroller of State securities. In administering the lottery the department develops and promotes games, licenses lottery ticket agents, receives ticket sales revenue, and makes payments to prize winners.

Organizational History. During the Dutch colonial period, government revenue was derived primarily from customs duties and excise taxes. When these sources proved insufficient, the colony fell back on voluntary contributions, but as early as 1654 the home government also granted the colony permission to tax land and livestock directly. There was little change in the tax structure during the British colonial period.

Responsibility for tax collection and maintenance of public funds was vested in the office of receiver general under the Dutch, and in the office of collector and later receiver general during the first 50 years of British rule. In 1706, a treasurer was appointed and this office continued until the Revolution. The First Provincial Congress established an office of treasurer in 1775, and the office was continued in the first State constitution, which provided for appointment of a treasurer by the legislature with the nomination originating in the assembly. The treasurer was appointed annually by joint legislative ballot under the 1821 constitution and was chosen for a two-year term at a general election after adoption of the 1846 constitution.

After ratification of the United States Constitution and assumption by the Federal government of the powers to levy and collect excises and customs duties, New York State sought additional sources of revenue. During the late 18th century and the first half of the 19th century, the State obtained revenue primarily from land sales, lotteries, canal tolls, auction fees, taxes on salt works, and investment of State funds. Collecting revenue was largely the responsibility of the comptroller, while the treasurer had custody of the funds and disbursed them upon warrant of the comptroller.

The State also resorted to general property taxation, first from 1799 to 1802 and again from 1815 to 1826. By 1845, general property taxation became a necessary, permanent part of the revenue system, providing 98 percent of State tax revenue by 1879. Town and county officials assessed property and collected taxes for the State.

This system of local assessment caused inequities in the level of taxation between communities. In 1859 (Chapter 312), a State Board of Equalization was created to equalize the assessments among counties and to fix the total assessment of real and personal property on which the State tax was levied. The board consisted of the commissioners of the land office and three State assessors appointed by the governor. The office of State assessor was abolished in 1896 (Chapter 908) and was succeeded by a Board of Tax Commissioners, consisting of three gubernatorial appointees empowered to furnish technical and advisory services to local officials and to collect information and make reports on local assessment practices. The three tax commissioners and the land office commissioners continued to serve as the State Board of Equalization.

State government reliance on direct property tax revenue declined after 1880 and was discontinued entirely in 1928. Meanwhile a variety of other revenue-producing programs were established including corporation franchise taxes; estate and stock transfer taxes; fees on racing admissions, sale of alcoholic beverages, and motor vehicle registrations; and, beginning in 1919, a personal income tax. Assessment and tax-collection responsibilities were shared by the Board of Tax Commissioners, Board of Equalization, comptroller, secretary of state, and treasurer. Consolidation of these diverse functions began in 1915 (Chapter 317), when the State Tax Department was created. This department, headed by a three-member State Tax Commission (which succeeded the Board of Tax Commissioners), assumed the comptroller's duties relating to corporation taxes and continued the previous board's functions regarding the property tax, mortgage tax, and the problems of local property assessment. The State tax commissioners along with the commissioners of the land office continued to constitute the State Board of Equalization.

In 1921 (Chapter 90), most of the remaining tax-collection duties were transferred to the department, including responsibility for the property and stock transfer and personal income taxes from the comptroller and for the registration and licensing of motor vehicles and drivers from the secretary of state.

During the general reorganization of State government in 1925-26 the Tax Department was renamed the Department of Taxation and Finance (Laws of 1926, Chapter 553), headed by a commissioner appointed by the governor. The commissioner served as president of the State Tax Commission, which also included two other members appointed by the governor. The department assumed all functions of the comptroller under the judiciary, tax, military, or any other law relating to the assessment, levy, and collection of direct State taxes, took over the duties of the state treasurer and the commissioner of the canal fund, which were abolished, and took over custody of the State Teachers' Retirement Fund and other State employees' retirement and pension funds. The State Tax Commission constituted the State Board of Equalization, which was concerned with local government property assessment after the State property tax was discontinued in 1928.

The State Board of Equalization was removed from the department in 1949 (Chapter 346) and made an independent temporary state commission known as the State Board of Equalization and Assessment. In 1960 (Chapter 464), the department's semiautonomous Bureau of Motor Vehicles became the newly created Department of Motor Vehicles responsible for the registration and licensing of motor vehicles and their operators.

Several additional State taxes have been added since the 1920s, including a sales tax in 1965 (Chapter 93) that now is second only to the personal income tax as a source of revenue. A 1966 constitutional amendment allowed the operation of a State lottery. Enabling legislation in 1967 (Chapter 278) gave the department responsibility for administering the lottery and created within the department a State Lottery Commission (appointed by the governor) to serve in an advisory capacity. In 1973 (Chapter 346) all responsibility for administering the lottery was transferred to the newly created Racing and Wagering Board. Three years later (Chapter 92) the lottery was transferred back to the jurisdiction of the Department of Taxation and Finance to be administered by a "separate and independent" Division of the Lottery, whose director was appointed by the commissioner of taxation and finance.

In 1986 (Chapter 282), the State Tax Commission was abolished and replaced by a three-member Tax Appeals Tribunal appointed by the governor. The president of the tribunal serves as executive of the newly created Division of Tax Appeals, an independent division within the Department of Taxation and Finance. The Division of Tax Appeals holds hearings conducted by administrative law judges to resolve tax disputes between taxpayers and the department.

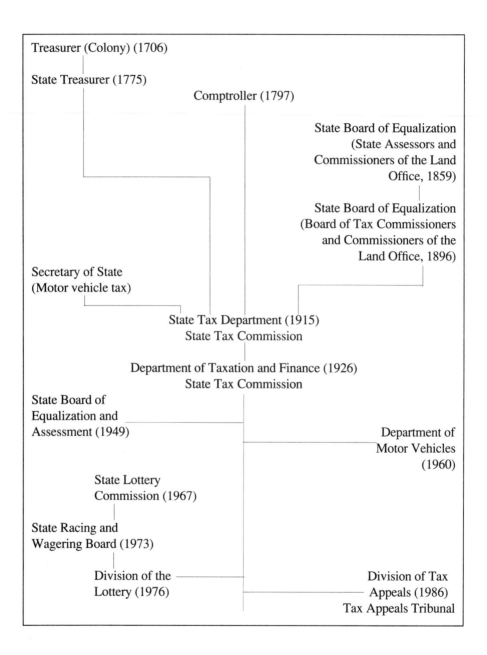

DEPARTMENT OF TAXATION AND FINANCE

General Agency-level Records

A3213   Files of the commissioner of Taxation and Finance, 1922-1942.
3 cu. ft.

B0969   Reports of sales of State lands, 1880-1939.
1 cu. ft. (5 volumes)

B0970   Register of title searches, 1900-1955.
.5 cu. ft. (6 volumes)

B0972   Monthly statements of mortgage taxes collected by counties, 1905-1931.
.5 cu. ft. (3 volumes)

B0980   Canal fund ledger, 1915-1930.
1 cu. ft. (2 volumes)

B0981   Special funds ledger, 1925-1927.
.3 cu. ft. (1 volume)

Law Bureau

15941   Real property tax correspondence, 1893-1969.
55 cu. ft.

15942   Lottery correspondence and regulations, 1966-1973.
3 cu. ft.

STATE TAX COMMISSION

B0984   Accounts of salaries, office and general expenses, 1919-1921.
.3 cu. ft. (1 volume)

B0999   Exhibit relating to real estate transfers and the rate of assessment of real property in the City of Buffalo, 1931.
.3 cu. ft. (1 volume)

STATE TAX DEPARTMENT

A3212   Appraisal of parcels, selected by the State Tax Commission, relating to the appeal by various towns from the assessment by the Board of Supervisors of Delaware County, ca. 1915-1917.
2.5 cu. ft.

A3214 Records of transfer tax for the estates of J.J. Astor, J.P. Morgan, W. Frear and F. Trowbridge, 1913-1917.
2 cu. ft.

TREASURER'S OFFICE

A3199 Abstracts of land grants, 1666-1775.
1.4 cu. ft.

A3190 Abstracts of warrants ("Payments from the Public Chest"), 1702-1705.
.1 cu. ft.

A3191 Accounts relating to excise tax of the Colony of New York, 1715-1733.
.1 cu. ft.

A3192 Accounts of quitrents and commutations, ca. 1728-1779.
4 cu. ft.

A0205 Books of entry, 1728-1766.
.5 cu. ft.

A3193 Accounts of revenue received, 1729-1783.
.5 cu. ft.

A3197 General accounts of provincial treasurer, ca. 1737-1767.
.5 cu. ft.

A3196 Reports of goods imported (manifest books) to New York, ca. 1740-1775.
5 cu. ft.

A3198 Entry documentation submitted to the treasurer, 1762-1772.
.1 cu. ft.

A3209 Accounts of land grants, 1766-1775.
.2 cu. ft.

A3203 Treasurer's ledger of financial transactions, 1775-1782.
.5 cu. ft.

A3200 Treasurer's journal, 1775-1784.
1 cu. ft.

A3201 Auditor's journal, 1775-1793.
1 cu. ft.

A3202   Treasurer's accounts of payments made, 1775-1797.
1 cu. ft.

A3204   General accounts, 1775-1797.
.5 cu. ft.

A0005   Journals, ledgers, and registers of receipts and payments by the State, 1775-1925.
350 cu. ft. (778 volumes)

A3205   Treasurer's daybook, 1778-1784.
.5 cu. ft.

A1201   Assessment rolls, 1779-1814.
.6 cu. ft.

A3210   Tax assessment lists, 1779-1788.
.5 cu. ft.

A3211   Register of abandoned children of slaves, ca. 1802-1866.
.1 cu. ft.

A1217   Treasurer's certificates to American Revolution veterans from New York State, ca. 1784.
.1 cu. ft.

A1090   Treasurer's account of canal tolls and salt duties deposited in banks, 1826-1832.
.6 cu. ft. (1 volume)

A3207   Statements, reports, and correspondence relating to State education funds, 1815-1842.
.1 cu. ft.

A3277   Accounts with county treasurers for sales of "The Natural History of New York," 1845-1871.
.3 cu. ft.

A3208   Correspondence from University of the State of New York to the comptroller relating to appointments, resignations and salaries of employees, 1857-1896.
.1 cu. ft.

B0979   General fund ledger, 1915-1926.
.5 cu. ft. (2 volumes)

B0978   Receipts journal, 1917-1923.
.5 cu. ft. (2 volumes)

B0977   Payments journal, 1921-1923.
         .3 cu. ft. (1 volume)

A3206   Tax assessment list for Van Rensselaer District, ca. 1750.
         .1 cu. ft. (1 item)

Department of Transportation

Current Functions. The Department of Transportation is responsible for planning, construction, maintenance, and supervision for New York's transportation network and infrastructure, including the State and local highway systems, canal system, five major ports, bus lines and public transportation organizations, and public and private airports. To fulfill these functions, the department engages in a number of activities, including coordinating and developing transportation policy and planning; coordinating and assisting in the planning, construction, maintenance, repair, and operation of transportation facilities and services, including highway, canal, rail, mass transit, port, and aviation facilities; planning for development of public and private commuter and general transportation facilities; administering a public safety program for rail and motor carriers in intrastate commerce; regulating rates and services of transportation corporations in the public interest; and investigating accidents on public transportation systems and evaluating the safety of such systems.

Organizational History. The origins of this department can be traced to the Dutch office of surveyor general established in 1642 to survey the lands of the Province of New Netherland. The office was continued under the British colonial government and reestablished after New York became a state (Laws of 1781, Chapter 32). The surveyor general was appointed by the Council of Appointment until 1821, when the new constitution provided for election by the legislature. Surveying the public lands continued to be the principal function of the office.

The major State involvement in transportation in the 19th century was the development of the canal system. Commissioners were appointed in 1810 and 1811 to report on possibilities for inland navigation in the State. In 1816 (Chapter 237), the legislature appointed five commissioners to oversee construction of a canal between the Hudson River and the Great Lakes. The following year (Laws of

1817, Chapter 262), the commissioners were made a permanent Board of Canal Commissioners, authorized to build canals between the Hudson River and Lake Erie, with branches to Lake Champlain and Lake Ontario. The same law established the commissioners of the canal fund, including the surveyor general, to administer a Canal Fund derived from canal tolls, other State revenues, and donations of land. After completion of the Erie Canal in 1825, legislation established a Canal Board comprised of the canal commissioners and the commissioners of the Canal Fund to fix tolls, make regulations, and hire employees (Laws of 1826, Chapter 314).

The Constitution of 1846 established the office of state engineer and surveyor. This office assumed the duties of the abolished surveyor general and was also given responsibility for carrying out engineering and surveying work on the canals. The Canal Board continued to appoint division canal superintendents and staff, but these people were to work at the direction of the state engineer and surveyor (Laws of 1848, Chapter 72).

An 1876 constitutional amendment abolished the canal commissioners and created the office of superintendent of public works, appointed by the governor. The superintendent was charged with executing all laws relating to canal maintenance and navigation except for those functions performed by the state engineer and surveyor, who continued to prepare maps, plans, and estimates for canal construction and improvement. The Canal Board (now consisting of the superintendent of public works, the state engineer and surveyor, and the commissioners of the canal fund) continued to handle hiring of employees and other personnel matters. The Barge Canal Law of 1903 (Chapter 147) directed the Canal Board to oversee the enlargement of and improvements to the Erie, Champlain, and Oswego canals.

The Department of Highways was established in 1908 (Chapter 330) to supervise bridges and highways financed by State funds. The department was originally headed by three commissioners appointed by the governor. A 1911 law (Chapter 646) designated the superintendent of highways, state engineer and surveyor, and superintendent of public works as highway commissioners. In 1913 (Chapter 80), a single highway commissioner replaced the three commissioners.

A 1923 law (Chapter 867) established the Department of Public Works, headed by the superintendent of public works. This department consolidated the offices of the superintendent of public works; superintendent and trustees of public buildings (established by Laws of 1909, Chapter 48, to care for all State buildings in Albany); Department of Highways; and Commission on Boundary Waters between the United States and Canada (created in 1920 to study the feasibility of a bridge between the United States and Canada; this commission included the state engineer and surveyor, superintendent of public works, and several other State officials).

Pursuant to the reorganization of State government in 1925-26, the Canal Board and the state engineer and surveyor were abolished and their functions assigned to the Department of Public Works. The commissioners of the canal fund were abolished, and responsibilty for the fund was transferred to the Department of Audit and Control.

Enabling legislation in 1926 (Chapter 348) established five divisions in the Department of Public Works: canals and waterways, highways, public building, engineering, and architecture. The department also absorbed the former Department of Architecture (created as the office of state architect in 1899 as the successor to the Office of Capitol Commissioner, then established as a department by Laws of 1914, Chapter 111, to prepare plans and specifications for State buildings); Bureau of Housing and Regional Planning (established within the Department of Architecture by Laws of 1923, Chapter 694); Salt Water Bays Commission (established in 1923 to survey waters of eastern Long Island); and Office of Harbor Masters (appointed by the governor after 1911 to regulate vessels in certain port cities north of New York City).

The Department of Public Works was reorganized in 1943 into three divisions: administration, construction, and operation and maintenance. An architecture division was added in 1955 and a finance and planning division in 1964.

The Department of Public Works was abolished in 1967 (Chapter 717), and its responsibilities for transportation planning, construction, and operation, including maintenance of the State barge canal system, were transferred to the new Department of Transportation. Also assigned to the new department were the duties and staff of the Office of Transportation (established in the Executive Department in 1959 to advise the governor on transportation policy); the duties and staff of the State Traffic Commission (created in 1936 to regulate traffic lights and signs, highway speeds, and safety programs); and the aviation functions of the Department of Commerce. Flood control, shore protection, and beach erosion control functions formerly exercised by the Department of Public Works were transferred to the Conservation Department. The duties and functions of the Architecture Division were transferred to the Office of General Services. In 1971, the department assumed from the Public Service Commission the regulatory functions relating to common carriers.

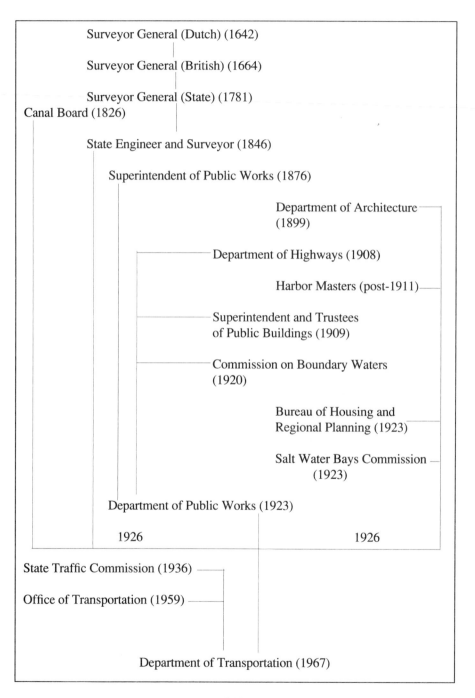

Surveyor General (Dutch) (1642)

Surveyor General (British) (1664)

Surveyor General (State) (1781)
Canal Board (1826)

State Engineer and Surveyor (1846)

Superintendent of Public Works (1876)

Department of Architecture
(1899)

Department of Highways (1908)

Harbor Masters (post-1911)

Superintendent and Trustees
of Public Buildings (1909)

Commission on Boundary Waters
(1920)

Bureau of Housing and
Regional Planning (1923)

Salt Water Bays Commission
(1923)

Department of Public Works (1923)

1926   1926

State Traffic Commission (1936)

Office of Transportation (1959)

Department of Transportation (1967)

DEPARTMENT OF TRANSPORTATION

Executive Deputy Commissioner

    B1334   Subject files, 1961-1967.
                 16 cu. ft.

Office of Planning and Development

    B0626   Highway development planning and progress files, 1921-1975.
                 3 cu. ft.

    11837   Transportation legislation planning files, 1953-1975.
                 7.2 cu. ft.

Regulation Division

    12393   Annual reports of stage coach and omnibus companies, 1909-1980.
                 86 cu. ft.

Highway, Aviation and Parts Division

   – Aviation Bureau

    13081   Airport construction project files, 1968-1985.
                 10 cu. ft.

Rail Operations Bureau

    13586   Rail subject files, 1954-1984.
                 29 cu. ft.

Legal Services Bureau

    13430   Files of the chairman of the task force investigating Love Canal, 1978-1979.
                 8 cu. ft.

Other Records

    14156   Route books for federal-aid highways, 1931-1977.
                 .5 cu. ft. (2 volumes)

    14155   Federal-aid urban area boundary maps, 1945-1975.
                 1 cu. ft. (1 volume)

DEPARTMENT OF PUBLIC WORKS

    10487   Commissioner's correspondence and subject files, 1943-1967.
                 147 cu. ft. R

B0251   Subject files of the deputy superintendent, 1950-1960.
         33 cu. ft.

B0171   Maps, blueprints, tracings, diagrams, plans, and cross sections of
         canal structures and sites, ca. 1830-1947.
         250 cu. ft.

B0392   Charts and maps of the State canal system, ca. 1923.
         1 cu. ft. (1 volume)

B0214   Barge Canal land appropriation maps, 1905-1925.
         14 cu. ft.

B0213   Barge Canal contract files, 1907-1944.
         85 cu. ft.

B0385   Barge Canal maintenance contracts, 1924-1931.
         3 cu. ft.

B1353   Plans, blueprints, and drawings relating to the operation and main-
         tenance of the Barge Canal, ca. 1902-1949.
         18 cu. ft.

A0133   Contracts for improvement of the Erie, Oswego, and Champlain
         Canals, ca. 1915-1925.
         .5 cu. ft.

B0693   Monthly time books for work done on the western division of the
         Barge Canal, 1905-1936.
         1 cu. ft. (9 volumes)

B0694   Distribution of expenses to engineers employed on the western
         division of the Barge Canal, 1927-1943.
         .3 cu. ft. (2 volumes)

B0381   Water gauge readings, ca. 1887-1951.
         20.5 cu. ft.

B0204   Index to Barge Canal minute books, ca. 1900-1931.
         3 cu. ft. (13 volumes)

B0208   Scrapbook regarding the Barge Canal, 1929-1932.
         .3 cu. ft. (1 volume)

B0746   File on All American Canal and St. Lawrence Ship Canal and
         Power Project, 1921-1932.
         .5 cu. ft.

10448   Maps, drawings and blueprints related to State waterways and canals, ca. 1851-1941.
24.8 cu. ft.

B0729   Roll maps and plans of the middle division of the Erie Canal, ca. 1850-1951.
139 cu. ft.

B1023   Unidentified maps, plans, and drawings of New York State canals, n.d.
5 cu. ft.

B0278   Records of petitions and details of roads built, 1898-1928.
5 cu. ft. (12 volumes)

B0745   Financial statements pertaining to highway contracts, 1914-1924.
.3 cu. ft. (1 volume)

B0320   State and federal-aid highway system planning maps, ca. 1921-1945.
.6 cu. ft.

B1349   State highway planning maps, ca. 1925-1950.
3.3 cu. ft.

14154   Federal-aid secondary highway system county maps, 1946-1947.
.9 cu. ft. (1 volume)

A0733   Urban arterial highway route planning files, 1947-1963, bulk 1947-1954.
3 cu. ft.

A4036   Highway planning aerial photographs of cities and villages, 1963-1966.
1 cu. ft.

B1355   Blueprints for Wards Island ferry, 1929.
1 cu. ft.

A0582   Exhibits from court case regarding elimination of grade crossings, ca. 1926-1929.
1.5 cu. ft.

B0714   Revolving account book of superintendent of grain elevators, 1922-1938.
.1 cu. ft. (1 volume)

Office of the Superintendent

B0737   Western division engineers' ledgers regarding division personnel, 1933-1944.
.5 cu. ft. (2 volumes)

Division of Administration, Bureau of Research and Statistics

A3229   State, district, county, and special highway maps, 1909-1955, bulk 1929-1949.
1 cu. ft.

Division of Canals and Waterways

A1276   Official orders, 1927-1930, 1934-1939.
3 volumes.

B1213   Plans, maps, and specifications relating to various Barge Canal contracts, ca. 1895-1935.
12 cu. ft.

– Syracuse Regional Office

B1069   Contract, computations, estimates, maps, sections, and charts concerning the U.S.—Barge Canal, 1933-1958.
2 cu. ft.

Division of Counsel

11074   Official orders, 1909-1930.
16 cu. ft. (36 volumes)

Division of Engineering

B1019   U.S.—Barge Canal contracts, estimates, and final accounts, 1941-1942.
1 cu. ft.

B0223   Negative photographs of State institutions, Barge Canal locations and structures, and highways, 1940-1944.
2 cu. ft. (ca. 1,500 items)

Division of Finance and Planning

10491   Minutes of meetings of Niagara Frontier Port Authority, 1959-1967.
2 cu. ft.

Division of Highways

B0228   Correspondence files regarding federally funded highway construction projects, 1917-1933.
1 cu. ft.

– Bureau of Highway Planning

A0766   Capital District transportation study aerial photographs, 1963.
3 cu. ft.

A4034   Statewide highway planning survey county maps, 1945-1949.
.5 cu. ft. (1 volume)

SUPERINTENDENT OF PUBLIC WORKS

B0382   Correspondence and subject files, ca. 1907-1921.
89 cu. ft.

B0330   Assistant clerk's letter book, 1903-1907.
.3 cu. ft. (1 volume)

B0201   Minutes of the canal commissioners and superintendent of public works, 1817-1889.
.6 cu. ft.

B0202   Index to minutes of the canal commissioners and superintendent of public works, 1817-1921.
1 cu. ft. (15 volumes)

B0216   Canal system contract agreements and specifications, ca. 1888-1904.
4 cu. ft.

B0220   Canal contract final accounts, 1896-1905.
1 cu. ft.

B0345   Advertising journal for the letting of canal construction contracts, 1903-1923.
.3 cu. ft. (1 volume)

B1354   Final estimate book for several Barge Canal Middle Division contracts, 1914-1915.
1 cu. ft.

A3261   Electrical inspector's Barge Canal construction correspondence, 1911-1914.
.2 cu. ft.

A1277 Notices of service upon owners of lands appropriated for the Barge Canal, 1906-1916.
3 volumes.

B0338 Depositions regarding notices of land appropriations for Barge Canal purposes, 1913-1916.
.3 cu. ft. (1 volume)

A0244 Land sale records and accounts, ca. 1790-1895.
3 cu. ft.

B0293 Index to canal structure map and plan books, ca. 1834-1905.
1 cu. ft.

A4290 Card index to Western Division canal maps, plans, estimates and related structures, ca. 1830-1925.
1.5 cu. ft. (ca. 7,000 cards)

B0738 Superintendent of Repairs' printed abstracts of expenditures for work on the western division of the Barge Canal, 1912-1923.
.5 cu. ft. (2 volumes)

B0386 Duplicate petitions submitted to the court of claims pertaining to canal related damages, 1897-1908.
2 cu. ft.

B0340 Assistant superintendent's record of bills pertaining to the eastern division, ca. 1911-1914.
1 cu. ft. (1 volume)

B0368 Journal of receipts and expenditures for construction of Barge Canal, 1915-1918.
.5 cu. ft. (1 volume)

B0346 Ledgers for canal related accounts, 1886-1899.
1 cu. ft. (4 volumes)

B0373 Journal pertaining to canals, 1893-1899.
.3 cu. ft. (1 volume)

B0342 Abstract registers of vouchers for money expended on State canals, 1916-1918.
1 cu. ft. (2 volumes)

B0337 Canal ice permits, 1895-1906.
.4 cu. ft. (1 volume)

B0334 Job application registers, 1891-1895.
.3 cu. ft. (2 volumes)

B1020   Construction permit files, 1903-1904.
         .5 cu. ft.

B0697   Newspaper clippings regarding events on the Barge Canal, 1902-
         1908.
         .5 cu. ft. (1 volume)

B0343   Journals pertaining to State institutional buildings, 1901-1914.
         1.5 cu. ft. (5 volumes)

B0344   Ledgers pertaining to engineering appropriations, 1903-1909.
         .5 cu. ft. (2 volumes)

B0709   Highway expenditure journals, ca. 1911.
         1 cu. ft., (2 volumes)

B0341   Abstracts of expenditures, 1916-1921.
         .8 cu. ft. (2 volumes)

Assistant Superintendent's Office

B0329   Letterbooks, 1899-1909.
         2.3 cu. ft. (16 volumes)

B1021   Photographs of culverts on the western division of the Erie Canal,
         ca. 1900.
         .5 cu. ft.

General Inspector's Office

B0328   Letterbooks, 1895-1905.
         1 cu. ft. (13 volumes)

B0332   Newspaper clippings regarding canal operations and conditions,
         1885-1912.
         2 cu. ft. (10 volumes)

Publicity Agent's Office

B0234   Correspondence files, 1921-1922.
         1 cu. ft.

Board of Consulting Engineers

B0225   Correspondence files, 1904-1906.
         1 cu. ft.

B0221   Reports and recommendations, 1913-1914.
         .5 cu. ft.

B0222   Weekly employment reports, 1914-1921.
.5 cu. ft.

COMMISSIONERS OF FORFEITURES

A4032   Lists of sales of and accounts of payments for confiscated lands, 1784-1788.
.5 cu. ft. (3 volumes, 1 disbound list)

SURVEYOR GENERAL

Land Grants, Sales, and Surveys

A4005   Abstracts of letters patent, 1665-1767.
.2 cu. ft. (2 volumes)

A4007   List of land patents granted by the State, 1784-1794.
.2 cu. ft.

A4013   Report and abstract of sales of land forfeited to New York State by Roger Morris and claimed by John Jacob Astor, 1781-1819.
.2 cu. ft. (2 volumes)

B0256   Records of applications for and sales of forfeited estates and military lots, 1783-1807.
.3 cu. ft. (1 volume)

A4008   List of grants to American Revolution soldiers, 1784-1790.
.2 cu. ft. (1 item)

B0255   Books of sales of State land, 1786-1927.
4 cu. ft. (17 volumes)

A4010   Description of lots granted to New Yorkers in compensation for land lost to Vermont, 1788.
.5 cu. ft. (1 volume)

A3267   Surveyor's bills and receipts for advertising sales of land, 1793-1826.
.3 cu. ft.

A0284   Register of lands sold, 1794-1812.
.3 cu. ft. (1 volume)

A4018   Maps of land purchased from the Holland Land Company, 1804-ca. 1849, bulk ca. 1840-1849.
6 cu. ft. (6 volumes) (1 microfilm reel)

A4027   Conveyances of Holland Land Company land, 1828.
.5 cu. ft. (1 volume) (1 microfilm reel)

A4019   Land survey field books, 1668-1848, bulk 1749-1830.
12 cu. ft. (61 volumes) (18 microfilm reels)

A4011   Survey maps of lands in New York and Vermont, 1736-1822, bulk 1760-1790.
116 maps.

A4038   Returns of surveys of State land, 1750-1787.
1 cu. ft. (4 volumes)

A4037   Field book of the boundary line between the Minisink and Hardenburgh patents, 1847.
.1 cu. ft. (1 volume)

Canals and Roads

A4006   Maps produced for the Commissioners to Report a Plan for Improving the Navigation of the Hudson River, 1820-1830, bulk 1820.
.5 cu. ft. (1 volume)

B0376   Index to contractors whose proposals were accepted for canal projects, ca. 1830-1840.
.1 cu. ft. (1 volume)

11835   Field notes, monthly work, material, and cost estimates, measurements for Erie Canal enlargement, 1835-1844.
2 cu. ft. (24 volumes)

B0722   Stone measurements and quantities used in the enlargement of the Erie Canal, 1837-1840.
.1 cu. ft. (1 volume)

A0855   Maps, profiles, and surveys of Erie and Hudson State roads, 1825.
5 cu. ft. (7 volumes)

Cities and Towns

A4026   Map of the Town of Brooklyn, Kings County, 1834.
.2 cu. ft. (1 volume)

A4276   Map of the village of Geddes, 1821-1822.
.1 cu. ft.

A4009   Register of town and city creation dates, 1801-1825.
.3 cu. ft. (1 volume)

STATE ENGINEER AND SURVEYOR

General Administrative Records

B0226	Correspondence files, 1848-1895. 1 cu. ft. (4 volumes)
B0250	Resident, division and assistant engineers' correspondence, 1904-1915. 1.3 cu. ft. (17 volumes)
B0247	Administrative subject files, 1922, 1925. 8 cu. ft.
B0268	Outgoing correspondence regarding land matters, 1890-1898, bulk 1890-1892, 1897-1898. 1 cu. ft. (2 volumes)
10482	Card index to correspondence of the State Engineer and Surveyor, 1901-1925. 40 cu. ft.
A1275	Special deputy State engineer's monthly reports, 1917-1920. 1 volume.
B0232	Monthly reports, 1921. .5 cu. ft.
B0248	Engravings of plans, profiles, and maps accompanying the annual report of the State Engineer and Surveyor, 1859. .5 cu. ft. (15 printed engravings)
B0267	Annual reports of bridge companies, 1864-1884. .3 cu. ft. (1 volume)
B0261	Register of expenditures for surveyor general and State engineer and surveyor's offices, 1839-1871, bulk 1839-1848. .3 cu. ft. (1 volume)
B0711	Monthly and final estimates for non-canal projects, 1879-1886. .3 cu. ft. (4 volumes)
B0230	Contractor's monthly estimates, ca. 1890-1902. 1 cu. ft.
B0245	Opinions and abstracts of attorney general's decisions, 1881-1895. .5 cu. ft.

A1143 Lists of appointments of assistant engineers and other employees, 1851-1900.
4 cu. ft.

A4021 Register of job applications, 1893.
.3 cu. ft. (1 volume)

A3260 Payrolls for employees in military service, 1917-1920.
.2 cu. ft.

B0249 Accounts of property first cleared and left at Boonville on the Black River Canal, 1857-1894.
3 cu. ft. (57 volumes)

B0673 Copy of Canal Commissioners' report to State Assembly and dock building permits regarding Erie Basin at Buffalo, 1863-1869.
.1 cu. ft. (1 volume)

Office of Special Deputy State Engineer

B0227 Correspondence files, 1904-1907.
7 cu. ft.

Western Division Engineer's Office

B0383 Correspondence and subject files, 1849-1908, bulk 1878-1897.
8.5 cu. ft.

B0331 Assistant engineer's letterbook, 1908-1909.
.3 cu. ft. (1 volume)

Land Records

A4016 Records of surveys and maps of State lands, ca. 1686-1892.
29 cu. ft. (29 volumes)

A0273 Survey maps of lands in New York State, 1711-1856, bulk 1772-1856.
36 cu. ft. (ca. 1,000 maps).

12405 Land survey maps, 1798-1888.
.9 cu. ft. (3 maps)

A4012 Holland Land Company field notebooks, 1798-1815.
4 cu. ft. (671 volumes) (23 microfilm reels)

B0254 Miscellaneous field notes relating to Holland Land Company holdings and adjoining tracts, 1806-1890, bulk 1806-1811.
.6 cu. ft. (4 volumes) (1 microfilm reel)

B0280 Holland Land Company deed books, 1803-1857.
24 cu. ft. (41 volumes)

B0277 Deed tables regarding sale of Holland Land Company lands, 1802-1833.
1 cu. ft. (3 volumes) (1 microfilm reel)

B0279 Ledgers of sales for purchases of Holland Land Company land, 1799-1842.
13 cu. ft. (23 volumes)

A4017 Cash books for survey and sale of State lands, 1823-1927.
1 cu. ft. (4 volumes)

A4003 Certificates and bonds for sales of State land, 1786-1903, bulk 1807-1903.
1.5 cu. ft. (17 volumes)

A4004 Records of sales of State lands belonging to various State funds, 1824-1860.
.5 cu. ft. (2 volumes)

A4014 Records relating to sales of State lands, 1796-1873.
.5 cu. ft.

B0369 Journal recording original land sales by the State engineer and surveyor, 1914-1928.
.3 cu. ft. (1 volume)

A3248 Survey descriptions and appraisals of Onondaga Salt Springs lands to be sold, 1851-1881, bulk 1851, 1879-1881.
.1 cu. ft.

A4025 Records of applications for and grants of land under water, 1875-1903, bulk 1875-1885 and 1901-1903.
.3 cu. ft. (2 volumes)

A4020 Description and map of Storm King grant to the New York Central Railroad, 1916-1917.
.1 cu. ft. (3 items)

A4035 Survey maps of village corporation boundary lines, 1870-1939.
.5 cu. ft. (48 maps)

B0244 Boundary line agreements and photographs, 1896-1911.
.3 cu. ft.

A4023   Drawings of State boundary monuments, ca. 1900.
         3 cu. ft. (3 volumes)

A3239   Inquiry regarding title to land in Buffalo, 1902.
         .5 cu. ft.

A4024   Indexes to maps and land records, 1850-1900.
         1 cu. ft. (6 volumes)

Canal Records

— General Canal Administration

B0702   Middle division letterbooks, 1850-1890.
         1.5 cu. ft. (13 volumes)

B0690   Western division letterbooks, 1854-1899.
         4 cu. ft. (32 volumes)

B0731   Western division resident engineer's letterbook, 1911-1912.
         .3 cu. ft. (1 volume)

B0325   Letters of instruction to western division engineers, 1903-1919.
         .5 cu. ft. (2 volumes)

B0740   Western division office report and letterbook, 1875.
         .3 cu. ft. (1 volume)

A4022   Copy of annual report on the canals, 1851.
         .2 cu. ft. (1 volume)

B0696   Report and estimates concerning the construction of gun boat
         locks on the eastern division of the Erie Canal, 1864.
         .4 cu. ft. (1 volume)

B0708   Reports, cost estimates, and certificates pertaining to the middle
         division of the canal system, 1862-1865.
         .1 cu. ft. (1 volume)

B0670   Western division engineers' annual reports, estimates of expenses,
         and other reports regarding canals, 1856-1901.
         .6 cu. ft. (9 volumes)

B0671   Western division resident engineer's annual report to division
         engineer, 1859-1860.
         .1 cu. ft. (1 volume)

B0668   Reports, statements, and estimates of expenses of western division
         engineer's office, 1850-1851.
         .1 cu. ft. (1 volume)

B0679 Engineers' progress reports regarding repairs and construction in western division of the Erie Canal, 1889-1890.
.1 cu. ft. (1 volume)

B0725 Engineers' diaries, 1905-1939.
20 cu. ft.

B0231 Weekly reports of engineers regarding the Barge Canal, 1921.
.5 cu. ft.

B0681 Histories of various canal projects on western division of the Erie Canal, ca. 1880-1919.
.4 cu. ft. (8 volumes)

B0712 Journal of proceedings in engineer's office at Whitehall, 1856.
.1 cu. ft. (1 volume)

B0688 Journals for western division accounts, 1870-1905.
2.5 cu. ft. (10 volumes)

B0372 Canal journals, 1891-1916.
1 cu. ft. (3 volumes)

B0352 Ledger, cash books, journal, and trial balance books, 1916-1920.
.6 cu. ft. (4 volumes)

B0378 Journal and voucher register for Barge Canal contracts, 1905-1924.
.5 cu. ft. (1 volume)

B0719 Resident engineer's ledger of expenses for the enlargement of the eastern division of the Erie Canal, 1854-1855.
.1 cu. ft. (1 volume)

B0354 Index to eastern division employees ledger, 1899-1902.
.3 cu. ft. (1 volume)

B0715 Employees' ledgers regarding Champlain Canal improvement expenses, 1890-1902.
2 cu. ft. (4 volumes)

B0689 Western division account ledgers, 1876-1904.
2 cu. ft. (5 volumes)

B0351 Canal ledger books, 1891-1921.
1.3 cu. ft. (6 volumes)

B0686 Canal construction projects and repairs ledger, 1887-1907.
.2 cu. ft. (1 volume)

B0377   Final estimates and accounts, ca. 1835-1905.
100 cu. ft. (215 volumes)

B0347   Certified final accounts for canal construction projects, 1841-1896.
3 cu. ft. (18 volumes)

B0654   Final accounts and estimates for Genesee Valley Canal and Ischua
Feeder, 1854.
.1 cu. ft. (1 volume)

B0359   Barge Canal final accounts, ca. 1906-1913.
.8 cu. ft. (2 volumes)

B0364   Barge Canal terminal final accounts, 1912.
.4 cu. ft. (1 volume)

B0698   Index to western division final accounts, ca. 1867, 1890.
.3 cu. ft. (2 volumes)

B0717   Cash accounts regarding the eastern division of the Erie Canal and
the Champlain Canal, 1884-1889.
.1 cu. ft. (2 volumes)

B0652   Account books for the Genesee Valley Canal, ca. 1843, 1863.
2 cu. ft. (10 volumes)

B0398   Cost account volumes for the western division of the Erie Canal
and Genesee Valley Canal, 1856-1878.
2 cu. ft. (33 volumes)

B0736   Account books of payments made to companies and employees for
work on the western division of the Barge Canal, 1905-1908.
.5 cu. ft. (2 volumes)

B0741   Account book listing expenditures and monthly balance statements
of the western division, 1911-1912.
.2 cu. ft. (1 volume)

B0733   Accounts of costs and payrolls pertaining to Barge Canal contract
59, ca. 1918-1923.
.3 cu. ft. (1 volume)

B0677   Division engineer's account book, 1872-1874.
.1 cu. ft. (1 volume)

B0669   Western division resident engineer's day book, 1852-1858.
.1 cu. ft. (1 volume)

B0371   Cash book for the Barge Canal, 1913-1916.
.1 cu. ft. (1 volume)

B0723   Record of payments on various contracts pertaining to the eastern division, 1850-1862.
.1 cu. ft. (1 volume)

B0705   Miscellaneous payments made for work done on the western division of the Erie Canal and the Genesee Valley Canal, 1848-1868.
.1 cu. ft. (1 volume)

B0706   Expenditures paid by engineers for work done on the western division of the Erie Canal and the Genesee Valley Canal, 1848-1858.
.1 cu. ft. (1 volume)

B0657   Division and assistant engineers' expense books regarding the western division, 1895-1899.
.2 cu. ft. (2 volumes)

B0703   Abstracts of accounts of labor and materials supplied for work done on the Erie and Genesee Valley canals, ca. 1840-1860.
.3 cu. ft. (1 volume)

B0718   Summaries of expenditures made for repair and improvement of the Champlain Canal, 1889-1895.
.1 cu. ft. (1 volume)

B0219   Abstracts of expenditures of Erie Canal contracts, 1900-1904.
2 cu. ft.

B0363   Monthly summaries of payment for improvement of the Erie, Champlain, and Oswego canals, 1903.
.4 cu. ft. (1 volume)

B0350   Abstracts of expenditures for construction of Barge Canal and terminals, 1903-1914.
2 cu. ft. (11 volumes)

B0362   Summary of engineering expenditures for constructing Barge Canal, 1904-1911.
.4 cu. ft. (1 volume)

B0349   Certified abstracts of expenditures, 1910-1914.
1 cu. ft. (4 volumes)

B0743   Western Division Engineers' abstracts of expenditures pertaining to employees, 1920-1926.
.3 cu. ft.

B0370   Trial balance book for the Barge Canal, 1913-1916.
.1 cu. ft. (1 volume)

B0353   Index to final estimates of contracts for the eastern division of the
Erie Canal, ca. 1880-1900.
.3 cu. ft. (1 volume)

B0393   Barge Canal contract final estimate folios, ca. 1915-1920.
10 cu. ft. (17 volumes)

B0397   Monthly estimates for improvement, repair, and enlargement of
the State's canal system, 1835-1907.
29 cu. ft. (115 volumes)

B0655   Estimates for the Genesee Valley Canal, 1851-1855.
.1 cu. ft. (1 volume)

B0374   Engineer's estimates of cost for canal contracts, ca. 1895-1915.
1 cu. ft. (3 volumes)

B0366   Monthly estimates for construction of Barge Canal, 1905.
.3 cu. ft.

B0365   Preliminary estimates for construction of Barge Canal, 1904-1916.
.4 cu. ft. (1 volume)

B0732   Preliminary estimates of quantities and costs for Barge Canal contracts, 1907-1909.
.3 cu. ft. (1 volume)

B0367   Preliminary estimates for construction of Barge Canal terminals,
1912-1918.
.4 cu. ft. (1 volume)

B0685   Summary of estimates for extraordinary canal repairs on the western division, 1895-1904.
.2 cu. ft. (1 volume)

B0699   Bills of materials used in canal construction and repair projects,
ca. 1854-1904.
1.2 cu. ft. (9 volumes)

B0720   Check register, 1920-1922.
.4 cu. ft. (1 volume)

B0672   Work force account, contract, and estimates of expenses regarding
Erie Basin and slips in Buffalo, 1858-1862.
.1 cu. ft. (1 volume)

B0680   Weekly employee reports, 1885-1895.
.2 cu. ft. (2 volumes)

B0742   Salaries paid to personnel temporarily employed on the middle division of the Erie Canal, 1893-1906.
.2 cu. ft. (1 volume)

B0684   Work force book for Section 13, 1898.
.1 cu. ft. (1 volume)

B0683   Personal and employment histories of western division employees, 1899-1907.
.1 cu. ft. (1 volume)

B0384   Eastern, middle, and western division canal records, ca. 1848-1900.
12.5 cu. ft.

B0326   Requisitions for supplies for construction of the Barge Canal, 1908.
.3 cu. ft.

B0682   Copies of permits issued by the superintendent of public works, 1853-1892.
.1 cu. ft. (1 volume)

– *Canal Contracts*

B0658   Contract and specification forms regarding the Genesee Valley Canal, 1838.
.1 cu. ft. (1 volume)

B0355   Contract proposals for the enlargement of the Erie Canal, 1847-1854, bulk 1847-1850.
1 cu. ft. (3 volumes)

B0659   Notices, written explanations, blank contracts, and specifications exhibited at lettings at Rochester and Clyde, 1850.
.2 cu. ft. (2 volumes)

B0660   Contracts and specifications exhibited and proposals received at letting in Lockport for Oak Orchard Creek Aqueduct, 1850.
.2 cu. ft. (2 volumes)

B0661   Register of contracts, field and office books, and other matters relating to the Erie Canal enlargement, 1851.
.1 cu. ft. (1 volume)

B0662   Index to proposals received at Albany, 1851.
.1 cu. ft. (1 volume)

B0735   Printed quantities exhibited at lettings for the western division of the Erie Canal and the Genesee Valley Canal, 1851.
.3 cu. ft.

B0734   Contract specimens pertaining to the 1854 enlargement of the State's canals, 1854-1859.
.3 cu. ft. (1 volume)

B0710   Letting records regarding various canals and locations of the western division, ca. 1860-1868.
.3 cu. ft. (1 volume)

B0663   Index to contractors' proposals for work on western division, ca. 1850-1901.
.2 cu. ft. (2 volumes)

B0687   Contract specifications, engineers' estimates, and related documents pertaining to the nine million dollar canal improvement, 1892-1905.
1 cu. ft. (6 volumes)

B0395   Contract plans relating to improvement of the Erie and Oswego canals, ca. 1895-1898.
36 cu. ft.

B0358   Canal contract registers, 1898-1926.
1 cu. ft. (3 volumes)

B0394   Barge Canal contract cross section sheets, 1916, 1922.
1 cu. ft. (2 volumes)

B0391   Barge Canal contract location maps, ca. 1904-1905.
2 cu. ft. (18 volumes)

B0236   Walters Act administrative files, 1918-1919.
1 cu. ft.

B0241   Card index to the Walters Act administrative files, 1918-1919.
.3 cu. ft.

– *Canal Construction, Maintenance, and Operation*

B0730   Engineers' field books for construction of the State's canal system, ca. 1830-1920.
160 cu. ft.

B0692   Final calculations for State canal construction, ca. 1831-1861.
9 cu. ft. (21 volumes)

B0399   Preliminary estimates, calculations, and measurements for canal system construction and repair, ca. 1835-1912.
17 cu. ft. (49 volumes)

B0724   Accounts, notes on damages, and survey computations for enlargement of the Erie Canal, ca. 1839-1845.
.3 cu. ft. (1 volume)

B0676   Engineer's formula book with specifications and drawings, ca. 1869-1878.
.1 cu. ft. (1 volume)

B0739   Record of cement received and used for Barge Canal contract No. 60, 1908-1909.
.3 cu. ft. (1 volume)

B0233   Card index to locations of Barge Canal construction records, 1917-1921.
1 cu. ft.

B0292   Canal structure map and plan books, ca. 1827-1905.
135 cu. ft. (135 volumes)

B0356   Index book to mechanical structures on canals, ca. 1850-1895.
.3 cu. ft. (1 volume)

A1272   Scrapbook of photographs, maps, and diagrams of canal, highway, and watershed construction, 1898-1907.
.9 cu. ft. (1 volume)

B0727   Glass plate negatives depicting construction of the western division of the Barge Canal, ca. 1907-1921.
92 cu. ft.

B0728   Index to glass plate negatives depicting construction of the western division of the Barge Canal, ca. 1907-1921.
2 cu. ft.

11833   Barge Canal construction photographs, 1905-1921.
21.3 cu. ft.

B0361   Bridge survey registers, 1877.
.6 cu. ft.

A3259   Canal bridge reference lists, ca. 1917.
.2 cu. ft.

B0678   Time book pertaining to locking procedures in the western division of the Erie Canal, 1879.
.1 cu. ft. (1 volume)

B0707   Gauge descriptions from various locations on State canals, 1905-1910.
.2 cu. ft. (1 volume)

B0389   Copies of hydrographs and flow data of the Canaseraga and Keshequa Creeks and the Genesee River, ca. 1910-1919, bulk 1918-1919.
.3 cu. ft. (1 volume)

B0388   Record books of watersheds and related improvements in the western division of the Barge Canal, 1919-1920.
.5 cu. ft. (9 volumes)

– *Canal Structures and Lands*

B0653   Profiles of Locks 98 and 99 on the Genesee Valley Canal, ca. 1843.
.1 cu. ft. (1 volume)

B0726   Maps of the 1854 enlargement of the western division of the Erie Canal, ca. 1850.
18 cu. ft. (48 items)

B0379   Maps, plans, details, and drawings of structures and locations of the middle and western divisions of the Erie, Genesee Valley, and Oswego canals, 1830-1900, bulk 1860-1900.
9 cu. ft. (27 volumes)

B0380   Western division canal maps and plans, ca. 1879-1925, bulk ca. 1896-1912.
174 cu. ft.

B0360   Index to maps and plans, ca. 1851-1895.
.6 cu. ft. (2 volumes)

B0675   Detailed estimates and location maps for proposed construction of gun boat locks on the western division of the Erie Canal, 1863.
.2 cu. ft. (2 volumes)

B0651   Original cross sections for 1876 survey of the western division of the Erie Canal, ca. 1877.
1.5 cu. ft. (13 volumes)

B0650   Original and preliminary cross sections for 1895 survey of Erie Canal improvement, ca. 1896.
6 cu. ft. (17 volumes)

B0396   Sectional canal survey maps of the 1895 improvement of the Erie Canal, ca. 1896-1897.
12 cu. ft.

B0253   Barge Canal sectional maps, ca. 1896.
132 cu. ft.

B1009   Barge Canal plans, 1920.
.1 cu. ft. (1 volume)

B1212   Roll survey maps relating to the 1854 Survey in the western division, ca. 1830-1890.
6 cu. ft.

B1211   Western division of the Erie and Barge canals roll maps, ca. 1850-1910.
27 cu. ft.

B1210   Middle and western division survey maps for the proposed 1895 Erie Canal enlargement, ca. 1895-1900.
32 cu. ft.

14068   Erie and Champlain canals topographic survey maps, ca. 1904-1915.
40 cu. ft.

B0224   Reports and supporting records regarding survey for proposed canal between the Barge Canal and Cayuga Lake, 1906.
.5 cu. ft.

B0695   Water supply computations for Black River survey, 1911.
.3 cu. ft. (2 volumes)

A0812   Map of improvements to state ditch off the Chemung Canal, ca. 1870.
.2 cu. ft. (1 map)

B0390   Survey records and estimates for proposed Chemung Canal reconstruction, 1913-1914.
1 cu. ft.

B0215   Abandoned canal lands and blue line survey files, 1914-1923.
8 cu. ft.

A0867 Blue line maps of the canal lands owned by the State, 1917-1948.
420 maps.

B0691 Copies of Monroe County clerk's office records of awards, deeds,
and claims for canal lands, 1822-1884, bulk 1822-1862, 1884.
.5 cu. ft. (1 volume)

B0664 Description of lands appropriated for Genesee Valley Canal, 1839-
1882.
.1 cu. ft. (1 volume)

B0656 Record of land appropriations and damage awards relating to the
Genesee Valley Canal, 1843-1847.
.1 cu. ft. (1 volume)

B0665 Copies of maps of lands appropriated for the enlargement of the
Erie Canal at Lyons and Palmyra, 1849.
.2 cu. ft. (2 volumes)

B0713 Maps of lands in the Rochester area claimed as damaged in the
Erie Canal Enlargement, ca. 1870.
.1 cu. ft. (1 volume)

B0667 Maps and descriptions of lands temporarily appropriated for State
canals, 1897-1907.
.1 cu. ft. (1 volume)

B0674 Maps and descriptions of western lands permanently appropriated
for use of the state canals, 1899-1907.
.1 cu. ft. (1 volume)

B0666 Checklist of maps and list of court of claims awards regarding land
appropriations, 1900-1901.
.1 cu. ft. (1 volume)

B0357 Index to Barge Canal releases, 1906-1926.
.3 cu. ft. (1 volume)

B0387 Stenographer's minutes of Jenkins and Perkins against the State of
New York in the court of claims, 1917.
.3 cu. ft. (4 volumes)

Roads, Bridges, and Waterways

B0272 Record of contracts awarded for improvement of public highways,
1898-1908.
.6 cu. ft. (2 volumes)

B0269   Monthly progress reports and record of petitions for work on highways, ca. 1898-1913.
1 cu. ft. (1 volume)

A4029   Specifications for work needed to improve roads, 1903-1905.
.2 cu. ft.

B0270   Engineers' estimates of costs for constructing public highways, 1906-1908.
.5 cu. ft. (1 volume)

B0271   Register of expenditures on public highways, 1904-1907.
.5 cu. ft. (1 volume)

B0327   Memoranda scrapbook pertaining to the Utica and Oneida Castle Road, 1903.
.3 cu. ft.

A3258   Bridge construction planning and supervision files, 1904.
.3 cu. ft.

B0375   Proceedings and financial statements regarding the improvement of the Hudson River, 1863-1892.
.1 cu. ft. (1 volume)

A4033   Maps of pierhead and bulkhead lines in State waterways, 1786-1920, bulk 1882-1920.
.5 cu. ft. (2 volumes)

CANAL BOARD

B0212   Printed proceedings of the canal board and the canal contracting board, 1857-1871.
.6 cu. ft. (2 volumes)

B0209   Record of canal contracts, 1898-1907.
.5 cu. ft. (1 volume)

B0348   Registers of contract proposals regarding the enlargement of the Erie Canal, 1851.
.6 cu. ft. (7 volumes)

A0853   State engineer and surveyor's maps and plans for the Hudson and Champlain Improvement survey, 1866.
.5 cu. ft. (1 volume)

B0206   Record of petitions for Barge Canal terminals, 1911-1913.
.2 cu. ft. (1 volume)

CANAL COMMISSIONERS

B0716   Expenditures made for improvement and repair of the middle division, 1840-1846.
.1 cu. ft. (1 volume)

B0704   Proposals and lists of proposals received for work done on the middle division, 1873-1894.
.1 cu. ft. (1 volume)

CONTRACTING BOARD

B0207   Rough minutes, 1854-1861.
.5 cu. ft. (2 volumes)

A4028   Bid proposals for construction work on Black River Canal reservoirs, 1859.
.2 cu. ft. (1 volume)

JAMAICA BAY—PECONIC BAY CANAL BOARD

B0238   Administrative files, 1917-1921.
1 cu. ft.

B0239   Card index to the board's administrative files, 1917-1921.
.3 cu. ft.

DEPARTMENT OF HIGHWAYS

A3227   State highway planning and maintenance maps books, ca. 1910.
1 cu. ft. (2 volumes)

A4030   Negatives and photographs of roads and road construction, 1917-1921.
6 cu. ft.

B0275   Highway construction and maintenance payment journal, 1922-1923.
.5 cu. ft. (1 volume)

B0721   Register of deposits made and checks issued, 1921-1922.
         1 cu. ft. (1 volume)

Bureau of Town Highways

B0235   Bridge files, 1918-1923.
         1 cu. ft.

STATE COMMISSION OF HIGHWAYS

A4031   Topographical and geological highway and canal planning maps
         of New York, ca. 1900-1921.
         2 cu. ft. (4 volumes, 2 boxes)

A0577   State highway records, 1904.
         2 cu. ft.

A3228   State highway planning and maintenance maps, ca. 1913.
         1 cu. ft.

Bureau of Maintenance and Repairs

B0747   Correspondence and reports, ca. 1921-1922.
         .5 cu. ft.

TRAFFIC COMMISSION

09723   Minutes of meetings and annual reports, 1936-1967.
         2 cu. ft.

Public Benefit Corporations and Authorities

Bridge Authority

Current Functions. The New York State Bridge Authority operates four bridges that span the Hudson River. The authority is authorized to sell bonds for the construction, maintenance, operation of the bridges, and to charge tolls to pay the bonded debt.

Organizational History. The New York State Bridge Authority was established within the Department of Public Works by Laws of 1932, Chapter 548. This act was amended the following year (Laws of 1933, Chapter 67), removing the Authority from the Department.

The Authority was originally governed by three gubernatorial appointees and has been headed by five appointees since 1949.

The Bridge Authority controls and operates the Mid-Hudson Bridge spanning the Hudson River at Catskill; the Rip Van Winkle Bridge at Catskill; the Bear Mountain Bridge spanning the Hudson River below West Point; the Kingston-Rhinecliff Bridge above Kingston and the twin spans at Newburgh-Beacon. The Mid-Hudson Bridge was opened to traffic in 1930, and the Rip Van Winkle on September 26, 1940. The Kingston-Rhinecliff Bridge was opened in 1957. The North Span of the Newburgh-Beacon Bridge opened to traffic in 1963, the South Span opened in 1980.

BRIDGE AUTHORITY
General Agency-level Records

> A3162   Files relating to acquisition of the Bear Mountain Bridge, 1922-1942.
> 1 cu. ft.

Dormitory Authority

Current Functions. The Dormitory Authority is responsible for providing financing, construction management, planning, design, and equipment-purchasing services for higher education, health care, and other institutions as authorized by the Public Authorities Law. It also provides long-term low-interest loans to college students to supplement grants from State, Federal, and private sources.

Organizational History. This authority was established in 1944 (Chapter 524) as a public-benefit corporation to finance and prepare plans, designs and cost estimates for construction, and to operate and maintain dormitories for the state colleges for teachers. The enabling legislation designated a governing board of eight: the commissioner of education, the comptroller, and six members appointed by the Board of Regents of the University of the State of New York.

Over the next two decades, numerous amendments expanded the Dormitory Authority's responsibilities to include colleges under the jurisdiction of the State University of New York, private institutions of higher learning, institutions for the training of nurses, regional boards of cooperative educational services, health facilities, community colleges, and facilities for the aged. Several other amendments have authorized the Dormitory Authority to construct specific cultural and educational facilities. In 1984 (Chapter 216) the Dormitory Authority was given responsibility to provide loans to college and graduate students who could demonstrate financial need.

The composition of the governing board has also changed over time to its present membership of three ex officio members (the commissioner of education, the state comptroller or a designee, and the director of the budget), as well as four members appointed by the governor.

No records in the State Archives

Energy Research and Development Authority

Current Functions. The New York State Energy Research and Development Authority promotes the development and use of new energy sources and technology, and the conservation of energy resources. It conducts energy research, development, and demonstration projects; issues tax-exempt bonds to finance installation of waste-disposal and energy-production facilities; and is responsible for statewide management of low-level radioactive waste disposal.

Organizational History. The authority was created in 1962 (Chapter 210) as the New York State Atomic Research and Development Authority, a public-benefit corporation with three members. Its purpose was to promote the development and use of atomic energy in New York State. To do this the authority was empowered to conduct atomic energy research and development activities; provide services necessary for the development and use of atomic energy, including the establishment and use of atomic energy facilities; serve as a clearinghouse for information on the uses of atomic power; and issue bonds to raise money to support its mandated activities.

In 1964, the authority was renamed the New York State Atomic and Space Development Authority, and its powers were enlarged to include the development of

339

space activities within the State as well as atomic energy activities. In addition, the membership of the authority was increased from three to five.

In 1975, the authority was renamed the New York State Energy Research and Development Authority, and its mission was substantially redefined. Rather than focus on atomic power, the authority was directed to develop and promote new energy sources and technologies and to encourage energy-conservation technologies. Members of the new authority were the commissioner of the Department of Environmental Conservation, who served as chairperson, the chairpersons of the Public Service Commission and the New York State Power Authority, and eight members appointed by the governor. Membership of the authority was increased to thirteen in 1980 (Chapter 196) by adding the commissioner of the State Energy Office, who served as chairperson, and an additional appointed member.

As a result of the Federal Low-Level Radioactive Waste Policy Act of 1985, all states were required to provide for the disposal of their own low-level radioactive wastes. In 1986 (Chapter 673), management of this type of waste was made the responsibility of the Energy Research and Development Authority. Under this statute, the authority must obtain the necessary licenses for, and construct and operate a permanent low-level radioactive waste disposal facility in the State.

No records in the State Archives

Environmental Facilities Corporation

Current Functions. The Environmental Facilities Corporation is a public benefit corporation created to protect the environment by assisting municipalities and private industries in implementing environmental projects, managing the wastes they produce, and complying with environmental regulations. The Corporation plans, designs, finances, constructs, and operates facilities for solid and hazardous waste management, as well as for air and water pollution abatement. Under the Industrial Finance Program the Corporation provides loans to finance environmental improvement projects for municipalities and industries. In addition, the Corporation manages the New York State Water Pollution Control Revolving Fund which provides low interest loans to municipalities to finance the construction of water pollution control facilities. Through the

Industrial Materials Recycling Program, the Corporation provides technical assistance to industry to help reduce, recycle, and reuse solid and hazardous wastes.

Organizational History. The Corporation was created by the Laws of 1970, Chapter 744. The Corporation is a reconstitution and continuation of the New York State Pure Waters Authority created in 1967 (Chapter 722) to plan, finance, construct, and operate sewage treatment and solid waste disposal facilities. The Corporation is governed by a Board of Directors consisting of seven members: the Commissioner of the Department of Environmental Conservation (Chairman and Chief Executive Officer); the Commissioner of the Department of Health; the Secretary of State; and four members appointed by the governor.

No records in the State Archives

Facilities Development Corporation

Current Functions. The Facilities Development Corporation (FDC) serves the design, construction, and real property needs of several State agencies and municipalities. FDC provides capital project management services to acquire, plan, design, construct, renovate and equip public facilities. FDC's principal State clients are the Office of Mental Health, the Office of Mental Retardation and Developmental Disabilities, the Division of Alcoholism and Alcohol Abuse, the Division of Substance Abuse Services, and the Department of Social Services' Commission for the Blind and Visually Handicapped. FDC also provides technical assistance to the Department of Social Services' Homeless Housing and Assistance Program and has provided project management services to over thirty municipalities in the areas of health, mental health, and correctional facilities.

Organizational History. Legislation in 1963 (Chapters 932 and 933) established and specified the functions of the Mental Hygiene Facilities Improvement Fund. The Fund was created as a public benefit corporation to expedite planning, construction, and reconstruction of State hospitals, schools, and other mental hygiene care, maintenance, treatment, and research and training facilities.

A 1968 law (Chapter 359) abolished the Mental Hygiene Facilities Improvement Fund and created the Health and Mental Hygiene Facilities Improvement

Corporation as a public benefit corporation to assist the departments of Health and Mental Hygiene with the management and construction of new, improved health and mental health facilities needed to house the increasing population of mentally ill and disabled persons. This law also authorized assistance to cities and counties in design, construction, and financing of community mental health and retardation facilities. The agency's name was changed to the New York State Facilities Development Corporation in 1973 (Chapter 658).

During the 1960s, most of FDC's work was new construction—as part of the State's master plan to upgrade and replace aging public facilities built in the nineteenth and early twentieth centuries. Since the 1970s, emphasis has turned to preservation, renovation, and adaptive reuse of existing facilities. Most of FDC's work, therefore, has changed from long-term new construction projects to shorter-term but higher-volume maintenance and rehabilitation projects. However, FDC continues to be involved in some design and construction of new buildings, especially in support of community residence programs for the mentally and developmentally disabled.

The Facilities Development Corporation is governed by five directors: the commissioner of health, the chair of the Inter-Office Coordinating Council of the Department of Mental Hygiene, and three gubernatorial appointees who are traditionally from outside State government. The corporation is directed by an executive director, who is the chief operating officer.

No records in the State Archives

Higher Education Services Corporation

Current Functions. The Higher Education Services Corporation (HESC) seeks to improve postsecondary educational opportunities through centralized administration of all of the State's college student financial aid and loan programs. The programs it administers include the Tuition Assistance Program; the Supplemental Tuition Assistance Program; the Liberty Scholarship Program; a variety of scholarship programs, including the Regents Scholarships; and the Federal Guaranteed Student Loan Program.

Organizational History. The first State financial aid to students at institutions of higher learning was a program of scholarships to Cornell University set up when the university was established in 1865 (Chapter 585). These scholarships were administered by the Department of Public Instruction and later by the State Education Department, and the first awards were made in 1868. In 1913 (Chapter 292), the Regents College Scholarships were established. These scholarships were awarded through a competitive examination and could be used at any approved college in New York State. Beginning in the 1930s, several additional scholarship programs were legislated, some awarded through examinations and others to members of targeted populations. These included scholarships for war service veterans; children of deceased or disabled veterans; and nursing, medical, and dental students. In 1961 (Chapter 389) the legislature created the Scholar Incentive Program of noncompetitive grants awarded largely on the basis of financial need. All of these programs were administered by the State Education Department.

The State program of educational loans for higher education began in 1957 (Chapter 367) with the establishment of the Higher Education Assistance Corporation (HEAC). This nonprofit corporation guaranteed repayment of loans made by private lenders to students. The Federal government began guaranteeing most such loans in 1965 after passage of the Higher Education Act, and HEAC administered the Federal program in New York State.

In 1974 (Chapter 942), HEAC was abolished and its loan programs were combined with the scholarship and grant programs administered by the State Education Department under a new nonprofit corporation, the Higher Education Services Corporation (HESC), established in the State Education Department. The same law abolished the Scholar Incentive Program and replaced it with a larger entitlement program, the Tuition Assistance Program. In 1988, the legislature established a new program, Liberty Scholarships, to cover the nontuition costs of attendance. New York State thus became the first state to offer full cost of attendance funding to needy students.

HESC is administered by a board of trustees consisting of the commissioner of education, the chancellors of the state and city universities of New York, and 10 gubernatorial appointees—6 representatives of colleges, the banking industry, and the public; and 4 students.

No records in the State Archives

Housing Finance Agency

Current Functions. The Housing Finance Agency provides financial assistance for construction of public housing and facilities. It is a public-benefit corporation issuing notes and bonds to finance the construction of facilities for the State University of New York, the Department of Mental Hygiene and its component offices, and facilities for numerous public and private programs. These programs include housing, hospitals and nursing homes, youth facilities, community mental health facilities, municipal health centers, and senior citizen centers. The agency also finances the Secured Loan Rental Housing Program, providing below-market mortgages for multifamily rental housing. In addition, the agency administers two State-funded programs to provide rent subsidies to low-income families and to support repair of construction-related problems at low-income housing sites.

Organizational History. The Housing Finance Agency was created by the Laws of 1960 (Chapter 671). The commissioner of housing and community renewal serves as chairperson and chief executive officer of the agency. In addition to the commissioner of housing, the members of the agency include the director of the budget, the commissioner of taxation and finance, and four others appointed by the governor.

No records in the State Archives

Power Authority

Current Functions. The Power Authority is responsible for providing an adequate supply of safe and economical power for the citizens of New York State. It accomplishes this by financing, constructing, and operating electric generation and transmission facilities in New York State. Construction is financed through the sale of tax-exempt bonds and may be undertaken by the authority on its own or in cooperation with private utilities. Operational costs are funded by revenue raised by the sale of power to public agencies, industries, investor-owned utilities, and municipalities. The authority operates a variety of facilities, including nuclear and hydroelectric facilities, and also investigates other alternative sources of power.

Organizational History. The Power Authority of the State of New York (PASNY) was created in 1931 (Chapter 772) as an agency to improve, along with appropriate

Canadian and United States authorities, the International Rapids Section of the St. Lawrence River near Massena as a means of commerce and navigation and to develop available hydroelectric power sources. In 1950, additional power resources of the Niagara River were made available to the United States under a treaty with Canada, and the following year PASNY was authorized by statute to develop additional power sources of this river.

In 1953, the authority was granted a license by the Federal Power Commission to construct, maintain, and operate the St. Lawrence Power Project. As a public benefit corporation, the Power Authority sold revenue bonds to defray the cost of the project. In 1958, the authority was granted another license to construct, maintain, and operate the Niagara Power Project, completed in 1963. In the case of both projects, contracts for the sale of power are expected to pay off debts incurred by construction and operation of the facilities.

In 1968, the authority was granted the right to construct nuclear facilities and hydroelectric pumped storage projects within specified areas, either alone or in cooperation with private utilities. The authority has completed projects at Blenheim-Gilboa (Schoharie County) and Nine Mile Point (on Lake Ontario near Oswego). In 1974, the authority also acquired and now operates power facilities in Astoria (Queens County) and Indian Point (a nuclear plant in Westchester County) to supply electricity to the New York City metropolitan area.

The Public Authorities Law was amended in 1978 to permit the Power Authority to develop small-scale hydroelectric projects. A number of such projects have been undertaken, including those on the Ashokain Reservoir (Ulster County), the Kensico Reservoir (Westchester County), and at Hinckley Dam and Reservoir (Oneida and Herkimer Counties).

In 1978, the Power Authority also completed a transmission line to import power from Hydro-Quebec; in 1982 a 13-year contract was signed for importing hydroelectric energy.

No records in the State Archives

State University Construction Fund

Current Functions. The State University Construction Fund is a public-benefit corporation responsible for construction projects on all State-operated campuses of the State University of New York (SUNY). It provides for planning, design, and construction of new facilities and rehabilitation of existing facilities. The Construction Fund consults with SUNY on space requirements, as outlined in the SUNY Master Plan, and then contracts with private architects, engineers, and builders to produce facilities. In addition, the fund provides in-house design services for a variety of rehabilitation/alteration types of projects. New projects are primarily funded with the proceeds from bond sales. Until 1981, the Housing Finance Agency was the bonding agent. Bonding is now performed for the Fund by the Dormitory Authority of the State of New York.

Organizational History. The State University Construction Fund was established as a public-benefit corporation in 1962 (Chapter 251) to reduce the time between inception and completion of new facilities for SUNY campuses. The fund was to be guided by the assumption that SUNY's enrollment would more than double in the next 10 years. Before the fund was created, construction of SUNY facilities was chiefly the responsibility of the Department of Public Works with the Division of the Budget closely monitoring expenditures. In 1959 the governor and the Board of Regents of The University of the State of New York appointed a three-member Committee on Higher Education to review and make recommendations concerning higher education needs and facilities in New York State. The committee reported in 1960 that the process by which facilities planning and construction was carried out was not satisfactory to meet the expected rapid growth in SUNY enrollments. The committee's report was partly responsible for the eventual creation of the fund.

The State University Construction Fund is administered by a board of three trustees appointed by the governor, at least one of whom must be a trustee of the State University.

STATE UNIVERSITY CONSTRUCTION FUND

Office of the General Manager

    B0622   Subject files, 1960-1978.
                 39 cu. ft.

B0621 Campus design and construction files, 1963-1978, bulk 1971-1978.
12 cu. ft.

13782 General manager's weekly reports to the trustees, 1962-1978.
5 cu. ft.

Physical Plant Support Services

15592 Documentation photographs of Comstock Hall, Cornell University, 1986.
.5 cu. ft.

15821 Architectural floor plans and elevations of Comstock Hall, Cornell University, ca. 1986.
1 cu. ft.

Thruway Authority

Current Functions. This public corporation is responsible for constructing, maintaining, and operating a central highway route across New York State. The authority is empowered to issue bonds to finance its operation, acquire property rights along the highway route, enter into contracts to construct and maintain the road, and collect tolls and other fees for road use.

Organizational History. The Thruway Authority was created as a public corporation in 1950 (Chapter 143). The 559-mile Thruway was completed in 1960, connecting New York City with Buffalo, and having additional links to expressways in Connecticut, Massachusetts, New Jersey, and Pennsylvania. In 1964 the highway system was officially named The Governor Thomas E. Dewey Thruway.

The Thruway Authority operates without State financial assistance, although the State guaranteed half the bond issue used to finance initial road construction. This bond debt and ongoing operational costs are paid for by the proceeds of tolls and fees. The authority is governed by a board of three members, appointed by the governor.

THRUWAY AUTHORITY

Department of Information and Commercial Affairs

B0589 Public relations planning and publications files, 1950-1969.
3 cu. ft.

B0588   Press clippings file, 1950-1972.
           21 cu. ft.

B0591   Files relating to the "Betterments" court case, 1964-1969.
           1 cu. ft.

Department of Public Information

B0590   Speech and news release file, 1946-1961.
           1 cu. ft.

14512   Motion pictures of Thruway construction and related matters, ca.
           1951-1967.
           15 cu. ft.

B0592   Negatives and prints of Thruway interchanges and facilities, ca.
           1960.
           .4 cu. ft. (ca. 250 negatives/prints)

Department of Public Information and Business Promotion

B0593   Audio recordings of programs about the Thruway, 1954.
           .2 cu. ft. (2 16" audio disks)

Urban Development Corporation

Current Functions. The Urban Development Corporation (UDC) is a public
finance and development authority that initiates and assists in a broad range of development projects. UDC's overall goal is to create and retain jobs, particularly in economically distressed areas and in circumstances where it is not financially or organi-
zationally feasible for the private sector to do so alone. To accomplish this, the State
legislature has provided UDC with unique statutory powers, including the powers to
condemn real property, to invest in property at below-market interest rates, to issue
tax-exempt and nontax-exempt bonds, to offer tax benefits to developers, and to provide flexibility in the application of local codes. UDC addresses the economic needs
of the State in the following seven areas: industrial development, downtown development, university research and development, regional economic development, minority and women-owned business development, new communities, and planning and
special projects.

Organizational History. The UDC was created as a public benefit corporation pursuant to the Laws of 1968 (Chapter 174). It originally concentrated on initiating and implementing large-scale housing development to low- and moderate-income people. In the mid-1970s, UDC's focus shifted away from housing development, in large part because of difficulties that arose in financing the completion of the extraordinary amount of housing launched by the corporation. In recent years, UDC has financed no new residential projects and has focused its efforts on the broader issues of economic development.

In contrast to its activities prior to 1975, UDC does not rely on its general credit to finance new projects but rather relies solely on State appropriations, grants, nonrecourse public borrowings secured by a particular project, or combinations of these mechanisms.

The corporation is headed by nine directors: seven gubernatorial appointees, the superintendent of banking, and the chairperson of the New York State Science and Technology Foundation.

UDC has the following four operating subsidiaries:

The 42nd Street Development Project. This project involves plans for the construction of four new office towers, the renovation of the Times Square subway station, and the acquisition of nine historic theaters in the Times Square area of New York City.

The Western New York Economic Development Corporation (WNYEDC). WNYEDC was created in 1984 in response to economic troubles and increased unemployment in western New York. It provides both leadership in rebuilding the regional economy and direct assistance in expanding the region's economic base through a variety of loans, training, and other initiatives.

The New York State Mortgage Loan Enforcement and Administration Corporation (MLC). The MLC was established as a joint venture of UDC and the Project Finance Agency (PFA) in 1979 to preserve and improve the financial and physical condition of UDC-built housing projects throughout the State. MLC manages the more than $1.2 billion housing portfolio that was developed by UDC from 1968 to 1978.

The Harlem Unit Development Corporation (HUDC). The HUDC was created in July 1971 through a memorandum of understanding between the Harlem Community and the New York State Urban Development Corporation. As a full-service development agency, HUDC is responsible for planning, feasibility studies, design, financing, construction supervision, and technical assistance.

URBAN DEVELOPMENT CORPORATION

General Agency-level Records

A0507   Reports and indexes to files, 1974-1975.
          .2 cu. ft.

Temporary War Emergency Agencies

Council of Defense

Functions. The Council of Defense was charged with conducting studies and formulating plans for the coodination of the State's agricultural, military, and commercial resources during World War I.

Organizational History. The State Council of Defense was established in 1917 (Chapter 369). It originally consisted of the governor, state engineer and surveyor, superintendent of public works, commissioner of agriculture, and a gubernatorial appointee representing New York City. Two additional members were appointed by the governor in 1918. The council was dissolved in 1920.

COUNCIL OF DEFENSE

General Agency-level Records

A4234   Correspondence files, 1917-1918.
          1 cu. ft.

A4242   Administrative and correspondence files, 1917-1918.
          .3 cu. ft.

A4241   Subject correspondence files, 1917-1918.
          .3 cu. ft.

A4240   Correspondence with State agencies, 1917-1918.
          .3 cu. ft.

A4235   Correspondence of county home defense committees, 1917-1918. 2 cu. ft.

A4237   Correspondence with National Council of Defense, 1917-1918. 1 cu. ft.

A4239   United States Public Service Reserve correspondence files, 1917-1918. 1 cu. ft.

A4238   Health and hospital resources files from the adjutant-general's office, 1917. 2 cu. ft.

War Council

Functions. The War Council was organized to coordinate war-related efforts necessary to ensure State and national defense during World War II. The council undertook a variety of activities, including conducting research on defense issues, especially those relating to supplying materiel for the war effort; providing the civilian population with civil defense training; administering federal rationing and price control; ensuring an adequate labor supply in war-production industries; and coordinating war efforts among State agencies and local war councils.

Organizational History. Governor Herbert H. Lehman appointed a State Council of Defense in 1940, consisting of representatives of industry, agriculture, labor, commerce, and public utilities. It became a statutory body the following year (Laws of 1941, Chapter 22). Following the passage of the New York State War Emergency Act (Laws of 1942, Chapter 445), the Council of Defense was replaced by the New York War Council, a temporary state commission. It was composed of the governor, certain legislative leaders, and 10 gubernatorial appointees.

The War Council actively coordinated war-related efforts in State government and cooperated with the federal government and local governments as well. The War Emergency Act had authorized the formation of local war councils; the councils were not mandatory but if formed were responsible to the State council. Eventually over 30 War Council agencies and programs were developed, many relating to either civilian protection or war-related production. The council was terminated in 1947.

WAR COUNCIL

General Agency-level Records

A0077	Administrative records, 1941-1944. 240 cu. ft.	
A4301	Agencies and local war councils general report files, 1942-1945. 8.5 cu. ft.	
A4302	Annual reports and war agency directories, 1942-1944. .25 cu. ft.	
A4303	Executive secretary's correspondence with local war councils, 1942-1945. 1.75 cu. ft.	
A4291	Governor's correspondence with citizens on war issues, 1942-1945. 3.8 cu. ft.	
A4295	Governor's office correspondence on war issues, 1940-1945. 7.5 cu. ft.	
A4294	Governor's media releases, 1941-1942. .3 cu. ft.	
A4299	Photographs of War Council agency activities, ca. 1942-1945. 2.2 cu. ft.	
A3081	Inventories of State war-related agency records, 1940-1945. 1 cu. ft.	
A4298	State records program organization files, 1947. .5 cu. ft.	
A3086	Printed copies of orders issued, 1942-1946. .2 cu. ft.	
A3087	Dispensation orders, 1943-1945. .3 cu. ft.	
A3085	Resolutions, 1942-1945. 2 cu. ft.	
A3091	War information publications file, ca. 1941-1945. 11 cu. ft.	
A4244	Agency monthly progress reports, 1941-1945 4 cu. ft.	

A4289   Citizen assistance and preparation films, 1942-1943.
1 cu. ft. (5 motion picture reels)

A4292   History of Westchester County defense and war councils, 1940-1945.
.8 cu. ft. (4 volumes)

A4284   Hospital staff draft status classification and recruit screening files, 1941-1945.
1 cu. ft.

A3080   State Defense Council history files, 1917-1918.
.25 cu. ft.

A3083   Petitions from the Bronx Coordinating Committee for Child Care, ca. 1944.
1 cu. ft.

Division of Public Relations

A4285   Defense digests and official bulletins, 1942-1945.
.6 cu. ft.

Nursing Council for War Service

A4277   Recruitment and classification files, 1942-1945.
24 cu. ft.

A4281   Newspaper clippings scrapbook, 1943-1944.
.3 cu. ft.

Office of War Information

A4287   Home front information publications file, 1942-1945.
8 cu. ft.

Division of Civilian Mobilization

– Section for Citizen Unity

A4270   General correspondence, 1942-1943.
2 cu. ft.

Division of Civilian Protection

– Office of Civilian Protection

A4305   Director's general correspondence files, 1941-1945.
2.95 cu. ft.

A4300   Director's correspondence with local civilian protection organizations, 1942-1945.
4 cu. ft.

A3082   Publications received from the U.S. Office of Civilian Defense, 1941-1945.
5.2 cu. ft.

A3090   Printed copies of regulations issued, 1942-1944.
.1 cu. ft.

— Emergency Medical Service

A4286   Survey and Planning Files, 1940-1945.
4 cu. ft.

— Highway Repair and Debris Clearance Committee

A4275   General correspondence, 1941-1945.
1 cu. ft.

A4274   Contractors files, ca. 1941-1945.
.3 cu. ft.

A4273   Personnel files, ca. 1941-1945.
.3 cu. ft.

A4272   Equipment and material inventories, ca. 1941-1945.
1.3 cu. ft.

— Committee on Fire Defense

A4271   Correspondence, bulletins and minutes, 1941-1944.
1 cu. ft.

Committee on Child Care, Development, and Protection

A4279   Local child care organization and assistance files, 1942-1945.
15.5 cu. ft.

A4283   Post-World War II day care center field reports, 1944-1947.
.5 cu. ft.

A4282   Mayor's Committee on Child Care for Schenectady administrative files, 1942-1947.
4.75 cu. ft.

Committee on Discrimination in Employment

A4278   Minutes and operations files, 1941-1945.
7.5 cu. ft.

War Emergency Dispensation Committee

A4280   Recommendations for labor dispensations for minors, 1943-1945.
.5 cu. ft.

Office of the Mileage Administrator

    A4243   Government agency automobile usage rationing coordination files, 1943-1945.
             2 cu. ft.

Vocational Education Program

    A3089   Vocational training manuals, 1942-1945.
             2 cu. ft.

Division of Records

    A4296   War records program organization file, 1943-1945.
             1 cu. ft.

    A4245   Local war council records inventory forms and correspondence, 1945-1946.
             2 cu. ft.

    A4236   Research and correspondence files for The Empire State at War: World War II, 1940-1949, bulk 1940-1945.
             2 cu. ft.

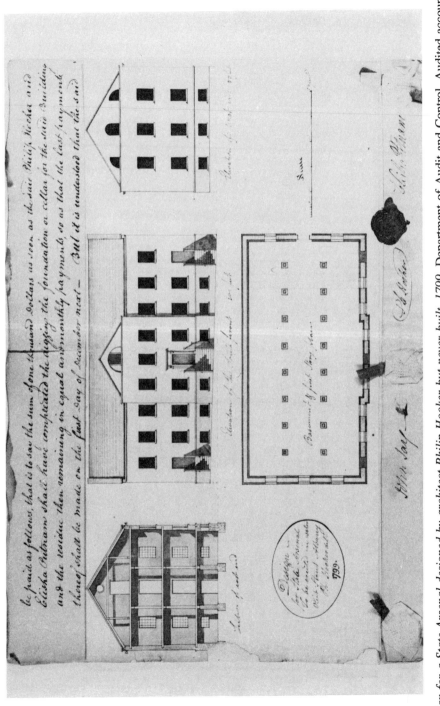

Plan for a State Arsenal designed by architect Philip Hooker but never built, 1799. Department of Audit and Control. Audited accounts, 1780-1938.

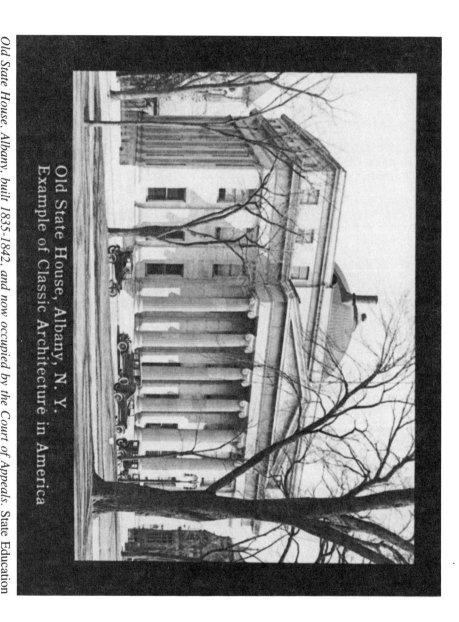

Old State House, Albany, N. Y.
Example of Classic Architecture in America

Old State House, Albany, built 1835-1842, and now occupied by the Court of Appeals. State Education Department. Division of Visual Instruction. Instructional lantern slides, ca. 1856-1939.

Construction of State Capitol, Albany, 1870. New Capitol Commission. Capitol construction progress photographs, ca. 1869-1900.

Assembly Chamber, State Capitol, ca. 1879. Temporary State Commission on the Restoration of the Capitol. Historic structures report for the Capitol, ca. 1982.

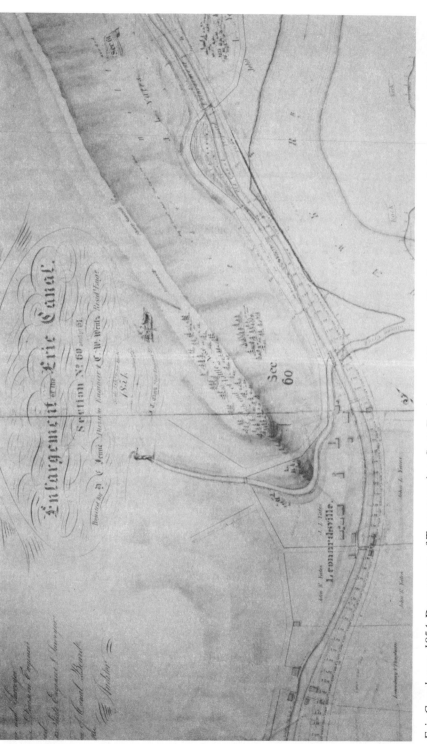

Erie Canal map, 1854. Department of Transportation. State Engineer and Surveyor. Canal structure map and plan books, ca. 1827-1905.

Erie Canal locks and towpath, Lockport, 1895. State Education Department. Division of Visual Instruction. Instructional lantern slides, ca. 1856-1939.

Woman being sentenced to State reformatory, ca. 1900. Albion State Training School. Inmate ledgers, ca. 1894-1935.

Young inmates at the State Agricultural and Industrial School, Monroe County, ca. 1910. New York State Agricultural and Industrial School (Western House of Refuge). Photographs of inmates, staff and facilities, ca. 1904-1930.

Dining Hall, Clinton Prison, ca. 1950. Clinton Prison. Photographs, ca. 1900-1969.

Cartoon relating to Theodore Roosevelt, Assemblyman and Governor of New York State, and President of the United States. Department of Civil Service. Photographs, press releases, and press clippings files, 1945-1971.

New York Governor Nelson A. Rockefeller and Albany Mayor Erastus Corning viewing architect's model of the State University of New York at Albany Campus. Governor. Public information photographs, 1910-1982.

Movie poster, 1947. State Education Department. Motion Picture Division. License application case files, 1921-1965.

Part II

LEGISLATIVE BRANCH

Legislature

Current Functions. The primary function of the New York State Legislature is to make laws. Article III of the State constitution vests the legislative power of the State in the senate and assembly. The legislature has nearly total control of the legislative process and is completely responsible for its own proceedings. There are, however, constitutional limits that prohibit the legislature from enacting certain types of laws. It may not pass laws that hinder the right of people to peaceably assemble or petition the government or that curtail freedoms of speech or press. The legislature also may not pass certain types of private or local laws (such as those changing a person's name or moving a county seat), and it may not grant divorces, annul court decisions, or audit claims made against the State.

Article IX of the State constitution requires the legislature to provide for the government of counties, cities, and incorporated villages. The legislature enacts general laws relating to localities, but legislation relating to a single locality generally can be passed only with the authorization of the locality.

The legislature passes resolutions that serve as formal statements of opinion or determination concerning a wide variety of matters. Legislative resolutions do not have the effect of law. Resolutions are used, for instance, to adopt internal rules, adjourn from annual sessions, adopt proposed constitutional amendments, establish legislative commissions, and issue congratulations on accomplishments of others.

The legislature is responsible for reviewing administrative action to ensure that it conforms to legislative intent and authorization. In performing this function, the legislature audits agency programs, investigates fiscal aspects of agency programs, and monitors agency rule-making activities. Various legislative committees also monitor and review the operations of those agencies that fall under the committee's area of responsibility.

Another major function of the legislature is to review the governor's annual budget. This function has expanded in the 1970s and 1980s and has increased the authority of the legislature in the governmental process. In reviewing the executive budget, the legislature may reduce a specific amount of money requested but may not increase a request. Any additional funding sought by the legislature must be added as a separate line item subject to veto by the governor.

The legislature also has an electoral function. The senate and assembly are the sole judges of the elections, returns, and qualifications of their members. While it rarely occurs, either house may refuse to seat any person whom a majority of its members finds unqualified. The legislature is responsible for electing its own officers. The legislature also elects members of the Board of Regents of The University of the State of New York.

Legislators provide a variety of services to their constituents. In particular, they intervene on behalf of their constituents with a State agency or local government to ensure that some need is being addressed.

The legislature has broad powers in ratifying proposed federal constitutional amendments referred to it, proposing State constitutional amendments, and convening constitutional conventions.

The senate is responsible (State constitution, Article V, Section 4) for reviewing and approving the governor's appointments of heads of most State agencies, members of boards and commissions, and judges of the court of appeals and court of claims.

The assembly has the authority (State constitution, Article VI, Section 24) to vote articles of impeachment against certain judicial and State officials. Upon an impeachment vote by a majority of the assembly, a court of impeachment is formed consisting of the president of the senate, members of the senate, and judges of the court of appeals. This court can vote to convict and remove these officials from office.

Other specific functions performed by the legislature include channeling federal grants to State agencies and loaning funds to public corporations.

Through standing and select committees and joint legislative commissions, the legislature gathers information from individuals and constituent groups to make more informed decisions concerning appropriate legislation.

Organizational History. The legislature can trace its origins to several representative councils that met during the 1640s and 1650s, the period of Dutch rule in New Netherland. The director general of the colony, assisted by an appointed council, held exclusive executive, legislative, and judicial authority. In 1641, representatives chosen by the people met and called for this authority to be limited. Over the next several years, similar meetings were called to represent popular interests before the colony's director general. In 1664, an Assembly was called by Peter Stuyvesant to consider the current state of affairs in the colony. However, England took control of

New York before this assembly was able to develop into a source of authority distinct from the appointed leaders.

Under the English governor Thomas Dongan, a representative assembly was convened in 1683. The first session of this assembly enacted a Charter of Liberties and Privileges, which called for certain basic rights, such as trial by jury and protection of property. The charter was approved by the royal governor but was vetoed in England. In 1686, King James II dissolved the assembly. In 1690, during a period of unrest, Jacob Leisler and his supporters organized an assembly, but this attempt was disallowed a year later.

A 1691 law (Chapter 10) finally established a continuing representative colonial assembly, which continued in existence throughout the colonial period until it was dissolved by Governor Tryon in 1776. The importance of this assembly grew as it gradually gained control over the province's taxation and expenditures. During this period, an appointed Governor's Council continued in existence, exercising both legislative and judicial functions.

In the Revolutionary era, the colonial assembly gave way in authority to the Provincial Congress. When the assembly refused to send delegates to the Second Continental Congress in 1775, the Provincial Congress convened and appointed delegates to the Continental Congress. This Provincial Congress also approved the Declaration of Independence on behalf of New York and proclaimed itself to be the Convention of the Representatives of the State of New York. In 1777, this convention approved a State constitution.

This constitution vested supreme legislative power in a two-house legislature. The lower house, the assembly, was roughly modeled on the colonial assembly. It consisted of seventy members representing fourteen districts who were to be elected annually by adult males meeting stipulated property requirements. The upper house, the senate, included twenty-four members representing four districts. The senate had power equal to that of the assembly although property-holding requirements for electors were higher and senators were to have four-year terms of office. The legislature was given broad governmental authority that has continued essentially unchanged to the present day. The powers of the legislature, however, were limited by two councils. The Council of Revision, including the governor, four supreme court justices, the chancellor, and four senators, had the authority to review and approve all bills passed by the legislature. Vetoed bills could be overridden by the legislature. The Council of Appointment, which included the governor and four senators, made appointments to nonelective government positions.

Constitutional revision in 1822 eliminated the councils of revision and appointment. The new constitution gave the governor veto power over legislation, although the veto could be overridden by a two-thirds vote of each house. The chief officers of the State, including the secretary of state, attorney general and comptroller, were to be selected by the legislature. Property-holding qualifications for voting were retained for blacks, but virtual universal suffrage was established for white males. The number of assembly members increased to 128 and the number of senators was set at 32.

A new State Constitution of 1846 determined that senators and assembly members were thereafter to represent single-member districts and that the term of office for senators was to be two years. The new constitution reduced the legislature's appointive powers by making the secretary of state, attorney general and comptroller elective offices. The constitution also increased the power of the legislature in other areas, especially in regard to the operations of the State's municipal and county governments.

The 1894 State Constitution mandated that there be 150 assembly members and at least 50 senators. The number of assembly members has remained at 150 while the number of senators has increased to 60. The electorate now includes all persons over 18 years of age who have been residents of the State for three months prior to an election.

Leadership in the legislature is centered in the speaker of the assembly and the senate majority leader who control the organization and most of the important functions of their respective houses. One function of the speaker and majority leader is to appoint the chairpersons of the assembly and senate standing committees. A major part of the work of the legislature is accomplished through these committees. These committees are organized around a subject area or based on a functional responsibility. Subcommittees often exist to divide the work of larger committees. In addition to standing committees, select committees are often appointed to help the legislature on a temporary basis. The legislature also uses joint legislative commissions to support legislative work, particularly by allowing special long-term attention to certain areas of concern to legislators. In the 1970s, these commissions replaced joint legislative committees that previously had done similar work.

ASSEMBLY

Speaker's Office

L0017   Subject files, 1977-1986.
26 cu. ft.

Office of the Majority Leader

L0174   Memoranda and draft legislation submitted to the Assembly by departments, 1982-1984.
2 cu. ft. R

L0173   Majority leader's bill files, 1981-1982, 1985-1986.
106.5 cu. ft. R

Clerk of the Assembly

L0179   Certified copy of the Assembly journal, 1906-1984.
25 cu. ft.

L0053   Assembly introductory books, 1911-1962.
12 cu. ft. (52 volumes)

L0054   Assembly members' bill introduction books, 1911-1978.
45 cu. ft. (76 volumes)

L0055   Assembly progress records of bills passed by Senate, 1912-1966.
8 cu. ft.

L0056   Assembly progress records of Senate sponsors' bills passed, 1911-1980.
11 cu. ft.

L0051   Assembly committee reports, 1908-1983.
265 cu. ft. (363 volumes)

L0052   Registers of bills referred to the Assembly Committee on Rules, 1938-1958.
2 cu. ft. (18 volumes)

L0062   List of legislative appropriations, 1900-1905.
.5 cu. ft.

Program and Counsel Staff

L0002   Hearing files, transcripts, and audio tapes, 1956-1985.
           108 cu. ft.

L0007   Assembly bill files, 1975-1987.
           32 cu. ft.

Program and Committee Staff

— Office of Research and Analysis

L0145   Correspondence and subject files relating to television commeri-
           cals for food products aimed at children, 1975-1978.
           4 cu. ft.

Public Information Office

L0016   Transcripts of Assembly debates, 1974-1979.
           35.9 cu. ft.

L0147   Transcript of Assembly debate on rent control, 1971.
           .1 cu. ft.

Office of Legislative Oversight and Analysis

L0015   Correspondence and subject files, 1975-1979, bulk 1976-1978.
           7 cu. ft.

L0136   Generic drug investigation files, 1963-1979, bulk 1977.
           13 cu. ft.

L0137   Arab boycott investigation files, 1975-1977.
           3 cu. ft.

L0138   Investigation files relating to the Port Authority of New York and
           New Jersey, 1973-1979, bulk 1977.
           2 cu. ft.

Assembly Committees and Task Forces

L0127   Standing committee agenda and bill files, 1974-1978.
           32 cu. ft.

— Committee on Ways and Means

L0135   Correspondence and subject files, 1935-1951, bulk 1940-1947.
           31 cu. ft.

L0150   Appropriation requests submitted by State departments to the divi-
           sion of the budget, 1943-1944.
           2 cu. ft.

– Standing Committee on Agriculture

A0715   Preservation of the family farm hearing statements, 1977-1979.
.5 cu. ft.

– Standing Committee on Codes

L0166   Bill files, 1985-1986.
9 cu. ft.

L0165   Bill files for bills signed or vetoed by the governor, 1977-1986.
15 cu. ft.

– Standing Committee on Consumer Affairs and Protection

L0014   Generic drug hearing and report files, 1974-1978.
1 cu. ft.

– Standing Committee on Education

L0129   Incoming correspondence relating to proposed legislation, 1969.
2 cu. ft.

L0130   Memoranda relating to proposed legislation, 1968.
1 cu. ft.

– Committee on Environmental Conservation

L0186   Bill files, 1983-1988.
5 cu. ft.

L0131   Hearing files and transcripts, 1975-1977.
.5 cu. ft.

– Standing Committee on Governmental Operations

L0011   Hearing and subject files, 1975-1982.
2 cu. ft.

– – Sub-committee on Affirmative Action

L0103   Correspondence, reports, and testimony on work force composition and affirmative action in State and local government, 1981-
1986, bulk 1983-1985.
4 cu. ft. (14 volumes)

L0177   Reports, testimony, and background files, 1987-1988.
4 cu. ft.

– – Sub-committee on Casino Gambling

L0019   Hearing transcripts and subject files, 1977-1986.
6 cu. ft.

– Committee on Health

    L0167   Public hearing files, 1978-1986.
                    2 cu. ft.

– Standing Committee on Higher Education

    L0185   Committee bill files, 1985-1986.
                    2 cu. ft.

– Standing Committee on Housing

    L0148   Hearing files, 1973-1979.
                    .5 cu. ft.

– Standing Committee on the Judiciary

    L0010   Bill files, 1973-1974, 1983-1986.
                    16 cu. ft.

    L0175   Issue files, ca. 1973-1988.
                    19 cu. ft.

    L0178   Bottle bill files, 1981-1986.
                    3 cu. ft.

– Committee on Legislative Oversight and Investigation

    A0765   Annual report, 1980.
                    .5 cu. ft.

– Task Force on School Finance and Real Property Taxation

    L0146   Hearing transcripts, 1979-1980.
                    1 cu. ft.

– Task Force on Toxic Substances

    L0133   Interviews and hearing files regarding alleged Army toxic dumping, 1978-1980.
                    1 cu. ft.

    L0134   Reports file, 1978-1981.
                    1 cu. ft.

    L0132   Copies of federal government documents relating to toxic contamination in the Niagara Falls region, 1940-1980, bulk 1944-1959.
                    33 cu. ft.

Member Offices

– Assemblyman (1983-1984: John F. Duane)

    L0003   Bill files, 1983-1984.
                    .5 cu. ft.

– Assemblyman (1975- : Maurice D. Hinchey)

L0005   Bill files, 1979-1982.
         3 cu. ft.

L0006   Issue files, 1980-1983.
         1 cu. ft.

L0004   Bill files concerning the Environmental Conservation Law, 1981-
         1982.
         6 cu. ft.

– Assemblyman (1971-1982 : G. Oliver Koppell)

L0018   Subject files, 1971-1983.
         4 cu. ft.

– Assemblyman (1975-1990 : Mark Alan Siegel)

L0176   Subject files, 1975-1990.
         15 cu. ft.

Other Assembly Records

A0264   Transcripts of hearings, ca. 1906.
         .5 cu. ft.

L0164   State budget hearing files, 1941-1947.
         1 cu. ft.

L0162   Transcripts of hearings on department requests for appropriations
         for the 1942-1943 fiscal year, 1941.
         1 cu. ft. (9 volumes)

A1825   Petitions, correspondence, and reports relating to cities, 1780-
         1830.
         .3 cu. ft. (1 microfilm reel)

A1823   Petitions, correspondence, and reports relating to Indians, 1783-
         1831.
         .6 cu. ft. (1 microfilm reel)

A1816   Petitions, correspondence, and reports relating to forfeited estates,
         1778-1826.
         1.3 cu. ft. (2 microfilm reels)

A1824   Petitions and reports relating to colleges and schools, 1777-1831.
         .6 cu. ft. (2 microfilm reels)

A1817 Petitions, correspondence, and resolutions relating to estates of deceased persons, 1779-1831.
1.6 cu. ft. (2 microfilm reels)

A1821 Comptroller's reports on petitions to the legislature, 1793-1829.
.3 cu. ft. (1 microfilm reel)

A1820 Surveyor general's reports on petitions to the legislature, 1795-1829.
.6 cu. ft. (1 microfilm reel)

A1822 Reports on petitions for bounty lands for American Revolution service, ca. 1784-1815, bulk 1808-1815.
.3 cu. ft. (1 microfilm reel)

A0042 Transcripts of reports regarding claims for American Revolution service, 1783-1822.
.3 cu. ft. (1 volume) (1 microfilm reel)

A1827 Correspondence, petitions, and reports on defense of the frontier, Onondaga Salt Springs, and other subjects, 1791-1830.
.6 cu. ft. (1 microfilm reel)

L0158 Departmental estimates for capital projects, 1939.
1 cu. ft.

L0161 Summaries of requests for allocations to design State and municipal public works projects, 1946.
1 cu. ft.

L0157 Approvals of requests for expenditures for acquisition and improvements of land by the Conservation Department, Division of Parks, 1926-1928.
2 cu. ft.

L0111 Legislative Resolution, Assembly No. 69, celebrating the 100th anniversary of the presidential inauguration of Grover Cleveland, 1985.
.1 cu. ft.

SENATE

Clerk of the Senate

A0396 General orders, 1867.
.5 cu. ft.

Senate Committees

– Committee on Civil Service

L0139   Appraisal reports of staffing at State agencies and institutions, 1914-1916, bulk 1916.
.5 cu. ft.

– Committee on Environmental Conservation

L0168   Bill files for bills signed or vetoed by the governor, 1981-1984.
1.5 cu. ft.

– Committee on Finance

A0169   Correspondence, 1909.
.5 cu. ft.

L0140   Testimony relating to the nomination of Milton E. Gibbs as State hospital commissioner, 1913.
.2 cu. ft.

Member Offices

– Senator (1948-1972 : Earl W. Brydges)

L0104   Correspondence and subject files, 1948-1972, bulk 1965-1972.
15 cu. ft.

– Senator (1973-1978 : Karen Burstein)

L0101   Women's issues files, 1973-1979, bulk 1977-1979.
1 cu. ft.

– Senator (1957-1978 : William T. Conklin)

A0418   Constitutional Ball signature cards, 1977.
.3 cu. ft.

– Senator (1965- : James H. Donovan)

L0013   Hearing files, 1974-1977.
2 cu. ft.

– Senator (1948-1974 : Joseph Zaretzki)

A0132   Records, ca. 1960.
1.5 cu. ft.

Other Senate Records

L0151   Legislative bill and memoranda files, 1976-1979.
97 cu. ft.

L0128   Standing committee agenda and bill files, 1974-1978.
14 cu. ft.

L0109   Public hearing files, 1977-1984.
3 cu. ft.

A0203   Correspondence, petitions, and claims, 1780-1803.
4 cu. ft.

L0009   Legislative subject files, 1859-1861, bulk 1861.
.5 cu. ft.

JOINT LEGISLATIVE COMMITTEES, COMMISSIONS, AND TASK FORCES

Joint Legislative Committee on Charitable and Philanthropic Agencies and Organizations

A0181   Report, 1955.
.5 cu. ft.

Commission to Examine Laws Relating to Child Welfare

A0018   Correspondence, 1920-1922.
.3 cu. ft.

Joint Legislative Committee on Consumer Protection

L0020   Public hearing and subject files, 1965-1967.
1 cu. ft.

Legislative Task Force on Demographic Research and Reapportionment

B1300   Election district reapportionment maps, 1970-1979.
10 cu. ft.

Joint Legislative Committee on Discrimination in Employment of the Middle-Aged

L0021   Subject and survey files, 1937-1940.
2 cu. ft.

Temporary State Commission on the Environmental Impact of Major Public Utility Facilities

A0166   Electric generating plants and environmental policy hearing transcripts and reports, 1962-1972.
.5 cu. ft.

Legislative Commission on Public Management Systems

L0169   Subject files, 1975-1989.
9 cu. ft.

L0152 Project files, 1979-1988.
66 cu. ft.

Joint Legislative Committee on the State Education System

A3043 Original maps for school district atlas, 1943.
4 cu. ft. (77 maps)

Factory Investigating Commission

A3019 Correspondence of the commission, 1912-1916, bulk 1913-1915.
3 cu. ft. (5 microfilm reels)

A3018 Financial records of the commission, 1912-1914.
2 cu. ft. (7 volumes) (2 microfilm reels)

A3022 Press releases concerning commission hearings or statements, 1914-1915.
.1 cu. ft. (1 microfilm reel)

A3023 Press clippings concerning commission activities, 1911, 1913-1914.
.1 cu. ft. (1 microfilm reel)

A3011 Wage investigation planning and research files, 1913-1914.
1.8 cu. ft. (1 microfilm reel)

A3013 Wage legislation opinion files, 1914.
.3 cu. ft.

A3007 Establishment survey assignment cards, 1913-1914.
.1 cu. ft. (ca. 750 cards)

A3008 Staff daily work reports, 1913-1914.
.3 cu. ft. (ca. 1,400 cards) (1 microfilm reel)

A3010 Lists of businesses, occupations, and code numbers used in the Wage Investigation, ca. 1913-1914.
.1 cu. ft.

A3020 Correspondence concerning the field investigation in Upstate New York, 1914.
.1 cu. ft.

A3000 General Wage Investigation data cards, 1912-1914.
14 cu. ft. (ca. 70,000 cards) (22 microfilm reels)

A3014 Establishment financial analysis reports for the Wage Investigation, 1912-1913.
.2 cu. ft. (1 microfilm reel)

A3009   Statistical tables compiled for report on wage investigation, 1914.
          13 cu. ft.

A3032   Charts, graphs, and tables prepared for publication in the commis-
          sion's reports, 1913-1914.
          4 cu. ft.

A3030   Notes and tables for a study on "Dependence and Wages", 1914.
          .2 cu. ft.

A3026   Organizational and planning files concerning advisory committees
          on the proposed Labor Law recodification, 1907-1914.
          .1 cu. ft. (1 microfilm reel)

A3016   Cost of living report, draft and background notes, 1914.
          .5 cu. ft. (1 microfilm reel)

A3028   Correspondence, drafts, and printed material related to commis-
          sion investigation of fire hazards in stores, 1914.
          .1 cu. ft. (1 microfilm reel)

A3029   Glass plate negatives and photographic prints of factory and hous-
          ing conditions, 1911-1912.
          .5 cu. ft. (1 microfilm reel)

A3025   Research files on contract prison labor, 1900-1914.
          .1 cu. ft. (1 microfilm reel)

A3027   Questionnaires, drafts, and printed material relating to commission
          proposals to consolidate building inspection agencies in New York
          City, 1912-1914, bulk 1914.
          .1 cu. ft. (1 microfilm reel)

A3017   Background report on Buffalo department stores employees strike,
          1913.
          .1 cu. ft. (1 microfilm reel)

A3024   Proofs of brief supporting the conviction of Jacob Balofsky, 1914.
          .1 cu. ft. (1 microfilm reel)

Joint Committee on Fire Laws

A0223   Records, ca. 1959-1960.
          1.5 cu. ft.

Joint Legislative Committee on Good Roads

L0144   Hearing testimony, 1907.
          .5 cu. ft. (2 volumes)

Joint Legislative Committee on Housing

L0156   Investigation and reports files, 1919-1922.
15.6 cu. ft.

L0180   Investigation subject files, 1919-1922.
18.6 cu. ft.

L0181   Insurance companies investigation files, 1906-1922, bulk 1919-1922.
11.2 cu. ft.

L0182   Bank and trust company investigation files, 1919-1922.
8.7 cu. ft.

L0183   Building Trades Council investigation files, 1919-1922.
8 cu. ft.

L0184   Criminal investigation and prosecution files, 1919-1922.
7.9 cu. ft.

A0138   Bank and insurance company investment pattern exhibits, ca. 1919-1922.
1 cu. ft. (5 volumes)

Joint Committee on Industrial and Labor Conditions

L0069   Public hearing testimony files, 1939-1945.
1 cu. ft. (5 volumes)

L0070   Workers' compensation subject files, 1934-1944.
1.5 cu. ft.

L0072   Business migration survey files, 1930-1942.
8 cu. ft.

L0065   Collective bargaining survey files, 1938-1939.
2 cu. ft.

L0068   Labor union survey files, 1930-1941, bulk 1939.
.5 cu. ft.

L0066   Labor relations education survey files, 1940-1942.
2.5 cu. ft.

L0071   Postwar planning background files, 1940-1944.
2.5 cu. ft.

L0067   Textbook draft files, 1943.
.5 cu. ft.

Joint Legislative Committee to Inquire Into and Study Legislative Methods, Practices, Procedures and Expenditures

L0149   Research and report files, 1927-1945, bulk 1944.
5 cu. ft.

Joint Legislative Committee on Legislative Practices and Procedures

L0022   Administrative files, 1957-1959.
1 cu. ft.

L0023   Questionnaires on joint legislative committee practices, 1958.
.5 cu. ft.

L0024   Information file on joint legislative committees' staff, 1958.
.5 cu. ft.

Joint Legislative Committee on Matrimonial and Family Laws

A0767   Reports to the legislature, 1957-1958.
.5 cu. ft.

Joint Legislative Committee Appointed to Investigate the Public Service Commissions

L0141   Investigation files, 1913-1917.
6 cu. ft.

Joint Legislative Committee to Investigate Public Utilities

L0142   Report and resolutions files, 1934-1935.
.1 cu. ft. (1 folder)

Joint Legislative Committee to Investigate Seditious Activities (Lusk Committee)

L0040   Correspondence and administrative files, 1919-1920.
.8 cu. ft.

L0039   Investigation subject files, 1919-1920.
1 cu. ft.

L0038   Investigation files, 1918-1920.
5 cu. ft.

L0026   Hearing testimony and executive session transcripts, 1919-1920.
1.2 cu. ft.

L0027   Mass meetings investigation files, 1918-1920.
1 cu. ft.

L0028   Rand School seized files, 1913-1919.
1.4 cu. ft.

L0029   Suspected radical organizations seized files, 1916-1919.
             1 cu. ft.

L0030   Industrial Workers of the World seized files, 1918-1919.
             1.2 cu. ft.

L0031   National Civil Liberties Bureau subpoenaed correspondence files,
             1917-1919.
             5.25 cu. ft.

L0032   Russian Soviet Bureau seized files, 1918-1919.
             1 cu. ft.

L0033   Finnish Information Bureau seized files, 1918-1919.
             1.7 cu. ft.

L0034   Draft report file, 1919-1920.
             2.4 cu. ft.

L0035   Newspaper clippings files, 1919.
             14 cu. ft.

L0036   Radical propaganda file, 1892-1919.
             10 cu. ft.

L0037   Legal papers relating to searches and prosecutions of suspected
             radical individuals and organizations, 1919-1920.
             1 cu. ft.

L0041   New York City maps outlining concentrations of ethnic groups,
             1919.
             .2 cu. ft. (2 maps)

Legislative Commission on Science and Technology

L0110   Correspondence, subject files, and draft legislation relating to
             maintenance of the State's infrastructure, 1982-1984.
             1 cu. ft.

Legislative Commission on Solid Waste Management

L0102   "The Mountain in the City" video documentary on solid waste
             management, 1986.
             .1 cu. ft. (1 videocassette)

COLONIAL AND REVOLUTIONARY WAR ERA LEGISLATIVE RECORDS

New York (Colony). Council

A1809	Dutch colonial council minutes, 1638-1665. 4 cu. ft.
A1895	Council minutes, 1668-1783. 19 cu. ft. (97 volumes) (13 microfilm reels)
A0176	Original draft minutes, ca. 1668-1783. .5 cu. ft.
A1455	Photostats of transcripts of Council minutes, 1686-1726. 3 cu. ft.
A1894	Council papers, 1664-1781. 39 cu. ft. (144 volumes) (27 microfilm reels)
A0212	Original colonial laws, 1683-1775. 12 cu. ft. (41 volumes)
A1890	Bills placed before the Provincial Legislature which failed to become law, 1691-1770. 3 cu. ft. (2 microfilm reels)
A1810	Dutch colonial administrative correspondence, 1646-1664. 2.3 cu. ft.
A3169	General entries, 1665-1682. 1.3 cu. ft. (4 boxes) (1 microfilm reel)

Provincial Congress

A1814	Minutes of the Provincial Congress, Provincial Convention, Committee of Safety, and Council of Safety, 1775-1778. 2.5 cu. ft.
A0118	Correspondence of the Provincial Congress, Provincial Convention, Committee of Safety, and Council of Safety, 1772-1777. 8 cu. ft.
A1811	Administrative papers, 1775-1777. .1 cu. ft. (1 microfilm reel)
A1812	Petitions, 1776-1777. .3 cu. ft.
A0115	Credentials of delegates, 1775. .1 cu. ft. (1 microfilm reel)

A1815 Military returns, 1775-1780.
.2 cu. ft. (1 microfilm reel)

– Military Committee

A1813 Correspondence and administrative papers, 1775-1778.
.1 cu. ft. (1 microfilm reel)

OTHER LEGISLATIVE RECORDS

A1818 Correspondence and legislative action files, 1794-1827.
1.3 cu. ft. (2 microfilm reels)

A0204 Petitions, 1786-1910.
20 cu. ft.

A1819 Reports of the attorney general on petitions to the legislature, 1787-1829.
.6 cu. ft. (1 microfilm reel)

A1826 Petitions and correspondence regarding the New York-Vermont boundary dispute, 1777-1800.
.3 cu. ft. (1 microfilm reel)

A0242 School commissioners' annual reports of schools, 1796.
.2 cu. ft.

A0140 Records documenting claims and titles to Onondaga County lands, 1801.
1 cu. ft.

L0172 Name index of the members of the 1846 State Constitutional Convention and the 1848-1850 legislature, 1848-1850.
.3 cu. ft. (1 volume)

A0041 Memorandum relating to an act to revise the charter of the city of Buffalo, 1890.
.5 cu. ft.

B0303 Joint legislative resolution regarding the 332nd Regiment of the American Expeditionary Force, 1919.
.1 cu. ft.

L0008 Scrapbook on dedication of Father Isaac Jogues Memorial, Lake George, 1936-1939.
.5 cu. ft. (1 volume)

Board of Statutory Consolidation

L0112   Minutes and financial records, 1904-1908.
.6 cu. ft. (4 volumes)

1846 CONSTITUTIONAL CONVENTION

A0168   Records, 1846.
1 cu. ft.

1915 CONSTITUTIONAL CONVENTION

L0089   Transcript of proceedings, 1915.
.2 cu. ft.

L0090   Published record of selected Convention reports and proceedings, 1915.
.2 cu. ft.

L0076   Committee correspondence, minutes and proposals files, 1915.
18 cu. ft.

L0091   Committee hearing testimony, 1915.
1 cu. ft. (10 volumes)

L0075   Committee amendment tracking books, 1915.
4 cu. ft. (27 volumes)

L0088   File of amendments introduced, 1915.
2 cu. ft.

L0077   Amendment introduction and progress log, 1915.
.2 cu. ft. (1 volume)

L0078   Delegate and committee amendment introduction and progress log, 1915.
.2 cu. ft. (1 volume)

L0081   Committee clerks' log of amendments received, 1915.
.1 cu. ft. (1 volume)

L0082   Printed amendment filing log, 1915.
.1 cu. ft. (1 volume)

L0084   Log of amendments ordered to a third reading, 1915.
.1 cu. ft. (1 volume)

L0080   Secretary of state's log of amendments received, 1915.
         .2 cu. ft. (1 volume)

L0085   General orders tracking log, 1915.
         .1 cu. ft. (1 volume)

L0083   Printer's receipt book, 1915.
         .1 cu. ft. (1 volume)

L0079   Financial clerk's accounts for delegate and staff expenses, 1915.
         .2 cu. ft. (1 volume)

1938 CONSTITUTIONAL CONVENTION

L0092   Transcript of proceedings, 1938.
         8 cu. ft. (14 volumes)

L0094   Summary of proceedings, 1938.
         2 cu. ft.

L0170   Journal of the Convention, Aug. 18, 1938.
         .3 cu. ft.

L0095   Committee correspondence, hearings, minutes, and proposals files,
         1938.
         8 cu. ft.

L0093   Proposed amendments file, 1938.
         2 cu. ft.

L0105   Amendment introduction and progress log, 1938.
         .2 cu. ft. (1 volume)

L0100   Delegate and committee amendment introduction and progress
         log, 1938.
         .2 cu. ft. (1 volume)

L0106   Log of committee action on amendments, 1938.
         .5 cu. ft. (1 volume)

L0097   Log of amendments ordered to a third reading, 1938.
         .1 cu. ft. (1 volume)

L0099   Printed amendment filing log, 1938.
         .1 cu. ft. (1 volume)

L0098   General orders tracking log, 1938.
         .1 cu. ft. (1 volume)

A0400   Civil Service Committee files, 1937-1938.
         1 cu. ft.

L0108   Convention secretary's accounts for delegate expenses, 1938.
         1 cu. ft. (8 volumes)

L0107   Convention secretary's accounts for staff expenses, 1938.
         2 cu. ft. (2 volumes)

L0096   Newspaper clippings file, 1938.
         .1 cu. ft.

1967 CONSTITUTIONAL CONVENTION

L0114   Transcript of proceedings, 1967.
         2 cu. ft.

L0113   Committee correspondence, minutes, hearing transcripts, and
         propositions file, 1967.
         33 cu. ft.

L0115   Propositions file, 1967.
         2 cu. ft.

L0116   Proposition introduction and progress log, 1967.
         1 cu. ft. (1 volume)

L0117   Delegate and committee proposition introduction and progress log,
         1967.
         2 cu. ft. (2 volumes)

L0119   Log of propositions placed on the Convention calendar, 1967.
         .5 cu. ft. (1 volume)

L0118   File of propositions advanced to a third reading, 1967.
         .5 cu. ft.

L0121   Committee clerks' log of propositions received, 1967.
         .5 cu. ft. (1 volume)

L0123   Printed proposition filing log, 1967.
         .5 cu. ft. (1 volume)

L0122   Printer's receipt book, 1967.
         .2 cu. ft. (1 volume)

L0120   Log of committee roll call votes, 1967.
         1 cu. ft.

L0124   Log of propositions received by the Revision and Engrossment
         Committee and the Library Committee, 1967.
         .5 cu. ft. (1 volume)

L0155   Roll call votes, 1967.
         1 cu. ft.

L0153   Committee reports published as convention documents, 1967.
         2 cu. ft.

L0171   Transcript of the Minutes of a Public Hearing of the Subcommittee
         on Transportation and Highways, 1967.
         .3 cu. ft.

L0125   Resolution introduction and progress log, 1967.
         .5 cu. ft. (1 volume)

L0154   Original resolutions and messages from the governor, 1967.
         .5 cu. ft.

L0126   Certificates of election of Convention delegates, 1966-1967.
         .1 cu. ft.

Part III

JUDICIAL BRANCH

Unified Court System
Office of Court Administration

Current Functions

Unified Court System

New York's unified court system was organized pursuant to constitutional amendments and statutes which went into effect in 1962. Central administration of the court system was further specified by 1978 constitutional amendments and by laws passed in 1974 and 1978. The main objectives of the court system are to provide a forum for fair resolution of civil and family matters, juvenile and criminal charges, and citizen-State disputes; supervise administration of estates, consider adoption petitions, and preside over divorce matters; provide legal protection for children, the mentally ill, and others unable to manage their own affairs; and regulate admission to the bar and the conduct of lawyers.

The unified court system is comprised of trial courts (courts of original jurisdiction), which hear cases in the first instance, and appellate courts, which hear and determine appeals from decisions of trial courts. Trial courts of limited jurisdiction adjudicate misdemeanors, violations, and minor civil matters and preside over arraignments and other preliminary proceedings in felony cases (which are then prosecuted in county-level courts). Outside of New York City, various city, town, village, and district courts handle minor civil and criminal matters. The jurisdiction of the city courts varies according to the terms of the city charter: some handle only civil cases, some only criminal cases, and some both. In New York City, the civil court adjudicates civil matters involving amounts up to $25,000, including small claims and housing matters (e.g., landlord-tenant disputes), and other civil matters referred to it by the supreme court; the criminal court adjudicates misdemeanors, traffic infractions, and violations.

There are three county-level courts. The county court, established in each county outside of New York City, has jurisdiction over indictable crimes committed within the county and has jurisdiction in civil cases in which the amount demanded does not exceed $25,000. The family court, established in each county and in New York City, has jurisdiction over matters involving children and families, including support of dependents, juvenile delinquency, persons in need of supervision, child protection, review and approval of foster-care placements, adoption proceedings, paternity determinations, and family offenses. The surrogate's court, established in each county, has jurisdiction over cases involving affairs of decedents, including probate of wills, administration of estates, and adoption proceedings. The supreme court has both original and appellate jurisdiction. As a trial court, the supreme court possesses unlimited original jurisdiction in law and equity, but it generally hears cases not falling within the jurisdiction of other courts. The supreme court exercises civil jurisdiction in every county. In New York City and some upstate counties it also exercises jurisdiction over felony cases. The supreme court appellate division has 4 departments and 12 judicial districts. The appellate division third department reviews cases from administrative adjudication tribunals such as the Workers' Compensation Board, the Commissioner of Education, and the Public Service Commission.

The court of claims is a statewide court hearing claims for monetary damages against the State.

The court of appeals is New York State's highest court. It hears cases on appeal from lower appellate courts and, in some capital cases, directly from trial courts. Its review is usually limited to questions of law; in capital cases it may rule on questions of both law and fact. The court of appeals also reviews determinations of the Commission on Judicial Conduct.

Office of Court Administration

The State constitution (Article VI, Section 28) designates the chief judge of the court of appeals as the chief judge of the State and its chief judicial officer. The chief judge appoints a chief administrator of the courts (called chief administrative judge of the courts if the incumbent is a judge). The appointment is made with the advice and consent of the Administrative Board of the Courts, comprised of the chief judge as chair and the presiding judges of the four supreme court appellate division departments.

The chief judge consults with the administrative board to establish statewide standards and administrative policies, promulgating them after approval by the court of appeals.

The chief administrator directs the Office of Court Administration, the head administrative office for the courts. Through this office the chief administrator supervises the administration and operation of the trial courts, assisted by several other offices. Two deputy chief administrative judges supervise the day-to-day operations of the trial courts. The Office of Management Support, headed by the chief administrator for management support, provides personnel, budget administration, planning, education, public information, employee relations, records management, and other support services for all court and related operations. Counsel's office provides legal assistance to the chief administrator, including preparation and analysis of legislation and representing the unified court system in litigation.

Administrative judges in each judicial district are responsible for management of trial courts, managing court case loads as well as general administrative functions such as budgeting and personnel. The appellate division in each department is responsible for administration and management of its court.

Organizational History

Colonial New York's supreme judicial authority rested in the office of the governor. The governor, with an advisory council, established such inferior courts as were deemed necessary and usually served as the court of last resort. Under British rule, the court system evolved into a series of courts exercising superior jurisdiction including the supreme court of judicature, court of chancery, prerogative court (supervising the administration of estates), and court of vice admiralty (handling maritime cases). Courts exercising inferior jurisdiction included the county courts of common pleas, the mayor's courts, and criminal courts of general sessions (county) and special sessions (local).

The first State constitution of 1777 continued the colonial court system essentially intact. The court of probates was founded in 1778, replacing the prerogative court. The court for the correction of errors, organized in 1784, replaced the governor as New York's highest court.

The second State constitution of 1821 established eight judicial circuits. Each held its own circuit court presided over by a judge appointed by the governor with the consent of the senate. Circuit court rulings and verdicts could be appealed to the supreme court of judicature, comprised of a chief justice and two associates. The supreme court's business was principally hearing and deciding on appellate matters; the circuit judges presided over trials of supreme court cases. The constitution also allowed the circuit judges to be vested with equity powers, which the legislature conferred on them in 1823 (Chapter 182). Also in 1823 (Chapter 70), the court of probates was abolished. Its appellate jurisdiction was vested in the court of chancery; its other functions were given to the surrogate courts.

The third State constitution of 1846 reorganized the court system into a form more closely resembling today's system. The court for the trial of impeachments and the correction of errors was abolished. A new court of appeals was established as the State's highest appellate court. The court of chancery was abolished and its jurisdiction transferred to a reorganized, elective supreme court, which became the highest court of original, unlimited jurisdiction for questions of both law and equity. Eight general terms of the supreme court, one for each judicial district, were established as courts of intermediate appeal. The surrogate's court was given constitutional recognition. The jurisdiction of the county courts was significantly reduced and the legislature was empowered to establish additional inferior civil and criminal courts as necessary.

The judiciary article added to the constitution in 1869 further reorganized the court system. Effective in 1870, the State was divided into four departments, each with a supreme court general term to hear and decide appeals. The eight judicial districts were distributed among the departments. The composition of the reorganized court of appeals was set at seven elected judges with fourteen-year terms. A Temporary Commission of Appeals, lasting five years, was created to help dispose of the backlog of cases that had built up in the old court of appeals.

To deal with the large number of cases in the supreme court, the legislature increased the number of justices in 1879 and 1882. To reduce the backlog of cases in the court of appeals, an 1888 constitutional amendment provided for a second division of the court of appeals consisting of seven supreme court justices designated by the governor to act as associate judges.

The fourth State constitution of 1894 changed the organization of the supreme court. The circuit courts (civil) and courts of oyer and terminer (criminal) were abolished and replaced by trial terms of the supreme court. The second division of the court of appeals was abolished. Effective in 1896, an appellate division of the supreme court was created to hear all appeals previously heard in the supreme court general terms.

Several constitutional amendments passed between 1895 and 1915 helped the judiciary to cope with the increase in litigation. In 1897 the Board of Claims, a tribunal hearing claims against the State, was reorganized as the court of claims. In 1899 the court of appeals was temporarily expanded to handle its backlog of cases. A 1905 amendment enabled the legislature to set specified ratios of supreme court justices to population, increased the number of judges in the appellate division and allowed for the establishment of an additional judicial district. An 1896 statute and a 1915 constitutional amendment authorized the appellate division in the first and second departments to set up appellate terms as first-level appeal courts.

A Temporary Commission on the Courts was created in 1953 to study problems facing the judiciary. The study led to major reorganization of the judiciary in 1962 (constitution, article VI and Chapters 684 and 685) and to the establishment of the unified court system. The children's courts statewide, and the county courts and several other courts in New York City, were abolished. The Administrative Board of the Judicial Conference, comprised of the chief judge of the court of appeals and the presiding justices of the four appellate divisions, was created with responsibility for administering the unified court system. The Office of Court Administration was created in 1974 (Chapter 615) as the statewide administrative office for the courts. A law of 1978 (Chapter 156) assigned to the chief judge of the court of appeals responsibility for the administrative supervision of the court system and, with the Administrative Board, for establishing statewide administrative standards and policies. The chief judge was to appoint a chief administrator of the courts (called the chief administrative judge of the courts if the incumbent is a judge) to direct the Office of Court Administration and supervise the administration and operation of the trial courts.

LAW REPORTING BUREAU

    J0228   Minutes of Court of Appeals decisions, 1895-1897, 1900-1904, 1911-1915.
               1.5 cu. ft. (5 volumes)

Court of Appeals

Current Functions. The court of appeals is New York State's highest court and court of last resort with appellate jurisdiction only. It hears cases on appeal from the appellate division and from trial courts in capital cases. Its review is generally limited to questions of law; in capital cases it may rule on both law and fact. The court of appeals also reviews determinations of the Commission on Judicial Conduct.

Organizational History. Under British colonial rule, appeals from the supreme court of judicature in New York were made to the royal governor and his council, sitting as a court later referred to as the court for the correction of errors and appeals. The court of last resort was the King's Privy Council, which met in London.

The first State constitution in 1777 established the court for the trial of impeachments and correction of errors, replacing the governor and council as New York State's court of last resort. This court, known as the court for the correction of errors, exercised final appellate and impeachment jurisdiction. Modeled after the British House of Lords, which served as Great Britain's court of last resort, the court consisted of the president of the senate (lieutenant governor), the senators, the chancellor, and the supreme court justices.

The constitution directed the legislature to define details of court operation. A resulting 1784 law (Chapter 11) authorized the court for the correction of errors to handle cases from the supreme court of judicature, the court of chancery, and the court of probates. The law also established the court's basic operating procedures and directed the Council of Appointment to appoint a court clerk. In 1823 the court of probates was abolished and its appellate jurisdiction over the surrogate courts was transferred to the court of chancery.

The 1846 State constitution abolished the court for the correction of errors and transferred its functions as a court of last resort to the newly established court of appeals. The impeachment function was transferred to the new court for the trial of impeachments. A law of 1847 (Chapter 280) implemented these constitutional provisions, mandating the transfer of all undecided court of errors cases and all court of errors records to the court of appeals effective July 1847. Pursuant to the same statute, the court of appeals also assumed custody of most records of the abolished court of chancery, the Albany, Utica, and Geneva offices of the supreme court of judicature, and the court of probates.

The court of appeals consisted of eight elective judges until reorganized by the Judiciary Article of 1869. The number of judges was then set at seven, with 14-year terms and mandatory retirement at age 70. New judges were appointed in 1870. A Temporary Commission of Appeals, lasting five years, was set up to help dispose of the backlog of cases that had built up in the old court of appeals. Further steps were taken to reduce the backlog in 1888 when a constitutional amendment provided for a second division of the court of appeals consisting of seven supreme court justices designated by the governor to act as associate judges. This second division continued until the fourth State constitution of 1894 established (effective January 1, 1896) an appellate division of the supreme court with intermediate appellate jurisdiction, hearing appeals previously heard in the supreme court general terms.

When the unified court system was established in 1962 (Chapters 684 and 685), the chief judge of the court of appeals, along with the presiding justices of the four appellate divisions, comprised the Administrative Board of the Judicial Conference with responsibility for administering the unified court system. Court of appeals judgeships became appointive positions (they were previously elective positions).

A 1978 constitutional amendment and law (Chapter 156) assigned to the chief judge of the court of appeals responsibility for the administrative supervision of the court system and, with the Administrative Board, for establishing statewide administrative standards and policies. The chief judge was to appoint a chief administrator of the courts (called the chief administrative judge of the courts if the incumbent is a judge) to direct the Office of Court Administration and supervise the administration and operation of the trial courts.

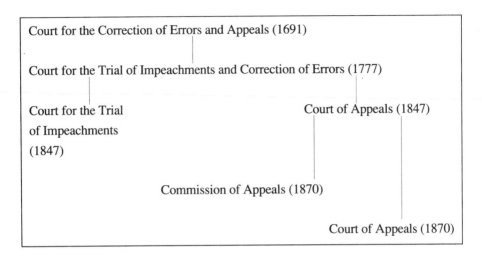

Court for the Correction of Errors and Appeals (1691)

Court for the Trial of Impeachments and Correction of Errors (1777)

Court for the Trial
of Impeachments
(1847)

Court of Appeals (1847)

Commission of Appeals (1870)

Court of Appeals (1870)

COURT OF APPEALS

General Agency-level Records

J1108	Engrossed minutes, 1847-1852. .3 cu. ft. (2 volumes)
J0212	Clerk's minutes, 1870-1903, 1914-1925, 1937-1952. 20 cu. ft. (56 volumes)
J2108	Rough minutes, 1870-1874. .3 cu. ft.
J2002	Cases and briefs on appeal, 1847-1983. 2,235 cu. ft. (14,563 volumes) R
J0312	Justices' registers, 1890-1907. 10 cu. ft. (30 volumes) R
J0232	Abstracts of opinions of Judge Edward T. Bartlett in reported cases, 1894-1909. .3 cu. ft. (1 volume)
J0107	Register of decisions, 1899-1901. .3 cu. ft. (1 volume)
J0105	Minutes of common orders, 1932-1934. .3 cu. ft. (1 volume)
J0224	Register of motions, 1926-1941. 1 cu. ft. (3 volumes)

J1224   Docket books of motions, 1950, 1952-1954, 1956.
1.5 cu. ft. (5 volumes)

J1200   Clerk's calendars, 1870-1957.
15 cu. ft. (97 volumes)

J2212   Docket books, 1880-1925.
3 cu. ft. (10 volumes) R

J3241   Register of disbursements, Chancery fund and Library fund, 1860-1879.
.3 cu. ft. (1 volume)

J0102   Certificates of commencement of clerkship, 1871-1938.
55 cu. ft. R

J0100   Index to certificates of commencement of clerkships, 1871-1903.
1 cu. ft. (5 volumes) R

J2102   Lists of attorneys admitted and disciplined in the Supreme Court, Appellate Division, 1896-1940.
.3 cu. ft.

J0109   Index to Regents' certificates of law students' qualifying education, 1881-1921.
1 cu. ft. (3 volumes) R

J1102   Law students' applications denied, 1897-1945.
10 cu. ft. R

J5102   Register of law student applications granted and denied, 1945-1958.
1 cu. ft. (5 volumes) R

J6000   Motion papers (examples), 1847-1878.
.4 cu. ft.

Court for the Trial of Impeachments and Correction of Errors

J0157   Record of appeals and cases in error, ca. 1784-1847.
19 cu. ft. (26 microfilm reels)

J0158   Index to appeals and cases in error, ca. 1784-1847.
.3 cu. ft. (1 volume) (1 microfilm reel)

J0159   Minutes, 1788-1846.
1.3 cu. ft. (4 volumes) (2 microfilm reels)

Commission of Appeals

J1212   Clerk's minutes, 1864-1874.
              2 cu. ft. (6 volumes)

J0108   Rough minutes, 1847-1872.
              2 cu. ft. (7 volumes)

J0200   Clerk's calendars, 1860-1873.
              5 cu. ft. (16 volumes)

J1232   Orders of dismissal, 1874.
              .3 cu. ft. (1 volume)

Supreme Court

Current Functions. The supreme court is the trial court of general unlimited juris-diction in law and equity, subject to the limited appellate jurisdiction of the court of appeals. The supreme court exercises jurisdiction over civil cases in every county; in New York City and some other parts of the State, it also exercises jurisdiction over felony cases. The supreme court appellate division hears appeals concerning civil and criminal cases and administrative adjudication decisions by State agencies.

Organizational History. Court of Assizes. Before the supreme court of judicature was established in 1691, other courts were operating in New York. Following the British conquest of New Netherland, the court of assizes was established in 1664 under the authority of the Duke of York, proprietor of the colony. Equity jurisdiction was conferred upon the court by a 1665 amendment to the Duke's Laws establishing the government of the colony.

The court consisted of the governor, his Council, and two justices from each of the three judicial districts (or "ridings") located in the southern part of the colony. After 1675, representatives from Kingston and Albany often sat as part of the court.

The court of assizes was the highest court of law and equity in the province. It exercised exclusive jurisdiction in cases of capital offenses and appellate jurisdiction in all criminal and civil matters. Its conduct of equity proceedings was modeled after the high court of chancery in England.

The court of assizes was abolished in 1684 (Chapter 31) by the colonial assembly, and its pending cases transferred to the court of chancery established the previous year.

Supreme Court of Judicature. The current supreme court evolved from a series of predecessor courts dating back to May 6, 1691, when New York's colonial assembly established the supreme court of judicature. Generally referred to as the supreme court, this was New York State's highest common-law court possessing both original and appellate jurisdiction. It combined the jurisdictions of three English courts: court of king's bench, the court of common pleas, and the court of exchequer.

The colonial supreme court of judicature and county-level courts had overlapping original jurisdiction over criminal cases, over civil actions in which the amount demanded was over a certain sum, and over actions concerning title to real property. The supreme court also possessed appellate jurisdiction over the lower courts.

Appeals from the supreme court were allowed in civil cases involving over 100 pounds (300 pounds after 1753). These appeals were made to the royal governor and his council (sitting as what later became known as the court for the correction of errors and appeals). The court of last resort was the Privy Council, which met in London.

The supreme court bench was comprised of a chief justice and two (three after 1758) associate justices appointed by the governor and commissioned by him to hold courts. Through the colonial period, the court held regular terms twice a year in New York City. An act of 1693 authorized the justices to hold courts in each county at least once a year to try civil and criminal cases. Most civil cases were tried in these courts. A justice holding a court was also empowered to hold a court of oyer and terminer, a criminal court in which grand juries returned indictments against suspects who were then tried in this court or in the supreme court.

Article 35 of the first State constitution of 1777 continued the colonial court system largely unchanged. Until the judicial reorganization of 1847, the supreme court of judicature, with five justices, remained the State's highest court of law holding original jurisdiction. However, Article 32 of the 1777 constitution established a court for the trial of impeachments and correction of errors, replacing the governor and council as the court of last resort in New York.

Supreme court justices continued to hold circuit courts, courts of oyer and terminer, and two regular terms each year. A law of 1785 required four annual regular terms, two in New York City and two in Albany. In 1820 one New York term was moved to Utica; in 1841, one Albany term was moved to Rochester. After 1823 there were eight separate circuit judges who presided over trials in circuit courts.

During its terms, the court heard arguments and ruled on points of law raised during pleading in supreme court or during trial proceedings in the circuit courts, and reviewed cases appealed from county-level civil and criminal courts and (before 1830) from justices' courts. Beginning in 1830, special terms were authorized to be held monthly to conduct business not on the court calendar, such as hearing motions for change of venue or for other special "rules." The third State constitution of 1846 abolished the court of chancery as of July 1, 1847. Original jurisdiction for equity matters was transferred to the supreme court.

Court of Probates. The court of probates originated in the late 17th century as the British authorities established a centralized probate system in the colony. It declined in importance during the late 18th and early 19th centuries as a decentralized probate system based on local surrogate courts developed.

During the Dutch colonial period, a will was signed by the testator, two witnesses, and a magistrate, who recorded it in a record book. This system continued briefly when the British gained control of the colony in 1664 but was soon replaced by the English system of probating wills. Under the Duke's Laws of 1665 the newly established court of sessions was empowered to probate wills, grant administration in cases of intestacy, order the final accounting of an executor or administrator, remove an executor or administrator, order the distribution of an estate, and appoint a guardian in English-speaking areas outside of New York City. In New York City, the mayor's court, established in 1664, performed these functions. On occasion the court of assizes handled probate matters.

The first step toward a centralized "prerogative" office or court came in 1670 when the court of assizes passed an ordinance requiring that all wills and grants of administration be recorded in the provincial secretary's office. In 1686 a *de facto* prerogative court was introduced into New York pursuant to royal instructions reserving the right to probate wills and grant letters of administration to the royal governor.

A 1691 law (Chapter 4) transferred civil jurisdiction, including that over probate matters, from the court of sessions to the courts of common pleas, newly established in every city and county in the colony. A 1692 law (Chapter 27) granted the royal governor or his "delegate under the seal of the Prerogative Office" the power to admit wills to probate and to grant letters of administration, thus legally establishing the prerogative court. Estates of all decedents in the counties of New York, Richmond, Westchester, Kings, and Orange (until 1750) were to be settled before this court. Probate and other estate proceedings in all other counties were to be conducted before the county court of common pleas, with appeals taken to the prerogative court in New York City.

The prerogative court consisted of the governor and a register who was the court's chief administrative and record-keeping officer. In the early eighteenth century the registers began using the title "principal surrogate" to describe their authority as delegate of the governor and deputy judge of the court. By the mid-18th century this officer conducted most of the court's business. "Surrogates" were also appointed by the governor in remote counties to take depositions of witnesses to wills and to administer oaths to executors and administrators who could not travel to New York City. These surrogates were not probate judges but agents of the prerogative court.

New York's first State constitution in 1777 granted the Council of Appointment the power to appoint surrogates. A year later the legislature replaced the prerogative court with a court of probates (Laws of 1778, Chapter 12) with a single judge appointed by the Council of Appointment. The judge was granted all powers formerly held by the royal governor in testamentary matters except for appointment of surrogates. Appeals were now made to the court for the trial of impeachments and correction of errors. The court of probates held sittings in different parts of the State until 1783, when it was held exclusively in New York City. In 1799 the court moved to Albany.

A law of 1787 (Chapter 38) radically changed New York State's probate system, establishing a surrogate's court in each county. The surrogates, now in effect probate judges, were empowered to take proof of wills, issue probates, and grant letters of administration for persons dying in their county and county residents dying elsewhere. The court of probates retained original jurisdiction only over the estates of decedents who were not New York State residents and New York residents who died out of state. This court also heard appeals from surrogate's courts and retained sole power to order the sale of property for payment of a decedent's debts, to decree final distribution of an estate among heirs, or to order an administrator or executor to exhibit accounts.

In 1823 (Chapter 70), the legislature abolished the court of probates and vested jurisdiction over all estates in the surrogate's courts. The chancellor now heard appeals from county surrogate's courts.

Court of Chancery. The first session of the colonial legislature in 1683 established the court of chancery (Chapter 7), consisting of the governor, his council and any officers he wished to appoint. The governor or his designee served as chancellor. The court of chancery held exclusive jurisdiction in matters not covered by common law, such as trusteeships, mortgages, mercantile law, women's property rights, and family property settlements. Like the court of assizes, the court of chancery was the colony's court of last resort in common-law matters as well as a court of equity.

In October 1688, New York was incorporated into the newly formed Dominion of New England, a royal colony created by King James II, formerly the Duke of York. Under the act creating the dominion, equity jurisdiction previously exercised by the court of chancery was now vested in the royal governor or his appointee.

In 1691, when New York was restored to separate provincial status, the assembly established a high court of chancery comprised of the royal governor and council (Chapter 4). This court exercised exclusive equity jurisdiction in the colony but had no common-law or appellate jurisdiction. The court was abolished in 1699, reestablished in 1701, suspended in 1702, and reestablished by council ordinance in 1704. Although politically controversial because it was not established by legislative enactment and because it had no juries, the court of chancery continued operating in New York until 1783 when the British evacuated New York City.

The high court of chancery consisted of the royal governor, council, and court officers: the register, who recorded court minutes and served as secretary to the chancellor; a clerk, who handled most of the paperwork; a sergeant-at-arms, who was the enforcement officer of the court; masters, who conducted investigations and performed various administrative duties; and examiners, who examined witnesses.

Much of this court's litigation concerned commercial relations, often involving disputes over profits or money received, bills of exchange, bonds, contracts, insurance policies, and fraud. Other cases involved mortgages and real property, execution of wills or other family property agreements, collection of quit rents, vacating of land patents, requests for discovery of evidence or property on which a judgment was levied, orders for performance of terms of a contract or agreement, appointment of guardians, and injunctions of various kinds.

The first State constitution of 1777 continued the colonial court system but established a court for the trial of impeachments and correction of errors as the State's new court of last resort. A law of 1778 (Chapter 12) organized the State court of chancery (coexisting with the British high court of chancery, which retained jurisdiction in British-occupied areas of New York until 1783). The chancellor was appointed by the Council of Appointment; other court officers were the same as those in the colonial court.

A law of 1804 (Chapter 58) established the Chancery Fund, giving the register and assistant register responsibility for depositing or investing funds coming to the court through fees, performance bonds, and estate cases.

Various statutes expanded and clarified the court's jurisdiction in family relations and competency matters during the period of the first constitution (1777-1821). The court was given authority to grant divorces, annulments, and legal separations. It was responsible for protecting the property of the mentally handicapped, mentally ill, and minors through the appointment of trustees. In 1813 the court was granted special jurisdiction over the management of the property and finances of religious institutions incorporated by the State.

The second State constitution of 1821 greatly changed the administration of equity in New York State. Pursuant to the constitution, an 1823 law (Chapter 182) established eight judicial circuits and vested circuit judges with power to hold a court of equity within their circuits. The chancellor shared equity jurisdiction with the circuit judges and also exercised appellate jurisdiction over them. He also had the sole authority to hear cases involving parties from different circuits or from out of State. The same year (Chapter 70), the court of probates was abolished. The chancellor henceforth heard most appeals from county surrogate's courts. The position of chancery clerk was abolished and its duties transferred to the register and assistant register.

The revised statutes of 1829 created a uniform statewide equity system under the direction of the chancellor. The courts of equity were abolished. The circuit judges retained their equity jurisdiction. In this capacity they were designated "vice chancellors" and acted as officials of the court of chancery subject to the authority of the chancellor. The court's jurisdiction over businesses and banks was expanded in the 1820s to include wide supervisory powers over corporations adjudged by the supreme court to be insolvent or in violation of their charters.

Supreme Court. The 1846 constitution established a new supreme court as the highest court of original jurisdiction in equity as well as law. The supreme court also heard appeals from the county courts. Eight general terms of the supreme court, one for each judicial district, were established as courts of intermediate appeal. The new court of appeals replaced the court for the trial of impeachments and correction of errors as the State's court of last resort.

The supreme court was restructured by the Judiciary Article added to the constitution in 1869. Effective in 1870, the State was divided into four departments and the eight judicial districts were distributed among the departments. Each district consisted of three justices and a presiding judge (except that New York City had five justices). The supreme court's jurisdiction remained the same, but judges could no longer sit in review of their own cases. The number of justices has been increased periodically to help deal with the growing case loads.

The fourth State constitution of 1894 changed the organization of the supreme court. The trial terms (known as circuit courts and courts of oyer and terminer) were abolished and reestablished as trial terms of the supreme court. Effective in 1896, an appellate division of the supreme court was created to hear all appeals previously heard in the supreme court general terms.

The supreme court structure and jurisdiction established by the 1894 constitution have remained essentially the same except for changes in the number of justices and judicial districts. The State is now divided into 12 judicial districts. The number of justices in each district may be increased by the Legislature up to one justice for each 50,000, or fraction over 30,000, of population. Justices are elected by voters of their respective districts, but their jurisdiction extends statewide. Justices normally preside over trial terms in their own districts but may be assigned to serve elsewhere in the State. County clerks are clerks of the supreme court in their respective counties.

The supreme court appellate division continues to operate in each of the four judicial departments of the State, hearing appeals from the trial courts and the administrative agencies. The governor designates justices of each appellate division for five-year terms. Each appellate division has its own clerk. Each appellate division has the power to establish an appellate term of the supreme court to be held in and for its department or any district within the department. Currently there are appellate terms in the first and second departments.

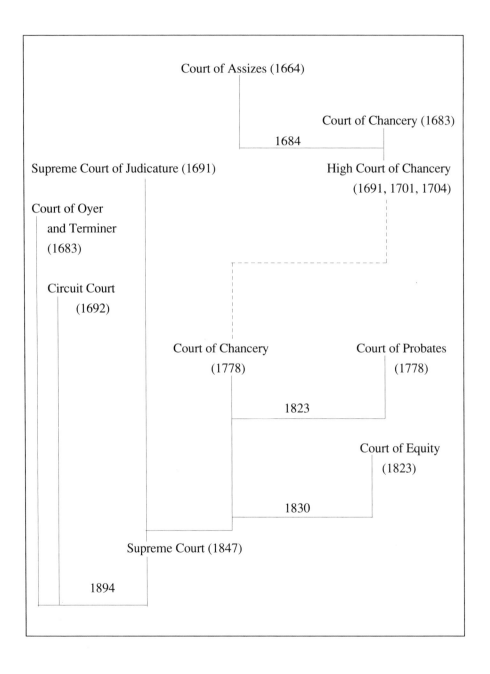

SUPREME COURT

General Agency-level Records

J1165   Common rule books, 1797-1849.
         58 cu. ft. (101 volumes)

J0014   Writs of commission, ca. 1802-1862.
         .8 cu. ft.

J1153   Registers of returns of writs of execution, 1837-1854.
         1 cu. ft. (4 volumes)

J0210   Index to returns of writs and executions, 1814-1858, bulk 1814-
         1817, 1826-1858.
         4 cu. ft. (7 volumes)

J1063   Orders transferring Court of Chancery papers to county clerks,
         1847-1886.
         1 cu. ft.

A0052   Minutes of the hearing in the matter of the acquisition of State
         Street from Broadway to the pier, 1912.
         5 cu. ft.

Appellate Division, First Department

B0815   Trial transcripts from New York County criminal courts, 1883-
         1927.
         425 microfilm reels

Appellate Division, Third Department

J2001   Records and briefs on appeal, 1896-1983.
         1,628 cu. ft. (7,413 volumes) R

J0037   Court minutes, 1896-1961.
         5 cu. ft.

J0018   Registers of orders, 1896-1956.
         19.2 cu. ft.

J0026   Registers of causes, 1896-1957.
         14.4 cu. ft.

J0035   Registers of decisions, 1896-1957.
         6.6 cu. ft.

J0008   Original proceedings case files, 1942-1954.
         .5 cu. ft.

J0042   Register of bonds and undertakings, 1896-1926.
.9 cu. ft.

J0060   Lists of attorneys admitted to the bar, 1934-1953.
.9 cu. ft.

New York County

J0218   Judgment books for mortgage foreclosures, 1868-1870.
1 cu. ft. (3 volumes)

3rd District

J0216   Special term minute book, 1854-1857.
.3 cu. ft. (1 volume)

Court of Assizes

A0271   Minutes, 1666-1670.
.1 cu. ft. (1 microfilm reel)

Supreme Court of Judicature

J0142   Index to dockets of judgments, 1829-1835.
1 cu. ft. (3 volumes) (1 microfilm reel)

J0222   Transcripts of docket of judgments in U.S. District and Circuit Courts, 1830-1836.
.5 cu. ft. (1 volume)

J6013   Transcripts of judgments in U.S. District and Circuit Courts, 1831-1836.
.2 cu. ft.

J3011   Summaries of testimony given in circuit courts and courts of oyer and terminer, 1823-1828.
2.6 cu. ft. (6 boxes)

J0007   Clerk's registers of cases in Supreme Court of Judicature and Courts of Common Pleas, 1797-1836.
.4 cu. ft. (4 volumes)

A0178   Book of entries of writs sealed, 1757-1762.
.5 cu. ft.

J0147   Writs of certiorari, ca. 1796-1847.
45.6 cu. ft.

J4013   Writs of mandamus, 1822-1844, bulk 1822, 1825-1844.
.4 cu. ft.

J0168 Precipes and original writs, 1815-1825.
.8 cu. ft. (2 boxes)

A0262 Miscellaneous writs and bail pieces, 1763-1824, bulk 1763, 1785-1824.
.5 cu. ft.

J0021 Bills of exceptions, ca. 1805-1847.
.9 cu. ft.

J1244 Ledgers of accounts with attorneys, ca. 1813-1844.
.4 cu. ft. (2 volumes)

B0318 Precepts for circuit courts and courts of oyer and terminer, Queens County, 1788-1794.
.1 cu. ft. (9 items)

J0124 Letter to James Kent, Chief Justice, concerning 1703 Rochester patent, 1811.
.1 cu. ft. (3 items)

– Albany

J0132 Transcripts of docket of judgments (New York), 1809-1847.
4.5 cu. ft. (11 volumes) (11 microfilm reels)

J0135 Transcripts of docket of judgments (Utica), 1807-1847.
7 cu. ft. (14 volumes) (14 microfilm reels)

J0138 Transcripts of docket of judgments (Geneva), 1829-1847.
4 cu. ft. (9 volumes) (9 microfilm reels)

J0130 General and special term minute books, 1797-1847.
11 cu. ft. (29 volumes)

J1130 Rough minute books, 1797-1807.
.5 cu. ft. (2 volumes)

J0079 Minute books for the Trial of Issues, 1798-1800.
.2 cu. ft. (3 volumes)

J2130 Partial index to minute books, 1797-1847.
.2 cu. ft. (1 volume)

J0140 Judgment rolls, 1797-1847.
326.4 cu. ft.

J0141 Docket of judgments, 1797-1847.
10 cu. ft. (28 volumes) (12 microfilm reels)

J1141   Transcripts of docket of judgments, 1808-1811.
             .2 cu. ft. (4 items)

J0154   Insolvency papers, 1795-1842.
             40 cu. ft. (17 microfilm reels)

J0041   Records of wills proved at Albany, 1799-1829.
             .3 cu. ft. (1 volume)

J0011   Motions and declarations, 1815-1847.
             187.9 cu. ft.

J0015   Declarations, 1838-1847.
             125.1 cu. ft.

J7011   Briefs, draft rules, and motions, 1812-1827.
             1.3 cu. ft.

J0241   Calendars of enumerated motions, 1806-1847.
             1.3 cu. ft. (68 volumes)

J0024   Writs of arrest and execution, 1797-1847.
             79.1 cu. ft.

J1025   Writs of certiorari, error, habeas corpus, and mandamus, ca. 1800-
             1847.
             9.9 cu. ft.

J0226   Registers of returns of writs, 1815-1847.
             .8 cu. ft. (6 volumes)

J0153   Registers of returns of writs, 1818-1825.
             1 cu. ft.

J3130   Minutes of return of writs by sheriffs, 1797-1799.
             .2 cu. ft. (1 volume)

J0022   Copies of pleadings furnished to circuit courts, 1797-1847.
             47.7 cu. ft.

J0096   Special bail pieces, 1797-1847.
             16.3 cu. ft.

J1202   Special bail books, 1807-1827.
             .3 cu. ft. (2 volumes, 1 item)

J0143   Committiturs and orders for exoneration of bail, 1829-1839.
             2.2 cu. ft.

J0002   Recognizance rolls, 1797-1834.
             2.6 cu. ft.

J0139   Satisfaction pieces, 1832-1839.
             1.3 cu. ft.

J1011   Fines and chirographs, 1793-1829.
             1 cu. ft.

J1041   Petitions and affidavits for proof of wills, 1801-1828.
             .2 cu. ft.

J2011   Criminal case documents, 1797-1808.
             .4 cu. ft.

J5011   Naturalization papers, 1799-1812.
             .2 cu. ft.

J8011   Assignments of error, 1837-1847, bulk 1837-1839, 1844-1847.
             .2 cu. ft.

J0152   Bonds of plaintiffs and appellants, 1808-1848.
             1.7 cu. ft.

J0019   Reports of commissioners to partition lands, 1802-1829, bulk
             1802-1819, 1824, 1829.
             1.7 cu. ft.

J6011   Affidavits of war service and property by Revolutionary War vet-
             erans, 1820.
             .4 cu. ft. (16 items)

J0104   Certificates of clerkships, 1809-1847.
             7.7 cu. ft.

J4011   Lists of freeholders qualified to serve as jurors, 1789-1821.
             1.3 cu. ft.

J9011   Lists of Supreme Court commissioners, 1788-1800.
             .1 cu. ft. (2 items)

J1150   Registers of agents, 1799-1813.
             .2 cu. ft. (4 volumes)

J0150   Notices of appointments of agents, 1826-1840.
             1.3 cu. ft.

J1152   Bills of costs, 1802-1812.
             .2 cu. ft.

J0214   Indexes and abstracts of attorneys' accounts, 1839-1847.
1 cu. ft. (5 volumes)

J7013   County treasurer's receipts for fees, 1841-1844.
.2 cu. ft.

J0230   Cash book for clerk's fees, 1846-1847.
.2 cu. ft. (1 volume)

– Albany and Geneva

J0001   Miscellaneous motions, 1798-1847.
6.4 cu. ft.

– Albany and Utica

J0170   Writs of commission, 1802-1843.
1.3 cu. ft.

– Albany, Utica, and Geneva

J0074   Transcripts of Chancery decrees, 1830-1847.
3.4 cu. ft. (8 boxes)

J0027   Writs of inquiry and inquisitions, 1823-1847.
12.5 cu. ft. (29 boxes)

– Geneva

J0129   Special term minute books, 1841-1846.
2 cu. ft.

J0137   Judgment rolls, 1827-1847.
111.8 cu. ft.

J0167   Common rule books, 1829-1847.
13 cu. ft. (79 volumes)

J1167   Common rule books for returns of writs of capias, 1829-1839.
.6 cu. ft. (10 volumes)

J2167   Common rule books for judgments on default, 1837-1847.
1 cu. ft. (9 volumes)

J5026   Orders for appointment of guardian or next friend, 1829-1847.
.4 cu.ft.

J6026   Orders for commissions, 1829-1847.
.4 cu. ft.

J8026	Orders of circuit judges on motions for new trials, 1833-1847. .4 cu. ft.
J0125	Motions and notices of joinder in demurrer, 1841-1846. .4 cu. ft.
J2241	Calendars of enumerated motions, 1841-1847. .3 cu. ft. (6 volumes)
J0017	Declarations, 1829-1847. 43 cu. ft.
J0025	Writs of execution, 1829-1847. 24.1 cu. ft.
J0028	Writs of capias ad respondendum, 1829-1847. 9.9 cu. ft.
J1026	Precipes and writs of summons, 1831-1842. .8 cu. ft.
J4026	Writs of possession, 1840-1843. .4 cu. ft.
J0030	Writs of replevin, 1838-1847. .8 cu. ft.
J0146	Copies of pleadings furnished to circuit courts, 1837-1847. 7.3 cu. ft.
J1012	Pleas and demurrers, 1837-1847. 1.3 cu. ft.
J0099	Special bail pieces, 1829-1847. 2.6 cu. ft.
J3202	Special bail book, 1829-1843. .5 cu. ft. (1 volume)
J3026	Affidavits of justification of special bail, 1839-1847. .4 cu. ft.
J1003	Recognizance rolls, 1829-1839. .4 cu. ft.
J0136	Satisfaction pieces, 1829-1842. 1.7 cu. ft.

J0004   Cognovits, 1829-1847.
         5.2 cu. ft.

J0005   Stipulations, 1844.
         1 cu. ft.

J2026   Assignments of errors, 1829-1842.
         .4 cu. ft.

J7026   Precepts and precipes, 1829-1847.
         .4 cu. ft.

J0006   Reports of referees, 1830-1847.
         .4 cu. ft.

J2104   Certificates of clerkships, 1838-1844.
         1.3 cu. ft.

J0012   Miscellaneous filed documents, 1829-1844.
         8 cu. ft.

J9813   Miscellaneous unfiled documents, ca. 1839-1844.
         .2 cu. ft.

J0244   Day book for clerk's fees, 1839-1847.
         .5 cu. ft. (1 volume)

– New York City

J0131   Docket of judgments, 1797-1810.
         1 cu. ft. (4 volumes)

J2000   Insolvency papers, 1784-1828, bulk 1786-1815.
         8.6 cu. ft.

J1014   Reports of commissioners appointed to appraise lands taken for
         street openings in New York City and Brooklyn, 1817-1845, bulk
         1817, 1830, 1837, 1845.
         .4 cu. ft.

– Utica

J0128   General term minute books, 1820-1846.
         3 cu. ft. (13 volumes)

J0134   Judgment rolls, 1807-1847.
         207.7 cu. ft.

J2165   Common rule books, 1807-1849.
         48 cu. ft. (90 volumes)

J0156   Insolvency papers, 1806-1847.
         5.6 cu. ft. (8 microfilm reels)

J0010   Declarations and motions before 1830, 1821-1829.
         1.3 cu. ft.

J0009   Declarations, 1831-1842.
         66.2 cu. ft.

J1013   Declarations and motions, 1841-1847.
         43.9 cu. ft.

J0126   Motions, 1820-1846.
         14.2 cu. ft.

J1126   Miscellaneous motions, 1832, 1837.
         1.3 cu. ft.

J2013   Motions denied, ca. 1841-1847.
         1.4 cu. ft.

J1241   Calendars of enumerated motions, 1820-1847.
         1.3 cu. ft. (28 volumes)

J0175   Orders of circuit judges on motions for new trials or for commissions, 1834-1847.
         .4 cu. ft.

J0013   Writs of arrest and execution, 1807-1847.
         63 cu. ft.

J0029   Writs of habeas corpus, 1807-1829.
         1.3 cu. ft.

J0031   Writs of error, 1807-1847.
         10.8 cu. ft.

J5013   Writs of dower, 1824-1829.
         .4 cu. ft.

J8013   Writs of attachment, 1825-1843.
         .4 cu. ft.

J1031   Writs of scire facias, 1843-1845.
         .3 cu. ft.

J0023   Copies of pleadings furnished to Circuit Courts, 1828-1847.
         22.8 cu. ft.

J0098	Special bail pieces, 1829-1847. 15.5 cu. ft. (36 boxes)
J2202	Special bail books, 1807-1826. 1 cu. ft. (5 volumes)
J0144	Committiturs and orders for exoneration of bail, 1807-1837. 2.2 cu. ft.
J1098	Affidavits of justification of special bail, 1807-1847. .4 cu. ft.
J0003	Recognizance rolls, 1807-1834. 1.3 cu. ft.
J0133	Satisfaction pieces, 1808-1845. 3.4 cu. ft.
J0020	Record of wills proved at Utica, 1818-1829. .2 cu. ft. (1 volume)
J1020	Wills and petitions for probate, 1820-1829. .4 cu. ft.
J3013	Issue rolls and continuance rolls, 1819-1830. .4 cu. ft.
J0151	Testimony taken conditionally, 1833-1846. .4 cu. ft.
J9013	Naturalization papers, 1822-1939, bulk 1822, 1838-1839. .2 cu. ft.
J9913	Reports of commissioners to partition lands, 1825-1830. .4 cu. ft.
J1104	Certificates of clerkships, 1807-1836. 1.3 cu. ft.
J0149	Notices of appointment of agents, 1809-1841. 2.2 cu. ft.

Court of Oyer and Terminer

A0237	Trial transcripts, 1865-1868. .5 cu. ft.

Court of Probates

J0038	Probated wills, 1671-1815. 9 cu. ft.

J0301   Inventories and accounts, 1666-1823.
         6 cu. ft.

J0032   Letters of administration, 1787-1799.
         .5 cu. ft. (2 volumes)

J0033   Administration papers, ca. 1700-1823.
         12.5 cu. ft.

J0034   Administration bonds, 1787-1823.
         .5 cu. ft. (5 volumes)

J0039   Exemplifications of wills and letters of administration, 1783-1801.
         .3 cu. ft. (1 volume)

J0043   Record of wills and probates, 1787-1822.
         .6 cu. ft. (2 volumes)

J0208   Orders and decrees, 1811-1823.
         .3 cu. ft. (1 volume)

J0036   Inventory of wills, administration papers and inventories trans-
         ferred from the secretary of state to the Court of Probates, ca.
         1783.
         .3 cu. ft. (1 volume)

J0302   Record of funds and cases transferred to the Court of Chancery,
         1823.
         .2 cu. ft.

Court of Chancery

J0059   Chancery minutes, 1781-1829.
         15 cu. ft. (47 volumes) (18 microfilm reels)

J0082   Chancellor's minutes, 1830-1833.
         5 cu. ft. (3 volumes)

J1059   Register's engrossed minutes, 1807-1812.
         .5 cu. ft. (3 volumes)

J0072   Register's minutes of causes, 1813-1847.
         5 cu. ft. (12 volumes)

J0069   Register's rough minutes, 1819-1821, 1827-1847.
         5 cu. ft. (16 volumes)

J0095   Chancery registers, 1780-1823.
         4 cu. ft. (26 volumes)

J2176   Register's statement of cases handled by the Court of Chancery,
        1794-1825.
        .1 cu. ft. (1 item)

J0070   Chancery papers, 1800-1847.
        108 cu. ft.

J1071   Index to Chancery papers, 1800-1847.
        .5 cu. ft. (1 volume) (1 microfilm reel)

J0057   In Re papers, ca. 1800-1847.
        21.5 cu. ft.

J0058   Index to In Re papers, 1800-1847.
        .3 cu. ft. (1 volume) (1 microfilm reel)

J2089   Chancellor's draft opinions, 1842, 1846.
        .5 cu. ft.

J0065   Pre-1800 Chancery decrees and papers, 1684-1815.
        57 cu. ft.

J1065   Pre-1800 defendant index to decrees and papers, 1684-1815.
        1.5 cu. ft.

J0063   Post-1800 Chancellor's enrolled decrees, 1801-1847.
        120 cu. ft. (151 microfilm reels)

J0064   Index of post-1800 enrolled Chancery decrees, 1801-1847.
        .5 cu. ft. (1 volume) (1 microfilm reel)

J0066   Index to pre-1800 enrolled decrees, 1712-1799.
        .1 cu. ft. (1 volume)

J0088   Index of post-1800 enrolled decrees, 1823-1847.
        .5 cu. ft. (1 volume)

J0089   Chancellor's draft decrees and orders, 1823-1847.
        29 cu. ft.

J0049   Register's minutes of decrees, 1830-1847.
        10 cu. ft. (28 volumes) (17 microfilm reels)

J0051   Register's docket of decrees, 1831-1835.
        1 cu. ft. (1 volume)

J0091   List of decrees entered in Register's office, 1819-1823.
        .1 cu. ft. (2 volumes)

J1049 Register's minutes of foreclosure decrees, 1840-1847.
4 cu. ft. (4 volumes) (3 microfilm reels)

J0092 Orders and decrees issued in the matters of the Utica and Schenectady Railroad Company, 1835-1839.
.3 cu. ft. (1 volume)

J0090 Orders in Chancery, 1701-1708, 1720-1770.
.6 cu. ft. (4 volumes)

J0045 Common order book, 1806-1830.
2 cu. ft. (6 volumes)

J0046 Register's minutes of common orders, 1830-1847.
6 cu. ft. (15 volumes)

J0087 Miscellaneous files, 1772-1847.
81 cu. ft.

J0071 Index to miscellaneous files in Chancery, 1772-1847.
.5 cu. ft. (1 volume) (1 microfilm reel)

J0053 Register's minutes of guardians, committees, and receivers, 1830-1847.
.6 cu. ft. (2 volumes)

J0054 Register's register of guardians, committees, and receivers, 1829-1833.
.3 cu. ft. (1 volume)

J0056 Accounts of infants with the New York Life Insurance and Trust Company, 1832-1838.
.3 cu. ft. (1 volume)

J4061 Mortgages filed in Register's Office, 1807-1826.
.5 cu. ft.

J0083 Index to mortgages filed in Register's Office, 1818-1823.
.3 cu. ft. (1 volume)

J3089 Notes of issue, 1814-1846.
.5 cu. ft.

J0093 Register's record of notices served, 1840-1847.
.4 cu. ft. (3 volumes)

J4089 Court calendars, 1830-1843.
.5 cu. ft.

J0040   Record of foreign and out-of-state wills proved, 1830-1848.
1 cu. ft. (3 volumes)

J0044   Oaths of office of attorneys, solicitors, and counsellors, 1796-1847.
.5 cu. ft.

J0238   Index to cases transferred by Clerk of Eighth Circuit to Supreme Court, 1847.
.3 cu. ft. (1 volume)

J0075   Chancery forms, ca. 1820-1847.
.2 cu. ft. (1 volume)

– Chancery Fund

J9076   Internal accounts and administration files, 1805-1847. .
.5 cu. ft.

J6076   Annual reports to comptroller on office expenditures, 1825-1830, 1832, 1834, 1838, 1843.
.5 cu. ft.

J7076   Register's and Assistant Register's reports to State Assembly, 1825, 1836, 1838.
.1 cu. ft. (9 items)

J0076   Annual statements of accounts of Register, Assistant Register, and Clerks, 1838-1847.
.5 cu. ft.

J4076   Register's and Assistant Register's reports of balances, bonds, and mortgages, 1823-1839.
.5 cu. ft.

J3076   Register's and clerks' reports of delinquent guardians, committees and receivers, 1830-1846.
.5 cu. ft.

J2276   Register's statement on mortgage foreclosures, 1838-1839.
.1 cu. ft. (1 item)

J0078   Ledger of fees paid by solicitors and counsellors, 1839.
.6 cu. ft. (3 volumes)

J0084   Receipts to the Register, 1823-1825.
.2 cu. ft. (1 volume)

J5076   Receipts and related records for accounts with the Court, ca. 1830-1855.
1 cu. ft.

– 1st through 8th Circuits

J0073   Clerk's minutes of causes, 1823-1847.
24 cu. ft. (48 volumes)

– 2nd Circuit

J1151   Appointments of agents, 1823-1842.
.5 cu. ft.

– 2nd through 8th Circuits

J0081   Minutes of Courts of Equity, 1823-1829.
5 cu. ft. (16 volumes) (7 microfilm reels)

J0061   Enrolled decrees, In Re papers, and other case files, 1823-1847.
378 cu. ft.

J0062   Index to enrolled decrees, In Re papers and other case files, 1823-1847.
1.5 cu. ft. (7 volumes) (1 microfilm reel)

J0047   Clerks' minutes of common orders, 1830-1847.
15 cu. ft. (43 volumes)

J0048   Clerks' minutes of decrees, 1830-1847.
33 cu. ft. (88 volumes) (47 microfilm reels)

J0052   Clerk's docket of decrees, 1830-1847.
2.6 cu. ft. (8 volumes)

– 3rd Circuit

J1089   Vice Chancellor's draft decrees and orders, 1830-1847.
7 cu. ft.

J1054   Clerk's register of guardians, committees, and receivers, 1829-1847.
.3 cubic ft. (1 volume)

J6061   Bonds of guardians, committees and receivers, 1823-1844.
.3 cu. ft.

– 3rd through 5th Circuits, Chancery Fund

J2076   Injunction Master's annual reports on the accounts of guardians, committees and receivers, 1830-1837, 1839-1841.
.2 cu. ft.

- 3rd through 8th Circuits

    J0068   Clerk's rough minutes, 1830-1847.
                  1.5 cu. ft. (13 volumes) (3 microfilm reels)

- 3rd through 8th Circuits, Chancery Fund

    J1076   Clerk's semi-annual report of accounts, 1833-1847.
                  .1 cu. ft.

- 3rd, 6th and 8th Circuits

    J5061   Masters' bonds, 1833-1847.
                  .5 cu. ft.

- 4th, 7th and 8th Circuits

    J0050   Clerk's minutes of foreclosure decrees, 1837-1847.
                  6 cu. ft. (17 volumes) (11 microfilm reels)

- 5th Circuit

    J2061   Draft orders, correspondence, reports and miscellaneous papers, 1830-1847.
                  .5 cu. ft.

- 5th, 6th, and 8th Circuits

    J1061   Naturalization papers, ca. 1830-1847.
                  1 cu. ft.

- 6th Circuit

    J3061   Vice Chancellor's opinions and decisions, 1823-1847.
                  .5 cu. ft.

- 7th Circuit

    J0085   Clerk's minutes of petition cases, 1837-1847.
                  .2 cu. ft. (1 volume) (1 microfilm reel)

    J0206   Common orders of reference in mortgage cases, 1843-1847.
                  .5 cu. ft. (1 volume)

- 8th Circuit

    J0055   Listing of receivers, committees, and guardians, 1830-1847.
                  .5 cu. ft. (1 volume)

    J0204   Orders for receivers, 1843-1847.
                  .5 cu. ft. (1 volume)

Court of General Sessions of the Peace

    J0016   Records on appeal remitted from the Supreme Court, Appellate Division, First Department, ca. 1886-1916. 84 cu. ft. R

Court of Claims

Current Functions. The Court of Claims is a statewide court responsible for hearing and determining claims for money damages against the State, by the State against a claimant, or between conflicting claimants.

Organizational History. The immediate predecessor to the court of claims was the Board of Claims, established in 1883 (Chapter 205) with three commissioners appointed by the governor. The Board of Claims took over all claims pending before the Canal Appraisers and the State Board of Audit. The Canal Appraisers, established in 1821 (Chapter 240) and continued by legislation of 1825 (Chapter 275) and 1836 (Chapter 287), heard claims for damages resulting from canal construction. The State Board of Audit was established in 1876 (Chapter 444) to hear all private claims against the State not falling under the jurisdiction of the Canal Appraisers. The Canal Appraisers and the State Board of Audit were abolished.

In 1897 (Chapter 36), the Board of Audit was reestablished as the court of claims with the same functions, powers, and jurisdiction, and the commissioners became judges of the court. In 1911 (Chapter 856), the court again became a Board of Claims with three commissioners. Legislation of 1915 (Chapter 1) restored the court of claims with three judges appointed by the governor, who also designated a presiding judge. The governor could appoint two additional judges if the case load became too heavy. In 1939 (Chapter 860), the court of claims was continued, this time with five judges. The number of judges has increased periodically since that time.

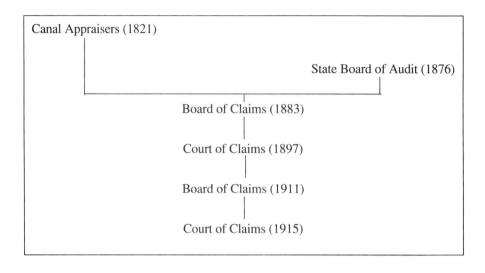

Canal Appraisers (1821)

State Board of Audit (1876)

Board of Claims (1883)

Court of Claims (1897)

Board of Claims (1911)

Court of Claims (1915)

COURT OF CLAIMS

General Agency-ievel Records

A0488   Exhibit map of Taggarts Paper Company land claim, 1910-1917. .3 cu. ft.

Court of Admiralty

Functions. Admiralty courts were responsible for determining cases involving maritime commerce. To carry out this responsibility, the courts heard cases concerning seamen's contracts and wages, capture of prizes on the high seas, customs tolls, ownership of shipwrecks and salvaged cargo, leases and mortgages of vessels, contracts for building and equipping vessels, and breaches of trade and navigation laws.

Organizational History. The colonial courts of admiralty were branches of the High Court of Admiralty in London. Originally, the colonial governor was commissioned as vice-admiral, and he appointed the presiding judge and other court officers. Beginning in 1697, governors needed authorization from the Crown to establish admiralty courts and make appointments to them. The Vice-Admiralty Court of the Province of New York covered New York, New Jersey, and Connecticut. Appeals were taken to the King in Council or the High Court of Admiralty.

In 1775, the Continental Congress authorized the states to establish courts of admiralty to determine cases of capture. Appeals were taken to Congress or commissions designated by Congress. In New York State, the colonial court of vice-admiralty was continued as the State Court of Admiralty with the same powers, and a judge was appointed with the same powers as the vice-admiralty judges. Although New York State provided for a court of admiralty in 1778 (Chapter 12), one did not actually operate until 1784, after the British evacuated the State's maritime counties. The court was abolished in 1789, when New York State adopted the Federal constitution, which vested admiralty authority in the Federal courts.

COURT OF ADMIRALTY

A3297   Case papers, 1784-1788.
         .1 cu. ft. (1 microfilm reel)

COURT OF VICE ADMIRALTY

A3296   Minutes and case papers, 1685-1838, bulk 1685-1775.
         .1 cu. ft. (1 microfilm reel)

APPENDICES

Appendix A

LOCAL GOVERNMENT RECORDS

The State Archives and Records Administration (SARA) does not accession or hold local government records, except for microfilm copies of local government records which may be deposited in the State Archives (see Appendix B).

The care, maintenance, and administration of local government records, including those with archival value, are the responsibilities of the local governments themselves. The State Archives and Records Administration's Local Government Records Services issues retention and disposition schedules that prescribe how long records must be retained; offers advice and guidance via workshops, publications, and consultation with local governments; and provides grants for records management and archival administration projects. The 1987 Local Government Records Law (Chapter 737) indicates that each local government must designate a Records Management Officer and support development of a coordinated records management program. The 1989 Records Management Improvement Act (Chapter 78) authorizes a grant-in-aid program and regional SARA field offices to provide advice and assistance to local governments. These laws and SARA's advisory services cover all local governments in New York State except New York City mayoral agencies. For more information about SARA's local records programs, contact the Local Government Records Services, 10A63 Cultural Education Center, Albany, NY 12230, phone 518-474-6926.

The New York City Department of Records and Information Services (DORIS) is responsible for records management and archival programs covering New York City mayoral agencies. DORIS operates an extensive City Archives program. For more information, contact the New York City Department of Records and Information Services, 31 Chambers Street, New York, NY 10007.

Appendix B

LOCAL RECORDS ON MICROFILM IN THE STATE ARCHIVES

This appendix lists microfilmed local records available from the New York State Archives. Most of the records were filmed during the period from 1974 to 1976 by the Office of State History as a project of the New York State American Revolution Bicentennial Commission. The 250 reels of microfilm produced by the project were given to the State Archives in 1976. The microfilmed records date from 1650 to 1975, with the bulk in the 1800-1850 era and only a few after 1900. The geographical coverage of the records is uneven; extensive film copies were made for some counties, but few or none for others. Most are public records, especially those of towns. The nonpublic materials microfilmed include church registers and minutes, store ledgers, business and commercial records, and records from private educational institutions.

In addition to the microfilm produced by the Bicentennial Commission project, the Archives holds a small amount of film obtained from other sources. The microfilm is available for use in the State Archives, and through the New York State Inter-Library Loan network. Copies of the film may also be purchased from the New York State Archives, Cultural Education Center, Albany, NY 12230.

The list of microfilmed local records is arranged alphabetically by county. If the name of a county does not appear, then no records were filmed. A few multicounty entries appear at the end. Under each county, records series entries are arranged according to the source or topic of the records, under the following headings:

> State Census Records
> County Government
> Town Government
> Village Government
> City Government
> Religious Organizations

Education-Public
Education-Nonpublic
Fraternal Organizations
Commercial-Retail Trade
Commercial-Transportation
Commercial-Manufacturing
Commercial-Services
Military
Individuals
Land Records
Cemeteries

Roll No.

ALBANY COUNTY

County government

74-40-1	Fort Orange proceedings 1652-60
74-40-1,2	Notarial papers, #s 1 & 2, 1660-95
74-40-6	Commissioners of Magistrates proceedings, 1676-80
74-40-16	Oaths of office, 1808-40
74-40-13	Account book for loan of 1792, 1792-ca. 1849
	Account book for loan of 1808, ca. 1808-50
74-40-2	Election result books, 1787-1815
74-40-17	Canvass of votes, 1820
74-40-3	Court minutes of Fort Orange (original), 1652-56; 1668-72; 1675-84
74-40-4,5	Court minutes of Fort Orange (copies and translations), 1652-1702
74-40-17	Court of Sessions minutes, 1685-89; 1717-23; 1763-82
74-40-7 to 10	Court of Common Pleas minutes, 1766-1850
74-40-11,12	Court of Common Pleas order books, 1803-32
74-40-12	Court of Common Pleas filings, 1790-1822
74-40-5	Justice of the Peace proceedings, 1680-85
74-40-12	Mayor's Court writ book, 1832-41
74-40-14,15	Mortgages, with discharges, 1765-75; 1787-89
74-40-6	Wills (affecting real estate), 1681-1835
74-40-5	Slave manumission register, 1800-1828
74-40-15	Church patents, 1784-1842; 1844-80
A3284-1 to 18	Common Council minutes, 1676-1848

Town government

Rensselaerville

76-33-1	Record books, 1795-1861

City government

Albany

76-3-11 to 31	Common Council documents, 1832-43
74-40-16	Oaths of office, 1826-45
76-3-9	Street records, 1832-33
	Street department performance bonds, 1830-43
74-40-18	Assessment rolls for first ward, 1817-23
76-3-1 to 9	Assessment rolls, 1846-59
76-3-32	Assessment and apportionment for Albany Basin, 1842
	Record of assessment bills delivered, Sept. 1842-Mar. 1845

Roll No.

74-40-3	City treasurer's record, 1702-21
76-3-32	Chamberlains' office ledgers, 1844-52
76-3-10, 11	Apportionments and miscellaneous financial documents, 1817-40
76-3-10	Shipping receipts, 1815
76-3-32	Report of the Albany pier commissioners, 1842

Commercial-transportation

Albany and Schenectady Turnpike Co.

| 74-40-18 | Stockholders' records 1830-31 |

Land records

74-40-18	Land commissioners' report, 1764
	Map index, 1767-1878
74-40-19	Highway field books, 1770-92
74-40-18	Description of reservoirs, 1844
74-40-19	Field book of City of Albany lands, 1804
74-40-18	Field notes in Bethlehem, 1803
74-40-19	Field book of Coeyman's patent, 1785-88
	Survey of lands granted to Anna Kast et al., 1768
	Field book of lands granted to Johannes Lawyer, Jacob Zimmer, et al., 1790-91; 1801
	Field book of lands south of the Mohawk, 1730
	Field book of lands in "Schaghcatot," n.d.
	Field book of West Troy, 1829
74-40-18	Saratoga and Hoosick patents-descriptions, 1769-72
	Watervliet and Hosack patents-descriptions, 1769-72

ALLEGANY COUNTY

County government

75-74-1, 2	Supervisors' minutes, 1812-47
75-74-2	Town charges, 1816; 1819; 1826
75-75-1	Court of Oyer and Terminer minutes, 1815-49

Town government

Angelica

| 75-74-2 | Assessment roll, 1817 |

Roll No.

CATTARAUGUS COUNTY

Town government

Little Valley
75-100-1   Record book, 1823-1914
Road commissioners' records, 1823-81
Book of marks and strays, 1822-98
School commissioners' records, 1828-1900

CAYUGA COUNTY

Town government

Aurelius
76-37-1   Record book, 1823-72
Highway record book, 1842-83

Brutus
75-49-1   Record book, 1827-68
Highway record book, 1803-26
Assessment rolls, 1844-55

Commercial-transportation

Auburn & Cato Plank Road Co.
Account book, 1848-77

CHAUTAUQUA COUNTY

State census records

Roll No.	
479631	1825, 1835, 1845
479634	1855 (part 1)
479635	1855 (part 2)
479638	1865 (part 1)
479639	1865 (part 2)
479640	1865 (part 3)
479643	1875 (part 1)
479644	1875 (part 2)
479645	1875 (part 3)
479648	1892
479649	1905 (part 1,2)
479650	1905 (part 3)
479651	1905 (part 4)

Roll No.

Town government

Busti
75-91-1   Record book, 1824-59
Assessment roll, 1844

Carroll
75-94-1   Record books, 1825-69

Ellington
75-95-1   Record books, 1825-59
Assessment roll, 1860
School district minute books, 1824-1947

French Creek
75-92-1   Record book, 1830-84

Harmony
75-93-1   Record book, 1816-51

Westfield
75-99-1   Record books, 1829-35; 1838-1900
Road books, 1829-99
Assessment roll, 1837
75-99-2   Military tax roll, 1853
Supervisors' book, 1829-54
Account book, 1829-99
75-99-2, 3   Justice dockets, 1830-63
75-99-2   Book of strays, 1829-81
75-99-1   School commissioners' records, 1838-1901

Village government

Westfield
75-98-1   Record books, 1833-76

Religious organizations

Ellington
First Congregational Church
75-96-1   Record book, 1828-50

Roll No.

Education-nonpublic

Fredonia Academy

75-97-2	Trustees' minutes, 1824-69
	Reports to regents, 1839-67
75-97-1	Correspondence, 1834-50
	By-laws and statistics, 1826-29
75-97-2	List of original subscribers, 1821
	Subscribers, 1821-65
75-97-1	Catalogues, 1827-65
	Student registers, 1831-60
75-97-2	Student bills, 1824-68
75-97-1	Diagram of Academy Square, n.d.

CHENANGO COUNTY

Town government

Columbus

76-17-1	Record books, 1805-63
	Road commissioners' reports, 1837-49
76-17-2	Assessment rolls, 1807-50
	Minutes of commissioners of excise, 1830-54
	Supervisors' accounts, 1830-62
	Chattel mortgage book, 1847-1911
	Book of strays, 1816-65
	School commissioners' reports, 1820-46

Smyrna

76-20-1	Minute books, 1809-53

Village government

Sherburne

76-19-1	Record book, 1863-91

CLINTON COUNTY

County government

76-39-1	Court of Oyer and Terminer minutes, 1796-1839; 1847-61
76-39-1, 2	Court of Common Pleas minutes, 1789-1819
76-39-2	Circuit Court minutes, 1796-1827
	Judgment book, 1798-1811

Roll No.

Town government

Peru
76-41-1 Record book, 1833-1909
 Highway book, 1831-1902

Plattsburgh
76-38-1 Record books, 1787-1859
 School record book, 1868-92
 School commissioners' records, 1868-92

COLUMBIA COUNTY

State census records

479098	1855
479100	1865
479102	1875
479105	1905

County government

74-1-1 Map of Columbia County, 1829

Town government

Canaan
74-26-1 Record book, 1772-1810

Chatham
74-2-1 Record book, 1795-1832
 Record of votes, 1804-27

Copake
75-33-1 Record book, 1824-65

City government

Hudson
75-54-2 Index to records, 1810-38
75-54-1 Common Council proceedings, 1806-51
75-54-2 Ordinance book #1, 1829-54
 Court record book, 1798
 Proprietors' minutes, 1784
75-54-1, 2 Register of firemen, 1809-73

Roll No.

75-54-2   Register of earmarks, 1808
        Stray animal book, 1787

Religious organizations

Claverack
Reformed Dutch Church
75-103-1   Record books, 1726-68; 1789-1810
        Record book #4A, 1810-28
        Record book #4B, 1816-25
        Record book #5, 1826-81
        Record book #6, 1819-1933
        Ouderlingen book, 1780-1821
75-103-2   Minutes of the consistory, 1831-78
        Consistory minutes and accounts, 1760-92;
        1817-30
        Account books, 1780-1801
        Account books, 1828-75
        Miscellaneous papers, -1875

North Chatham
Baptist Church
74-25-1   Minute book, 1795-1809

Education-public

75-32-1   Teacher of arithmetic instruction book, 1806-8

Commercial-retail trade

Van Schaak estates
Account book, 1785-1816

Van Schaack family
Business ledger, 1795-1831

Commercial-transportation

Columbia Turnpike Co.
Stockholders' ledger, 1811-98

Commercial-services

Aaron Jewett
74-1-1   Shoemaker's journal, 1764-89

Roll No.

Military

75-32-1   County revolutionary war pension claims, ca. 1830s

Individuals

Cornelius Van Schaack
75-32-2   Estate book kept by Peter Sylvester, 1776-90

Land records

75-32-1   Proprietors of Hudson, articles of agreement, 1785

CORTLAND COUNTY

Town government

Homer
75-52-1   Record books, 1797-1880
Road records, 1847-88
Supervisors' account book, 1832-60
School records, 1821-90

DELAWARE COUNTY

Town government

Dehli
74-53-1   Record books, 1823-62

Harpersfield
75-1-1   Record book, 1787-1855

Kortright
74-13-1   Record book, 1829-1928

Stamford
74-12-1   Record book, 1793-1840

Roll No.

DUTCHESS COUNTY

Town government

Beekman (precinct and town)
75-87-1   Record book, 1772-1825

Crum Elbow, Charlotte, Clinton (precincts)
75-10-1   Record book, 1783-99

Poughkeepsie
Record book, 1769-1833
Record book, 1742-1854
Road book, 1834-54
75-10-1, 2   Overseers of the poor record, 1807-15

Red Hook
75-14-1   Record book, 1813-66
Record book, 1849-78
Election result book, 1813-68

Rhinebeck
74-19-1   Record books, 1748-1877
Assessment roll, 1846

A3245-1 to 4   **Stanford**
Records, 1794-1982

Village government

Poughkeepsie
75-10-2   Record books, 1803-39

Commercial-retail trade

W. C. Cramer of Red Hook
75-32-1   Account book, 1775-1809

ERIE COUNTY

Buffalo
79-14-1 to 239   Common Council minutes, 1832-1900

Roll No.

ESSEX COUNTY

Town government

Elizabethtown
76-43-1 Record books, 1798-1902

Essex
76-42-1 Assessment roll, 1826
Register of voters, 1860

Minerva
74-20-1 Record books, 1817-35; 1837-82

Moriah
76-40-1 Record book, 1819-95
Justice docket, 1831-43

Willsboro
76-42-1 Record books, 1789-1905
Road records, 1840
Overseers of the poor record, 1794-1832

Village government

Port Henry
74-37-1 Record book, 1869-93

FULTON COUNTY

State census records

513993	1845
462875	1855
462876	1865
513995	1875
465984	1905 (part 1)
465985	1905 (part 2)

Village government

Johnstown
76-27-1 Record books, 1808-67

Roll No.

Religious organizations

Gloversville
Kingsborough Presbyterian Church
75-57-1 Record book, 1804-91
Papers, 1793-1812
Session minutes, 1822-53
Society of Kingsborough records, 1793-1908
Trustees' accounts, 1838-65
Marriage record, 1830-1904   ·
Journal of the Rev. Elisha Yale, 1803-17
Correspondence of the Rev. Elisha Yale, 1802-40

Johnstown
First Presbyterian Church
75-48-1 Registers, 1785-1890

St. John's Episcopal Church
76-28-1 Vestry records, 1809-63

Fraternal organizations

Johnstown Masonic Lodge
76-29-1 Proceedings, 1766-1865

GREENE COUNTY

State census records

480075	1855 (part 1)
480076	1855 (part 2)
480077	1865
480079	1875
480081	1892, 1905

HAMILTON COUNTY

State census records
550033 1892

HERKIMER COUNTY

Town government

Danube
74-44-1 Record books, 1828-90

Roll No.

74-9-1	Record book (ledger), 1828-78
	Record book (ledger), 1862-90
	Highway book, 1834-77
	Supervisors' record, 1825-77

Frankfort

74-10-1	Record book, 1798-1832
	Highway record books, 1832-52; 1854-98

Herkimer

74-21-1	Record book, 1789-1874

JEFFERSON COUNTY

Town government

Ellisburg

75-79-1	Record book, 1803-27
	Assessment rolls, 1855; 1859
	Register of chattel mortgages, 1850-66
	Election results, 1828; 1829; 1838
	School records, district #10, 1864-91
	School records, district #34, 1847-76

LIVINGSTON COUNTY

Town government

Avon

76-45-1	Record book, 1797-1874

Conesus

76-45-2	Record books, 1820-1917

Geneseo

76-45-3	Record book, 1797-1822

Lima

76-45-4	Record books, 1793-1812; 1818-60
	Assessment roll, 1878
76-45-5	Supervisor's account books, 1829-67; 1864-1933
76-45-4	Register of voters, 1869
	Military enrollment, 1863
76-45-5	School fund, 1856-1907

Roll No.

Ossian
76-45-6   Record book, 1808-39, 1902

West Sparta
76-45-7   Record book, 1847-66

Village government

Avon
76-45-8, 9   Record books, 1853-1918
76-45-8   Election results, 1906

MADISON COUNTY

State census records

53057 Pt. 3	1855 (volume 1,2)
53057 Pt. 4	1855 (volume 3)
53057 Pt. 7	1865 (volume 1)
53057 Pt. 8	1865 (volume 2)
53057 Pt. 9	1875
53057 Pt. 10	1875
53057 Pt. 13	1892
53057 Pt. 14	1905

Town government

Cazenovia
75-105-1   Record book, 1804-54
               Road book, 1804-90s
               Vital statistics, 1847-49

Georgetown
75-104-1   Record book, 1816-34
               Record book, 1816-88

Village government

Cazenovia
74-36-1   Minute books, 1810-76

Chittenango
75-106-1   Record book, 1842-58
               Enumeration, 1906

Roll No.

De Ruyter

75-53-1 Record book, 1834-70

Religious organizations

Chittenango
Reformed Dutch Church
76-18-1 Consistory minutes, 1828-88
Building committee accounts, 1828-32
Register of members, 1826-87

MONROE COUNTY

County government

76-11-1 Treasurers' record book, 1821-41

Town government

Chili
76-9-1 Record books, 1822-1929
76-9-2 Assessment rolls, 1853; 1855-59
76-9-1 Supervisors' account book and excise commissioners' minutes, 1830-79
76-9-2 Poormasters' accounts, 1823-62
Justice dockets, 1831-33; 1841-49
76-9-1 Military rolls, 1852; 1855-57
School minutes, 1822-93

Gates
76-8-1 Record book, 1809-1913

Henrietta
76-6-1 Record books, 1818-78

Mendon
75-80-1 Record books, 1813-97
Account book, 1821-1905

Penfield
76-7-1 Record book, 1811-64
Record book, 1816-51
Road survey book, 1811-64
Road survey, 1811-60
Supervisors' accounts, 1816-59

Roll No.

76-7-2	Account book, 1845-95
	Poormasters' minutes, 1821-43
	Justice dockets, 1838-41; 1843-45; 1851-52
	Military roll, 1852
76-7-1	School district minutes, 1817-74

Pittsford

76-10-1	Record books, 1796-1879
	Road record book, 1839-1910
76-10-2	Register of electors, 1864
	Justice docket, 1819
76-10-1	Justice docket, 1837-41
76-10-2	Book of strays, 1827-1903
	Cattle marks, 1799-1830
76-10-1	School district reports, 1821-50
	School record book, 1846-1921

Village government

Honeoye Falls

75-82-1	Record book, 1838-45

Rochester

76-12-1	Tax rolls, 1827; 1827-30

Religious organizations

Honeoye Falls
  First Presbyterian Church

76-13-1	Session minutes, 1831-1904
	Trustees' minutes, 1831-1925
	Church history, 1965

MONTGOMERY COUNTY

State census records

479195	1865
479334	1875
479335	1892
479336	1905

County government

74-52-7	Court of Common Pleas papers, 1789-1848

Roll No.

72-52-4 to 6	Court of Common Pleas papers, 1830-50
74-52-8, 9	Tryon County Court of Common Pleas minutes, 1772-91
74-52-8	Tryon County Court of General Sessions, 1772-1822
74-52-9 to 41	Miscellaneous fiscal, legal, and business papers, with index, 1770-ca. 1900

Town government

Amsterdam

74-52-3   Record book, 1852-85
Highway commissioners' minutes, 1857-86
School commissioners' minutes, 1841-79

Oppenheim

74-52-1   Record book, 1830-37

Palatine

74-52-2   Record book, 1828-1925
Record books, 1827-1911
Minute book, 1880-1911
74-52-3   Clerk's book, 1797-1803
74-52-2   District clerk's book, 1786-97

Root

74-52-1   Record book, 1823-88
Book of strays, 1823-76
Commissioners of common schools records, 1823-93
Commissioners' report of apportionment of school monies, 1851-1904

Commercial-retail trade

74-52-9 to 41   Miscellaneous fiscal, legal, and business papers, with index, 1770-ca. 1900

Commercial-transportation

Miscellaneous fiscal, legal, and business papers, with index, 1770-ca. 1900

Amsterdam & Fish House Plank Rd. Co.

74-52-1   Record book, 1848-58

Roll No.

Commercial-manufacturing

74-52-9 to 41   Miscellaneous fiscal, legal, and business papers, with index, 1770-ca. 1900

Commercial-services

Miscellaneous fiscal, legal, and business papers, with index, 1770-ca. 1900

NASSAU COUNTY

Town government

Hempstead

76-15-1, 2	Record books, 1644-1864
76-4-1, 2	Record books, 1657-1784
76-4-3	Duke's laws, 1664
	Land record book, 1723
	Court record book, 1657-60

North Hempstead

76-4-2, 3	Record books, 1784-1879
76-4-3	Records of the poor, 1785-1833
	Marriage records, 1830-50

NEW YORK COUNTY

Commercial-transportation

Sloop on Hudson River

75-32-1   Account book, 1771-73

ONEIDA COUNTY

Town government

Vernon

75-45-1   Record book, 1831-1902
Papers, ca. 1814-50
Highway book, 1802-1928
Highway books, 1849-69
Assessment rolls, prior to 1824; 1831; 1849
Register of chattel mortgages, 1849-63

Roll No.

Village government

Vernon
75-44-1   Minute book, 1827-93

Whitesboro
74-35-1   Record book, 1829-59

Religious organizations

Vernon
Mt. Vernon Presbyterian Church
75-46-1   Minutes, 1805-82
Session minutes, 1817-87
Record of members, 1841-87

New Hartford
First Religious Society of Whitestown
First Presbyterian Church
74-23-1   Session minutes, 1791-1802
Session minutes, 1791-1873
Session minutes, 1802-17; 1827-50

Whitesboro
First United Presbyterian Church
74-24-1   Session minutes, 1794-1859
Record of the United Society of Whitestown,
1794-1869
Records of the trustees: United Society of Whitestown,
1805-36
Register of members, 1795-1888
74-24-2   Canvass of families, 1813-16
74-24-1   Handbook of the Rev. Bethuel Dodd, 1794-1898
74-24-2   Abstract history, 1846

ONONDAGA COUNTY

Town government

Dewitt
75-86-1   Record book, 1835-99
Road record book, 1857-1905
Tax rolls, 1835; 1844
Supervisors' account book, 1835-89

Roll No.

Auditors' reports, 1838-1901
Book of strays, 1835-1902
School commissioners' minute book, 1835-1915

Manlius
75-18-1   Road books, 1794-1898

Marcellus
75-88-1   Record book, 1830-1901
Highway record book, 1830-98
Account book, 1830-1902
Earmarks and strays, 1830-99
School record book, 1830-88; 1896-97

Onondaga
75-89-1   Record books, 1798-1854
Road books, 1798-1916
School district records, 1812-79
Record of school officers, 1891-1911

Pompey
75-23-1   Road book, 1794-1901

Religious organizations

Fayetteville
    Baptist Church
75-19-1   Record books, 1811-68

    Presbyterian Church
Trustees' minutes, 1829-74
Session minutes, 1830-71
Ladies' Society record book, 1838-51

Manlius
    First Baptist Church
75-22-1   Pompey Church record, 1813-50
Records of the Pompey and Manlius Church and
         Society, 1822-1912

    Christ Church, Episcopal
75-29-1   Vestry minutes, 1804-73
Record book, 1811-57
Female Benevolent Society minutes, 1858-67
Subscribers for church building, 1805

Roll No.

Pleasant Valley Society

75-17-1   Oran Community Church record book, 1805-1913

Marcellus
First Presbyterian Church

75-90-1   Minutes, 1833-70

Skaneateles
First Presbyterian Church

75-21-1   Records of the session, 1801-41; 1854-1917
               Church register, 1853-1905

Education-nonpublic

Fayetteville Academic Society

75-20-1   Records, 1836-46

Fayetteville Academy
               Catalogues, 1839; 1840; 1849-50

Fraternal organizations

Manlius Chapter #72, Royal Arch Masons

75-107-1   Record books, 1822-30; 1854-66

ONTARIO COUNTY

Town government

Gorham

75-51-1   Record book, 1817-71
               Highway commissioners' records, 1806-31
               Highway book, 1823-62
               Supervisors' account books, 1830-65
               Justice Court record, 1828-35
               School record book, 1813-1913

Phelps

76-35-1   Record books, 1796-1859
               Election register, 1799-1846

Village government

Canandaigua

75-31-1   Record books, 1815-65

Roll No.

Geneva
75-30-1, 2   Record books, 1812
75-30-2   Miscellaneous financial papers, 1820-29
75-30-1, 2   Cemetery register, compiled 1882-83

ORANGE COUNTY

Town government

Goshen
75-40-1   Record book, 1846-96
             Supervisors' account book, 1837-1901

New Windsor
74-34-1   Record book, 1792-1917
             Road record, 1793-1884
             Precinct journal, 1763-1852

Warwick
76-23-1   Record books, 1789-1861
             Record book, 1801-13
             Highway commissioners' records, 1790-1870
             Tax rolls, 1813-30

Village government

Goshen
75-39-1   Record book, 1843-61

Montgomery
76-24-1   Record book, 1810-73
             Day book, 1810-1901

ORLEANS COUNTY

Village government

Medina
79-13-1 to 3   Village board minutes, 1832-1908

Roll No.

OSWEGO COUNTY

Town government

Mexico
75-78-1
Record book, 1796-1826
Record book, 1827-48
Highway commissioners' records, 1856-71
Road surveys, 1869-1911
Highway records, 1857-1907

Richland
75-77-1
Record book, 1823-82
Highway commissioners' minutes, 1841-1900

Sandy Creek
75-76-1
Record book, 1825-68
Road commissioners' records, 1825-69
Road district book, 1846-96

Village government

Fulton
74-30-2
Record books, 1849-67

Oswego Falls
74-30-1
Record books, 1853-85; 1855-92; 1896-97

OTSEGO COUNTY

Town government

Milford
75-43-1
Record book, 1796-1848

Springfield
74-22-1
Record book, 1797-1846

Unadilla
74-11-1
Record book, 1796-1860
Highway records, 1819-56
Assessment rolls, 1831-48
Poormasters' accounts, 1793-1828

Roll No.

Village government

Cooperstown
75-24-1   Record book, 1855-80
             Census, 1898

PUTNAM COUNTY

Town government

Philipstown
75-41-1   Record book, 1809-64
             Assessment rolls, 1815; 1818; 1824; 1828; 1829;
                 1831; 1834; 1836
             Poormasters' records, ca. 1794-1822

RENSSELAER COUNTY

State census records

549885   1855 (city of Troy)
549886   1855 (towns)
549887   1855 (towns)
549891   1865 (city of Troy)
549892   1865 (towns)
549893   1865 (towns)
549897   1875 (city of Troy)
549898   1875 (towns)
549899   1875 (towns)
549904   1905 (city of Troy)
549905   1905 (city of Troy)

Town government

Brunswick
75-60-1   Record book, 1807-44
             Miscellaneous record book, 1812-57
75-60-1, 2   Road record, 1845-74
75-60-2   Highway commissioners' account book, 1857-87
             Supervisors' account book, 1843-1921
             Overseers of the poor, 1807-68
             School district account book, 1856-1920

Stephentown
75-16-1   Record book, 1784-1877

Roll No.

Land Records

Albany and other counties
74-40-19   Highway field books, 1770-92

Schaghticoke
Field book, 1801

ST. LAWRENCE COUNTY

State census records

556597   1815
            1845
            1865

SARATOGA COUNTY

County government

74-48-1   Supervisors' minutes, 1791-1802
74-47-3, 4 Land records, ca. 1708-98
74-47-1   Circuit court minutes, 1791-1824
74-47-2, 3 Court of Common Pleas minutes, 1791-1805;
                1809-18
74-47-1   Court of Oyer and Terminer minutes, 1791-1842
74-47-3   Court of General Sessions minutes, 1791-1817

Town government

Corinth
75-45-1   Record books, 1819-42; 1844-85

Hadley
76-2-1   Record book, 1821-81
            Assessment rolls, 1849; 1855; 1857
            State census, 1845
            School record book, 1847-56
            Town map, 1867

Halfmoon
76-1-1   Record books, 1786-1830; 1833-55

Malta
75-6-1   Record books, 1802-1931

Roll No.

Highway papers, 1789-1859
School district #3 minutes, 1813-67

Milton
74-46-1   Record book, 1799-1846

Moreau
76-31-1   Record book, 1805-48
Assessment rolls, 1859-60

Saratoga
75-5-1   Record book, 1828-64

Saratoga Springs
76-30-1   Record book, 1820-64
76-30-2   Road district records, 1821-76
Assessment rolls, 1820-40
Excise commissioners' minutes, 1836-54
Supervisors' accounts, 1836-63
76-30-1   School district record, 1818-56
76-30-2   School district record, 1820-69
76-30-1   Library minute book, 1808-34

Stillwater
75-83-1   School reports and related records, 1818-47

Village government

Ballston Spa
74-16-1   Record book, 1807-52

Saratoga Springs
76-30-1   Record book, 1840-66

Stillwater
75-3-1   Record books, 1821-36; 1839-48

Religious organizations

Milton
     First Baptist Church (Old Stone Church)
75-15-1   Record books, 1797-1904; 1927-47

447

Roll No.

Stillwater
Second Baptist Church
74-5-2   Records, 1836-1932

Congregational Church
74-5-1   "Canaan Book of Church Records," 1752-1834
75-84-1   "Historical Reminiscences of the Congregational
                Church in Stillwater," 1752-1850

Methodist Church
74-5-2   Record book, 1866-87

Presbyterian Church
74-5-1   Record book, 1793-1856

First Presbyterian Church
                Historical notes, 1791-1852

Second Presbyterian Church
74-5-2   Records, 1865-77

Commercial-retail trade

Stillwater
David Newland, storekeeper
75-84-1   Account books, 1797-1839

David Weston, storekeeper
75-85-1   Day book, 1833-40

Land records

Albany and other counties
74-40-19   Highway field books, 1770-92

SCHENECTADY COUNTY

Town government

Duanesburg
76-32-1   Record book, 1832-1935

Roll No.

Land records

Albany and other counties
74-40-19   Highway field books, 1770-92

Commercial-transportation

Albany and Schenectady Turnpike Co.
74-40-18   Stockholders' records, 1830-31

SCHOHARIE COUNTY

Town government

Cobleskill
75-25-1   Record books, 1797-1879

Land records

Schoharie and Coeymans
74-40-19   Field book, 1790-91; 1801

SENECA COUNTY

Town government

Ovid
74-41-1   Record book, 1794-1841

Romulus
76-36-1   Record book, 1794-1863
Road district book, 1830-67
Supervisors' account book, 1833-69
Election register, 1804-22
School record book, 1822-68
School commissioners' records, 1849-64

Varick
76-36-1   School district #10 minutes, 1869-1914

STEUBEN COUNTY

State census records

512419   1825, 1835, 1845

Roll No.

512420	1855 (part 1)
512421	1855 (part 2)
512422	1855 (part 3)
512423	1865 (part 1)
512424	1865 (part 2)
512425	1865 (part 3)
512426	1875 (part 1)
512427	1875 (part 2)
512428	1875 (part 3)
512429	1875 (part 4)
512430	1892
512431	1905 (part 1,2)
512432	1905 (part 3)

County government

75-70-1, 2	Proceedings of board of supervisors, 1799-1856
80-23-1 to 16	Records, 1791-1909

Town government

Caton
75-72-1   Record book, 1840-1903
             Assessment roll and military roll, 1850-52
             Supervisors' account book, 1840-76

Village government

Corning
75-71-1   Trustees' proceedings, 1848-77

Religious organizations

Caton
  United Methodist Church
75-73-1   Record book, 1838-59

SUFFOLK COUNTY

Town government

East Hampton
76-14-2   Record book, 1650-70
76-14-1   Record book "A," 1657-1770
76-14-2   Record book "B," 1650-69

Roll No.

76-14-1	Record book "1 and 4," 1662-1717
	Record book "G" 1700-1874
	Record book "E," 1728-99
76-14-2	Record book "H," 1800-1834
	Record book "K," 1835-99
	Supervisors' accounts, 1833-82
76-14-3	Invoice book, 1833-66
	Day book, 1830-82
76-14-3	Cattle marks, 1714-1963
	Assorted documents, 17th and 18th centuries
76-14-2	Gov. Thomas Dongan's book of laws, 1665; 1666; 1672; 1674
	Gov. Thomas Dongan's patent, 1686

Islip
80-24-1 to 9   Records, 1720-1979

Religious organizations

Huntington
    The Rev. Joshua Hartt
76-5-1   Record of marriages and baptisms, 1772-1825

Commercial-retail trade

Huntington
    Nathaniel Potter, storekeeper
76-5-2   Day book, 1807-29

Commercial-manufacturing

Huntington
    Cider mill
76-5-1   Account book, 1826-29

    Geo. Crossman and Sons, brickmakers
76-5-1   Account books, 1826; 1827; 1829

    Lockwood Marble Works
76-5-2   Account books, 1837-69

Land records

Huntington
    Lyon Gardiner
76-5-1   Deed, 1659

Roll No.

John N. Lloyd, estate
Account book, 1842

Mark Oakley
76-5-2   Temperature record, 1807-24

Landholders
76-5-1   Legal documents and manuscripts, late 1600s-
          early 1800s

SULLIVAN COUNTY

Town government

Fallsburg
76-21-1   Record books, 1826-77

Mamakating
74-15-1   Record book, 1771-93

Thompson
76-22-1   Record book, 1805-42

TIOGA COUNTY

County government

County surrogate
75-62-1   Accounts with executors and administrators, 1825-54

County judge and surrogate
Fee book, 1856-72

County judge
Day book, 1847-54

Town government

Berkshire
75-59-1   Papers, 1830-99

Owego
75-61-1   Record books, 1800-1858
          Road records, 1808-57
          Assessment rolls, 1843; 1847; 1848

Roll No.

75-59-1	Overseers of the poor accounts, 1800-1817
	Justice dockets, 1840-64; 1844-58
75-61-1, 2	Justice dockets, 1843-45; 1847-50
75-61-1	Book of strays, 1834-71
	School district records, 1813-61

Tioga

75-59-1	Record book, 1800-1833
	Election results, 1801-22

Religious organizations

Owego
  Congregational Church

75-59-2	Session records, 1817-1912
	Record book, 1867-1901
	Society record book, 1849-78

Commercial-services

Avery's Tavern in Owego

75-59-1	Day books, 1809-14; 1817-27

Springsteen's Machine Shop in Owego
Account book, 1834-37

Military

Roster of officers and enlisted men, 1814

ULSTER COUNTY

Town government

Marbletown

74-6-1	Book of conveyances, Vol. A, 1704-35
	Book of conveyances, Vol. B, 1734-66
	Book of conveyances, Vol. C, 1765-1820
74-6-2	Book of conveyances, Vol. E, 1773-1847
	Highway survey book and record of strays, 1808-85
	Book of town officers, 1808-1903

Marlborough

74-17-1, 2	Record books, 1772-1875

Roll No.

Warwarsing
74-14-1   Record book, 1806-29

Woodstock
75-9-1   Record book, 1805-29

Village government

Kingston
74-42-1   Record book, 1805-30

WARREN COUNTY

State census records

473270   N.Y.S. Agricultural census, 1855

County government

76-46-34	Supervisors' minutes, 1862-85
76-46-1, 2	Supervisors' minutes, 1886-1901
76-46-3	County court minutes, 1852-95
76-46-3, 4	Circuit court minutes, 1824-89
76-46-4	Court of Common Pleas minutes, 1813-52
76-46-18	Court of Oyer and Terminer minutes, 1816-88
76-46-3	Court of Oyer and Terminer minutes, 1888-95
76-46-4	Court of Sessions minutes, 1813-57
76-46-11	Court of Sessions minutes, 1858-96

Town government

Bolton

76-46-9, 10	Record books, 1799-1893
76-46-5 to 8	Record books, 1905-64
76-46-10	Account books with tax schedules, 1830-1912
	Tax rolls and election results, 1892-1905
76-46-8, 9	Election records, 1854-1911
76-46-9	Justice docket of Justice of the Peace Thomas McGee, 1818-32
	Military roll and account book, 1862-67

Chester

76-46-14, 15	Record books, 1906-61
76-46-11 to 14	Tax rolls, 1859-1900

Roll No.

Hague

76-46-17, 18	Record books, 1922-67
76-46-53	Tax rolls, 1858-60
76-46-16, 17	Tax rolls, 1861-1900

Horicon

76-46-19, 20	Record books, 1910-67

Johnsburg

76-46-24 to 27	Record books, 1808-1965
76-46-15	Tax rolls, 1858; 1860
76-46-21 to 23	Tax rolls, 1860; 1870-1900

Lake George

76-46-29 to 31	Record books, 1936-67
76-46-32 to 34	Tax rolls, 1858-99
76-46-28	Board of health minutes, 1885-1908

Queensbury

76-46-35	Record books, 1796-1897
76-46-36 to 40	Record books, 1850-1966
76-46-36	Highway commissioner's minutes, 1850-1927
	Field book, 1885
76-46-40 to 45	Tax rolls, 1854-99
76-46-36	Account book, 1820-41
76-46-35	Assessor's military roll book, 1851
	Financial war commission minutes, 1861-65
76-46-36	Board of health minutes, 1897-1914
76-46-35	Timber marks, 1831-1933

Stony Creek

76-46-23	Tax rolls, 1859-63; 1865-66
76-46-27	Tax rolls, 1867-69
76-46-46	Tax rolls, 1869-79; 1884-87

Warrensburg

76-46-47 to 51	Record books, 1838-86; 1903-4; 1920-68
76-46-51 to 53	Tax rolls, 1864-1900

WASHINGTON COUNTY

State census records

513913	1825, 1835
513915	1855 (part 1)

Roll No.

513916	1855 (part 2)
513918	1865 (part 1)
513919	1865 (part 2)
512701	1875 (part 1)
512702	1875 (part 2)
512705	1892
512706	1905

Town government

Argyle
74-50-2	Records, 1771-1819
	Records, 1804 onward
74-50-1	Record book, 1827-67
	Record book, 1837-91
	Supervisors' account book, 1830-63
	Loan commissioners' ledger, 1833-45
	Vote results book, 1799-1881
	Poormasters' account book, 1814-28

Cambridge
75-2-1	Record book, 1773-1816

Easton
75-4-1	Record book, 1789-1852
	Record book, 1799-1849
	Account book, 1793-1853

Fort Edward
75-7-1	Record books, 1771-1876
75-7-2	Assessment rolls, 1819-52
75-7-3	Excise records, 1819-1919
75-7-2	Audit ledger, 1819-54
75-7-3	Absentee voting forms, 1864
75-7-1, 2	Justice dockets, 1842-56; 1869-72
75-7-3	Jury lists, 1821-77
	School commissioners' records, 1819-53
	School inspector's acceptance, 1842
	Military exemptions, 1862
75-7-2	Military rolls, 1851-54; 1862; 1864; 1866

Granville
74-3-1	Record book, 1787-1826

Roll No.

Greenwich

74-4-1   Record book, 1803-55

Hebron

75-58-1   Record books, 1784-1886
Supervisors' account book, 1831-74
Certificates of election, 1827-34
Records of overseers of the poor, 1792-1832
Supervisors' school accounts, 1864-1901

Kingsbury

75-8-1   Record book, 1841-69
Road book, 1785-1930s

White Creek District

74-8-1   Proprietors' book, 1762-83

Village government

Salem

74-51-1   Trustees' record books, 1803-84
74-51-2   Assessment roll, 1885
74-51-1, 2   Board of education minutes, 1851-1902

Land records

Albany and other counties

74-40-19   Highway field books, 1770-92

WAYNE COUNTY

Town government

Arcadia

74-27-1   Record book, 1825-58
Road book, 1825-79

Galen

74-39-1   Record book, 1830-92

Lyons

75-28-1   Record book, 1802-33
School commissioners' minutes, 1828-1917

Marion

75-50-1   Record books, 1825-95

Roll No.

Palmyra

74-29-1   Record book, 1827-73

Road records, 1793-1901

Sodus

74-38-1   Record books, 1799-1893

74-38-1, 2   Road books, 1799-1899

74-38-2, 3   Election record, 1830-63

74-38-2   Justice docket, 1829

Justice docket, 1829-32

74-38-3   Sheep marks, 1831-35

Book of strays, 1830-44

Chattel mortgage index, 1832-80

74-38-2   School commissioners' minutes, 1830-90

School monies apportionment, 1844-67

Village government

Palmyra

74-28-1   Record books, 1852-73

Commercial-transportation

Clyde and Rose Plank Road Company

74-39-1   Minutes book, 1848-87

WESTCHESTER COUNTY

County government

75-102-1   Criminal register, 1864-67

Town government

Cortlandt

74-33-2   Highway commissioners' records, 1877-88

74-33-1, 2   Road book, 1829-83

74-33-1   Road survey book, 1796-1906

74-33-2   Justice docket, 1835-37

School district record book, 1829-1901

Eastchester

75-55-1   Minute books, 1666-1870

75-55-2   Highway department reports, 1800-1850

Road alterations and book of strays, 1790-1861

Roll No.

Oaths of office, 1790-1850
Election returns, early 1800s
Record of overseers of the poor, 1788-1824
Inn and tavern licenses, early 1800s
Book of colored people, 1785-1822
School board minutes, districts 1,2,3,5, 1800-1850

Harrison

75-13-1   Record book, 1774-1855

Greenburgh

74-54-1   Record books, 1845-78
74-54-1, 2   Road records, 1792-1884
74-54-2   School records, 1836-80

Mamaroneck

74-31-1   Record book, 1697-1881
                 Record book, 1756-1878
                 Record of black children born in the town,
                     1799-1818

Mount Pleasant

76-25-1   Record book, 1788-1802
                 Highway record book, 1827-93

New Castle

74-32-1   Record book, 1791-1851

North Castle

75-56-1   Record book, 1736-1848

North Salem

75-11-1, 2   Town papers, 1789-1850

Pelham

75-12-1   Record book, 1801-51

Rye

75-42-1, 2, 3   Record books, originals and transcriptions,
                     1672-1859

Village government

Peekskill

76-26-1, 2, 3   Record books, 1879-1901
76-26-3   Index, grantor to grantee, 1674-1836

Roll No.

Yonkers
75-27-1, 2, 3   Record books, 1855-70

Religious organizations

North Salem
St. James Episcopal Church
75-11-2   Minute book, 1797-1874

First Universalist Society
Minute book, 1841-1945

Commercial-retail trade

New Castle
Isaac Carpenter, storekeeper
75-101-1   Day book, 1818-20

C. & C. Kipp, general store
Day book, 1838-39

New Rochelle
Robert Underhill & Co., general store
75-102-1   Store ledger, 1786-93

Military

75-102-2   Revolutionary war soldiers, "McDonald Papers,"
1776-83

Individuals

Keeler family, North Salem
75-11-2   Deeds, 1731-1823

Stater, Lyon, Merritt families
75-26-1, 2   Business records, ca. 1680-1850

Residents of Westchester County
75-102-1   Miscellaneous colonial and revolutionary documents,
1689-1819

Roll No.

WYOMING COUNTY

County government

75-63-1, 2	Supervisors' minutes, 1841-77
75-81-1	Common rules, minutes, 1841-48
	Grand jury lists, 1841-52
	Court of General Sessions minutes, 1841-53
	Mortgage book, 1837-64

Town government

Castile

75-66-1	School district #2 minutes, 1868-1945
	School district #2 list of scholars, 1842-49
	School district #4 minutes, 1844-1926
	School district #4 minutes, 1841-1934
	School district #5 minutes, 1830-85
	School district #8 list of scholars, 1842-61
	School district #8 library book, 1844-57
	School district #9 minutes, 1825-75
	School district #11 minutes, 1841-1907
	School district #13 minutes, 1829-1933
	School district #18 minutes, 1824-90

Covington

75-36-1, 2	Record books, 1817-1920
75-36-1	Road book, 1812-91
75-36-2	Assessment roll, 1840
	School district #6 minutes, 1817-85
	School district #16 minutes, 1825-61
	School finance record book, 1853-1913

Java

75-68-1	Record book, 1833-97

Middlebury

75-35-1	Assessment roll, 1847
	Day book/justice docket, 1842-43
	School district #2 records, 1843-61

Religious organizations

Attica
  First Baptist Church

75-67-1	Record books, 1846-59; 1880-1927

Roll No.

First Presbyterian Church

75-37-1 First Presbyterian Church and Congregational
Society records, 1809-75

Castile
First Christian Church

75-66-2 Minutes, 1822-62

Christian Society
Records, 1825-71

United Church of Christ
Sesquicentennial history, -1975

United Community Church
History of the church, -1962

Middlebury
First Congressional Society

75-65-1 Minutes, 1819-1949

Strykersville
Congregational Church

75-69-1 Record book, 1848-99

Wyoming
First Baptist Church

75-35-1 Record book, 1820-58

Methodist Episcopal Church

75-64-1 Minute book, 1835-1910
Sunday school record book, 1841-67

First Presbyterian Church

75-65-1 Sunday school record book, 1831-35

Education-nonpublic

Middlebury Academy

75-35-1 Miscellaneous records, 1807-75

Roll No.

Commercial-retail trade

Covington
Benedict Brooks, businessman
75-36-2   Business ledger, 1833-47

Gordon's Store
75-36-1   Day book, 1845; 1850

Ebenezer Mix
75-36-2   Personal journal, 1787-1811

Middlebury
Amzi Wright, storekeeper
75-35-1   Day book, 1824-86

Storekeeper
Store ledger, 1833-63

Storekeeper (Middlebury?)
Day book/justice docket, 1842-43

Land Records

Surveyor of Cottringer tract
75-34-1   Notes, map, and survey, 1807-77

Cemeteries

Brainard Cemetery Association, Attica
75-38-1   Record book, 1814 to date

MULTICOUNTY

Religious organizations

Albany area churches
74-40-15   Patents, 1784-1842; 1844-80

Commercial-transportation

Sloop on Hudson River
75-32-1   Account book, 1771-73

Roll No.

Military

Issacher Bates, Shaker, revolutionary war veteran

74-1-1   "Sketch of the Life and Experience of Issachar
Bates," 1758-1836

Timothy Pickering, Quarter-master General et al.

76-5-2   Revolutionary war papers, letters, orders, 1778-85

Veterans, revolutionary war, War of 1812

74-1-1   "Schedule of Pensioners from Revolution and War of
1812," n.d.

Individuals

Thomas Paine

75-102-1   Correspondence, 1780-1824

Land records

Albany and vicinity

74-40-19   Field book covering lands south of the Mohawk,
1730

Appendix C

Research Libraries Information Network (RLIN)
Archives, Manuscripts, and Special Collections Members in New York State

The following institutions are members of the RLIN network's Archives, Manuscripts, and Special Collections (AMSC) program. Individuals interested in searching RLIN should contact the repository directly for information about its searching policy and services. In addition to these repositories, many libraries have dial-up access for RLIN searching or are RLIN members who do not participate directly in the AMSC program. Researchers should ask at their local libraries about the availability of such searching.

New York State Archives and Records Administration
Research Services Unit
Cultural Education Center
Albany, NY 12230

518-474-8955

New York State Library
Manuscripts and Special Collections Section
Cultural Education Center
Albany, NY 12230

518-474-6282

Cornell University
Department of Manuscripts and University Archives
101 Olin Library
Ithaca, NY 14851-5301

607-255-3530

State University of New York at Albany
University Library
Reference Department or University Archives
1400 Washington Avenue
Albany, NY 12222

518-442-3552/518-442-3544

State University of New York at Buffalo
University Archives
420 Capen Hall
Buffalo, NY 14260

716-636-2916

New York Public Library
Rare Books and Manuscripts
The Research Libraries
5th Avenue and 42nd Street
New York, NY 10018-2788

212-930-0804

Rockefeller Archive Center
Pocantico Hills
North Tarrytown, NY 10591

914-631-4505

New-York Historical Society
Library
170 Central Park West
New York, NY 10024

212-873-3400

New York University
Bobst Library, Archives
70 Washington Square South
New York, NY 10012

212-998-2644

Columbia University
Rare Books and Manuscripts
801 Butler Library
New York, NY 10027

212-280-2231

City of New York Department of Records and Information Services
31 Chambers Street
New York, NY 10007

212-566-3106

Syracuse University
University Archives
George Arents Research Library
Syracuse, NY 13244-2010

315-443-2697

University of Rochester
Department of Rare Books, Manuscripts, and Archives
Rush Rhees Library
Rochester, NY 14627

716-275-4477

INDEXES

Index to Agency Functions

Index to Agency and Office Names

012606
92-072

Notes

Notes

Notes